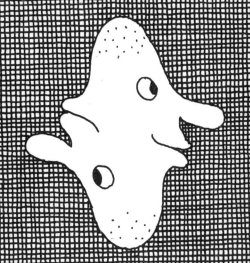

THE BOOK OF ENGLISH HUMOUR

MOSCOW

RADUGA PUBLISHERS

THE
BOOK
OF
ENGLISH
HUMOUR

Moscow
Raduga Publishers
1990

Составление и комментарии А. Я. ЛИВЕРГАНТА
Художник А. Б. МАРКЕВИЧ
Редактор С. Б. БЕЛОВ

Антология английского юмора: Сборник./Сост.
А. Я. Ливергант. На англ. яз.—М.: Радуга.—
1990.—432 с.

Англия—страна, породившая великую плеяду юмористов, клас-
сиков мировой литературы. Традиции, заложенные Шекспиром,
Филдингом, Стерном, Диккенсом, продолжают и развивают английские юмористы XIX—XX столетий: Джером К. Джером,
Г. К. Честертон, Х. Беллок, Дж. Микеш и другие, с творчеством
которых и познакомит данный сборник.
Издание предназначено как владеющим английским языком, так
и изучающим его.

А $\frac{4703010100\text{-}258}{031(01)\text{-}90}$ 442-90

ISBN-5-05-003241-5

ОТ СОСТАВИТЕЛЯ

«Отечество карикатуры и пародии», как назвал Англию
А. С. Пушкин, предоставляет составителю антологии английского юмора практически неограниченный выбор авторов, жан-
ров, сюжетов, отчего, впрочем, его задача лишь усложняется.
Достойных претендентов столько, что приходится ограничивать
себя определенными — и по необходимости весьма узкими —
рамками, в том числе и временными. В настоящем сборнике
представлены последние сто лет английской комической литературы: от «нонсенсов» Эдварда Лира и Льюиса Кэрролла
до «театра абсурда» Гарольда Пинтера, от добродушного Джером К. Джерома до весьма язвительных, а порой и мрачноватых
Дж. Б. Мортона и Дж. Кольера, от классических пародийных
стилизаций Макса Бирбома до современных бурлесков Мо-
риса Бэринга, Дж. К. Сквайра и др.

Трудно припомнить хотя бы одного крупного английского писателя нашего столетия, который не отдал бы должного юмористике. Веселые рассказы, комические эпизоды, юмористические мотивы встречаются не только у признанных мастеров английской литературы смеха Хиллари Беллока, Ивлина Во, Олдо-
са Хаксли, Энтони Поуэлла, Уиндэма Льюиса, Тома Шарпа, но
и у Грэма Грина, В. С. Притчетта, У. Х. Одена, Т. С. Элиота —
авторов, казалось бы, весьма далеких от комической традиции.
Обращает на себя внимание и тот факт, что для многих английских писателей юмористика является чем-то вроде хобби, от-
дохновения, часто плохо сочетающегося с «основной профес-
сией». Так, А. Э. Хаусмен, поэт и филолог-античник, М. Бирбом,
театральный критик, М. Брэдбери, прозаик, литературовед и со-
циолог, прославились остроумными пародиями, математик
Л. Кэрролл, как известно, стал создателем одной из самых смешных книг прошлого столетия, а Хиллари Беллок, автор ряда
серьезных исторических исследований, и Гарри Грэхем, сочини-
тель сентиментальных пьес, останутся в литературе в совершенно
ином качестве — как блестящие острословы и эпиграмматисты.

Представлены в нашей антологии и «профессионалы юмора»,
которых в Англии, особенно с появлением журнала «Панч»,
этого неизменного «порта приписки» всех англоязычных юмористов, всегда было предостаточно. Это и Гектор Манро, который пользуется репутацией английского О. Генри, и поэт Эдмунд Клерихью Бентли, чьи шуточные куплеты украшают мно-
гочисленные юмористические антологии, и неистощимый на вы-
думки издатель «Панча», сатирик и юморист Эдмунд Нокс, и,

разумеется, П. Г. Вудхаус, являющий собой нечастый пример сверхплодовитости, сочетавшейся с отменным качеством его юмористической продукции. В этой связи нельзя не упомянуть и современных фельетонистов, ведущих разделы юмора в крупных британских газетах и журналах и соревнующихся между собой в нелегком искусстве острить на злобу дня.

Последним, пожалуй, приходится особенно тяжело. Ведь, с одной стороны, у каждого из них должна быть своя постоянная комическая маска, а с другой, им ни под каким видом нельзя повторяться, муссировать одну и ту же, пусть даже вполне выигрышную тему. Надо признать, что многие из них с честью выходят из положения. Дж. Б. Мортона и Э. Нокса, А. Херберта и П. Флеминга отличает поразительное умение шутить изо дня в день, из номера в номер, из рассказа в рассказ столь вдохновенно и столь непредсказуемо, что рутинная работа на заказ выглядит у них, как правило, лихим и оригинальным экспромтом.

Когда рассматриваешь карикатуры, читаешь пародии, эпиграммы, юморески «Панча», «Соглядатая» и других периодических изданий, то становится очевидным, что в юморе англичане верны традиции, восходящей к Аддисону, Филдингу, Теккерею, Диккенсу, что юмористический взгляд на вещи словно бы передается английским писателям по наследству. С другой стороны, то обстоятельство, что в «Панче» печатались в свое время Диккенс и Теккерей, накладывает на нынешних английских юмористов особую ответственность, тем более, что мишени, по которым метко бьют многие поколения английских острословов, не меняются: это и «вульгарная» Америка с ее рекламой, нуворишами, безвкусицей, это и родная британская эксцентричность, это штампы бульварного чтива и стереотипы массового сознания.

Впрочем, в юморе — как и в искусстве вообще — не в одних темах дело. Талант проявляется в нюансах, в мелочах, в неожиданном подходе к вроде бы традиционнейшим предметам. Остается надеяться, что эта антология станет подтверждением того, что лучшим английским сатирикам и юмористам конца XIX—XX века удается, оставаясь в русле традиций, запомниться «лица необщим выраженьем».

CONTENTS

I. PROSE

11

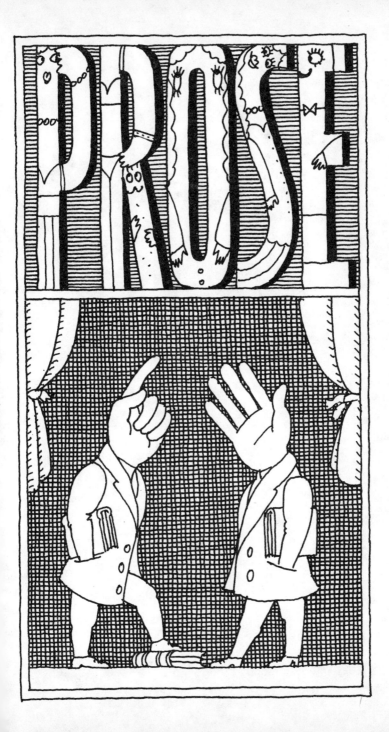

F. ANSTEY

A CANINE ISHMAEL

"Tell me," she said suddenly, with a pretty imperiousness that seemed to belong to her, "are you fond of dogs?" How we arrived at the subject I forget now, but I know she had just been describing how a collie at a dog-show she had visited lately had suddenly thrown his forepaws round her neck in a burst of affection — a proceeding which, in my own mind (although I prudently kept this to myself), I considered less astonishing than she appeared to do.

For I had had the privilege of taking her in to dinner, and the meal had not reached a very advanced stage before I had come to the conclusion that she was the most charming, if not the loveliest, person I had ever met.

It was fortunate for me that I was honestly able to answer her question in a satisfactory manner, for, had it been otherwise, I doubt whether she would have deigned to bestow much more of her conversation upon me.

"Then I wonder," she said next, meditatively, "if you would care to hear about a dog that belonged to — to someone I know very well? Or would it bore you?"

I am very certain that if she had volunteered to relate the adventures of Telemachus, or the history of the Thirty Years'

15

War, I should have accepted the proposal with a quite genuine gratitude. As it was, I made it sufficiently plain that I should care very much indeed to hear about that dog.

She paused for a moment to reject an unfortunate *entrée* (which I confess to doing my best to console), and then she began her story. I shall try to set it down as nearly as possible in her own words, although I cannot hope to convey the peculiar charm and interest that she gave it for me. It was not, I need hardly say, told all at once, but was subject to the inevitable interruptions which render a dinner-table intimacy so piquantly precarious.

"This dog," she began quietly, without any air of beginning a story, "this dog was called Pepper. He was not much to look at—rather a rough, mongrelly kind of animal; and he and a young man had kept house together for a long time, for the young man was a bachelor and lived in chambers by himself. He always used to say that he didn't like to get engaged to anyone, because he was sure it would put Pepper out so fearfully. However, he met somebody at last who made him forget about Pepper, and he proposed and was accepted—and then, you know," she added, as a little dimple came in her cheek, "he had to go home and break the news to the dog."

She had just got to this point, when, taking advantage of a pause she made, the man on her other side (who was, I daresay, strictly within his rights, although I remember at the time considering him a pushing beast) struck in with some remark which she turned to answer, leaving me leisure to reflect.

I was feeling vaguely uncomfortable about this story; something, it would be hard to say what, in her way of mentioning Pepper's owner made me suspect that he was more than a mere acquaintance of hers.

Was it *she*, then, who was responsible for——? It was no business of mine, of course; I had never met her in my life till that evening—but I began to be impatient to hear the rest.

And at last she turned to me again: "I hope you haven't forgotten that I was in the middle of a story. You haven't? And you would really like me to go on? Well, then—oh yes, when Pepper was told, he was naturally a little annoyed at first. I daresay he considered he ought to have been consulted previously. But, as soon as he had seen the lady, he withdrew all opposition—which his master declared was a tremendous load off his mind, for Pepper was rather a difficult dog, and slow as a rule to take strangers into his affections, a little snappy and surly, and very easily hurt or offended. Don't you know dogs who are sensitive like that? *I* do, and I'm always so sorry for them—they feel little things so much, and one never can find out what's the matter, and have it out with them! Sometimes it's shyness; once I had a dog who was quite painfully shy—self-consciousness it was really, I suppose, for he always fancied everybody was looking at him, and often when people were calling he would come and hide his face in the folds of my dress till they had gone—it was too ridiculous! But about Pepper. He was devoted to his new mistress from the very first. I am not sure that she was quite so struck with him, for he was not at all a lady's dog, and his manners had been very much neglected. Still, she came quite to like him in time; and when they were married, Pepper went with them for the honeymoon."

"*When they were married!*" I glanced at the card which lay half-hidden by her plate. Surely Miss So-and-so was written on it?—yes, it was certainly "Miss". It was odd that such a circumstance should have increased my enjoyment of the story, perhaps—but it undoubtedly did.

"After the honeymoon," my neighbour continued, "they came to live in the new house, which was quite a tiny one, and Pepper was a very important personage in it indeed. He had his mistress all to himself for the greater part of most days, as his master had to be away in town; so she used to talk to him intimately, and tell him more than she would have thought of confiding to most people. Sometimes, when she thought there was no fear of callers coming, she would make him play, and this was quite a new sensation for Pepper, who was a serious-minded animal, and took very solemn views of life. At first he hadn't the faintest idea what was expected of him; it must have been rather like trying to romp with a parish beadle, he was so intensely respectable! But as soon as he once grasped the notion and understood that no liberty was intended, he lent himself to it readily enough and learnt to gambol quite creditably. Then he was made much of in all sorts of ways; she washed him twice a week with her own hands—which his master

17

would never have dreamt of doing—and she was always trying new ribbons on his complexion. That rather bored him at
first, but it ended by making him a little conceited about his
appearance. Altogether he was dearly fond of her, and I don't
believe he had ever been happier in all his life than he was in
those days. Only, unfortunately, it was all too good to last."

Here I had to pass olives or something to somebody, and the
other man, seeing his chance, and, to do him justice, with no
idea that he was interrupting a story, struck in once more, so
that the history of Pepper had to remain in obeyance for
several minutes.

My uneasiness returned. Could there be a mistake about
that name-card after all? Cards *do* get re-arranged sometimes,
and she seemed to know that young couple so very intimately.
I tried to remember whether I had been introduced to her as
a Miss or Mrs. So-and-so, but without success. There is some
fatality which generally distracts one's attention at the critical
moment of introduction, and in this case it was perhaps easily
accounted for. My turn came again, and she took up her tale
once more. "I think when I left off I was saying that Pepper's
happiness was too good to last. And so it was. For his mistress
was ill, and, though he snuffed and scratched and whined at
the door of her room for ever so long, they wouldn't let him
in. But he managed to slip in one day somehow, and jumped
up on her lap and licked her hands and face, and almost went
out of his mind with joy at seeing her again. Only (I told you
he was a sensitive dog) it gradually struck him that she was not
quite so pleased to see him as usual—and presently he found
out the reason. There was an other animal there, a new pet,
which seemed to take up a good deal of her attention. Of
course you guess what that was—but Pepper had never seen
a baby before, and he took it as a personal slight and was
dreadfully offended. He simply walked straight out of the
room and downstairs to the kitchen, where he stayed for days.

"I don't think he enjoyed his sulk much, poor doggie; perhaps he had an idea that when they saw how much he took it
to heart they would send the baby away. But as time went on
and this didn't seem to occur to them, he decided to come out
of the sulks and look over the matter, and he came back quite
prepared to resume the old footing. Only everything was dif-

18

ferent. No one seemed to notice that he was in the room now, and his mistress never invited him to have a game; she even forgot to have him washed—and one of his peculiarities was that he had no objection to soap and warm water. The worst of it was, too, that before very long the baby followed him into the sitting-room, and, do what he could, he couldn't make the stupid little thing understand that it had no business there.If you think of it, a baby must strike a dog as a very inferior little animal: it can't bark (well, yes, it *can* howl), but it's no good whatever with rats, and yet everybody makes a tremendous fuss about it! The baby got all poor Pepper's bows now; and his mistress played games with it, though Pepper felt he could have done it ever so much better, but he was never allowed to join in. So he used to lie on a rug and pretend he didn't mind, though, really, I'm certain he felt it horribly. I always believe, you know, that people never give dogs half credit enough for feeling things, don't you?

"Well, at last came the worst indignity of all: Pepper was driven from his rug—his own particular rug—to make room for the baby; and when he had got away into a corner to cry quietly, all by himself, that wretched baby came and crawled after him and pulled his tail!

"He always *had* been particular about his tail, and never allowed anybody to touch it but very intimate friends, and even then under protest, so you can imagine how insulted he felt.

"It was too much for him, and he lost the last scrap of temper he had. They said he bit the baby, and I'm afraid he did—though not enough really to hurt it; still, it howled fearfully, of course, and from that moment it was all over with poor Pepper—he was a ruined dog!

"When his master came home that evening he was told the whole story. Pepper's mistress said she would be ever so sorry to part with him, but, after his misbehaviour, she should never know a moment's peace until he was out of the house—it really wasn't safe for baby!

"And his master was sorry, naturally; but I suppose he was beginning rather to like the baby himself, and so the end of it was that Pepper had to go. They did all they could for him; found him a comfortable home, with a friend who was looking out for a good housedog, and wasn't particular about breed,

19

and, after that, they heard nothing of him for a long while. And, when they did hear, it was rather a bad report: the friend could do nothing with Pepper at all; he had to tie him up in the stable, and then he snapped at everyone who came near, and howled all night — they were really almost afraid of him.

"So when Pepper's mistress heard that, she felt more thankful than ever that the dog had been sent away, and tried to think no more about him. She had quite forgotten all about it, when, one day, a new nursemaid, who had taken the baby out for an airing, came back with a terrible account of a savage dog which had attacked them, and leaped out at the perambulator so persistently that it was as much as she could do to drive it away. And even then Pepper's mistress did not associate the dog with him; she thought he had been destroyed long ago.

"But the next time the nurse went out with the baby she took a thick stick with her, in case the dog should come again. And no sooner had she lifted the perambulator over the step, than the dog *did* come again, exactly as if he had been lying in wait for them ever since outside the gate.

"The nurse was a strong country girl, with plenty of pluck, and as the dog came leaping and barking about in a very alarming way, she hit him as hard as she could on his head. The wonder is she did not kill him on the spot, and, as it was, the blow turned him perfectly giddy and silly for a time, and he ran round and round in a dazed sort of way — do you think you could lower that candle-shade just a little? Thanks!" she broke off suddenly, as I obeyed. "Well, she was going to strike again, when her mistress rushed out, just in time to stop her. For, you see, she had been watching at the window, and although the poor beast was miserably thin, and rough, and neglected-looking, she knew at once that it must be Pepper, and that he was not in the least mad or dangerous, but only trying his best to make his peace with the baby. Very likely his dignity or his conscience or something wouldn't let him come back quite at once, you know; and perhaps he thought he had better get the baby on his side first. And then all at once, his mistress — I heard all this through her, of course — his mistress suddenly remembered how devoted Pepper had been to her, and how fond she had once been of him, and when she saw

20

him standing, stupid and shivering, there, her heart softened to him, and she went to make it up with him, and tell him that he was forgiven and should come back and be her dog again, just as in the old days!——"

Here she broke off for a moment. I did not venture to look at her, but I thought her voice trembled a little when she spoke again. "I don't quite know *why* I tell you all this. There was a time when I never could bear the end of it myself," she said; "but I have begun, and I will finish now. Well, Pepper's mistress went towards him, and called him; but—whether he was still too dizzy to quite understand who she was, or whether his pride came uppermost again, poor dear! I don't know—but he gave her just one look (she says she will never forget it—never; it went straight to her heart), and then he walked very slowly and deliberately away.

"She couldn't bear it; she followed; she felt she simply *must* make him understand how very, very sorry she was for him; but the moment he heard her he began to run faster and faster, until he was out of reach and out of sight, and she had to come back. I know she was crying bitterly by that time."

"And he never came back again?" I asked, after a silence.

"Never again!" she said softly; "that was the very last they ever saw or heard of him. And—and I've always loved every dog since for Pepper's sake!"

"I'm almost glad he did decline to come back," I declared; "it served his mistress right—she didn't deserve anything else!"

"Ah, I didn't want you to say that!" she protested; "she never meant to be so unkind—it was all for the baby's sake!"

I was distinctly astonished, for all her sympathy in telling the story had seemed to lie in the other direction.

"You don't mean to say," I cried involuntarily, "that you can find any excuses for her? I did not expect you would take the baby's part!"

"But I did," she confessed, with lowered eyes—"I *did* take the baby's part—it was all my doing that Pepper was sent away—I have been sorry enough for it since!"

It was her own story she had been telling at second-hand after all—and she was not Miss So-and-so! I had entirely forgotten the existence of any other members of the party but our two selves, but at the moment of this discovery — which was doubly painful — I was recalled by a general rustle to the fact that we were at a dinner-party, and that our hostess had just given the signal.

As I rose and drew back my chair to allow my neighbour to pass, she raised her eyes for a moment and said almost meekly: "I *was* the baby, you see!"

JEROME K. JEROME

OVERHAULING A BICYCLE

I have had experience on the "overhauling." There was a man at Folkestone; I used to meet him on the Lees. He proposed one evening we should go for a long bicycle-ride together on the following day, and I agreed. I got up early, for me; I made an effort, and was pleased with myself. He came half an hour late: I was waiting for him in the garden. It was a lovely day. He said:

"That's a good-looking machine of yours. How does it run?"

"Oh, like most of them!" I answered, "easily enough in the morning; goes a little stiffly after lunch."

He caught hold of it by the front wheel and the fork, and shook it violently.

I said: "Don't do that; you'll hurt it."

I did not see why he should shake it; it had not done anything to him. Besides, if it wanted shaking, I was the proper person to shake it. I felt much as I should had he started whac-king my dog.

He said: "This front wheel wobbles."

I said:"It doesn't if you don't wobble it." It didn't wobble, as a matter of fact—nothing worth calling a wobble.

He said: "This is dangerous; have you got a screw-hammer?"

23

I ought to have been firm, but I thought that perhaps he really did know something about the business. I went to the tool-shed to see what I could find. When I came back he was sitting on the ground with the front wheel between his legs. He was playing with it, twiddling it round between his fingers; the remnant of the machine was lying on the gravel path beside him.

He said: "Something has happened to this front wheel of yours."

"It looks like it, doesn't it?" I answered. But he was the sort of man that never understands satire.

He said: "It looks to me as if the bearings were all wrong."

I said: "Don't you trouble about it any more; you will make yourself tired. Let us put it back and get off."

He said: "We may as well see what is the matter with it, now it is out." He talked as though it had dropped out by accident.

Before I could stop him he had unscrewed something somewhere, and out rolled all over the path some dozen or so little balls.

"Catch 'em!" he shouted; "catch 'em! We mustn't lose any of them." He was quite excited about them.

We grovelled round for half an hour, and found sixteen. He said he hoped we had got them all, because, if not, it would make a serious difference to the machine. He said there was nothing you should be more careful about in taking a bicycle to pieces than seeing you did not lose any of the balls. He explained that you ought to count them as you took them out and see that exactly the same number went back in each place. I promised, if ever I took a bicycle to pieces I would remember his advice.

I put the balls for safety in my hat, and I put my hat upon the doorstep. It was not a sensible thing to do, I admit. As a matter of fact, it was a silly thing to do. I am not as a rule addle-headed; his influence must have affected me.

He then said that while he was about it he would see to the chain for me, and at once began taking off the gear-case. I did try to persuade him from that. I told him what an experienced friend of mine once said to me solemnly:

"If anything goes wrong with your gear-case, sell the machine and buy a new one; it comes cheaper."

He said: "People talk like that who understand nothing

about machines. Nothing is easier than taking off a gear-case."

I had to confess he was right. In less than five minutes he had the gear-case in two pieces, lying on the path, and was grovelling for screws. He said it was always a mystery to him the way screws disappeared.

We were still looking for the screws when Ethelbertha came out. She seemed surprised to find us there; she said she thought we had started hours ago.

He said: "We shan't be long now. I'm just helping your husband to overhaul this machine of his. It's a good machine; but they all want going over occasionally."

Ethelbertha said: "If you want to wash yourselves when you have done you might go into the back kitchen, if you don't mind; the girls have just finished the bedrooms."

She told me that if she met Kate they would probably go for a sail; but that in my case she would be back to lunch. I would have given a sovereign to be going with her. I was getting heartily sick of standing about watching this fool breaking up my bicycle.

Common sense continued to whisper to me: "Stop him, before he does any more mischief. You have a right to protect your own property from ravages of a lunatic. Take him by the scruff of the neck, and kick him out of the gate!"

But I am weak when it comes to hurting other people's feelings, and I let him muddle on.

He gave up looking for the rest of the screws. He said screws had a knack of turning up when you least expected them; and that now he would see to the chain. He tightened it till it would not move; next he loosened it until it was twice as loose as it was before. Then he said we had better think about getting the front wheel back into its place again.

I held the fork open, and he worried with the wheel. At the end of ten minutes I suggested he should hold the forks, and that I should handle the wheel; and we changed places. At the end of his first minute, he dropped the machine, and took a short walk round the croquet lawn, with his hands pressed together between his thighs. He explained as he walked that the thing to be careful about was to avoid getting your fingers pitched between the forks and the spokes of the wheel. I replied I was convinced, from my own experience, that there was much truth in what he said. He wrapped himself up in a couple of dusters, and we commenced again. At length we did get the thing into position; and the moment it was in position he burst out laughing.

I said: "What's the joke?"

He said: "Well, I am an ass!"

It was the first thing he had said that made me respect him. I asked him what had led him to the discovery.

He said: "We've forgotten the balls!"

I looked for my hat; it was lying topsy-turvy in the middle of the path, and Ethelbertha's favourite hound was swallowing the balls as fast as he could pick them up.

"He will kill himself," said Ebbson —— I have never met him since that day, thank the Lord; but I think his name was Ebbson —— "they are solid steel."

I said: "I am not troubling about the dog. He has had a bootlace and a packet of needles already this week. Nature's the best guide; puppies seem to require this kind of stimulant. What I am thinking about is my bicycle."

He was of a cheerful disposition. He said: "Well, we must put back all we can find, and trust to Providence."

We found eleven. We fixed six on one side and five on the other, and half an hour later the wheel was in its place again. It need hardly be added that it really did wobble now; a child might have noticed it. Ebbson said it would do for the present. He appeared to be getting a bit tired himself. If I had let him, he would, I believe, at this point have gone home. I was determined now, however, that he should stop and finish; I had abandoned all thoughts of a ride. My pride in the machine he had killed. My only interest lay now in seeing him scratch and bump and pinch himself. I revived his drooping spirits with a glass of beer and some judicious praise. I said:

"Watching you do this is of real use to me. It is not only your skill and dexterity that fascinates me, it is your cheery confidence in yourself, your inexplicable hopefulness, that does me good."

Thus encouraged, he set to work to refix the gear-case. He stood the bicycle against the house, and worked from the off side. Then he stood it against a tree, and worked from the near side. Then I held it for him, while he lay on the ground with his head between the wheels, and worked at it from below, and dropped oil upon himself. Then he took it away from me, and doubled himself across it like a pack-saddle, till he lost his balance and slid over onto his head. Three times he said:

"Thank Heaven, that's right at last!"

And twice he said:

"No, I'm damned if it is after all!"

What he said the third time I try to forget.

Then he lost his temper and tried bullying the thing. The bicycle, I was glad to see, showed spirit; and the subsequent proceedings degenerated into little else than a rough-and-tumble fight between him and the machine. One moment the bicycle would be on the gravel-path, and he on top of it; the next, the position would be reversed — he on the gravel-path, the bicycle on him. Now he would be standing flushed with victory, the bicycle firmly fixed between his legs. But his triumph would be short-lived. By a sudden, quick movement it would free itself, and, turning upon him, hit him sharply over the head with one of its handles.

At a quarter to one, dirty and dishevelled, cut and bleeding, he said: "I think that will do," and rose and wiped his brow.

The bicycle looked as if it also had had enough of it. Which had received most punishment it would have been difficult to say. I took him into the back kitchen, where, so far as was possible without soda and proper tools, he cleaned himself, and sent him home.

The bicycle I put into a cab and took round to the nearest repairing-shop. The foreman of the works came up and looked at it.

"What do you want me to do with that?" said he.

"I want you," I said, "so far as is possible, to restore it."

"It's a bit far gone," said he; "but I'll do my best."

He did his best, which came to two pounds ten.

THE STATUES OF PRAGUE

It was in Prague that Harris and I did a kind and friendly thing to George. We had noticed for some time past that George was getting too fond of Pilsener beer. This German beer is an insidious drink, especially in hot weather; but it does not do to imbibe too freely of it. It does not get into your head, but after a time it spoils your waist. I always say to myself on entering Germany:

"Now, I will drink no German beer. The white wine of the country, with a little soda-water; perhaps occasionally a glass of Ems or potash. But beer, never — or, at all events, hardly ever."

It is a good and useful resolution, which I recommend to all travellers. I only wish I could keep to it myself. George, although I urged him, refused to bind himself by any such hard and fast limit. He said that in moderation German beer was good.

"One glass in the morning," said George, "one in the evening, or even two. That will do no harm to anyone."

Maybe he was right. It was his half-dozen glasses that troubled Harris and myself.

"We ought to do something to stop it," said Harris: "it is becoming serious."

"It's hereditary, so he has explained to me," I answered. "It seems his family have always been thirsty."

"There is Apollinaris water," replied Harris, "which, I believe, with a little lemon squeezed into it, is practically harmless. What I am thinking about is his figure. He will lose all his natural elegance."

We talked the matter over, and, Providence aiding us, we fixed upon a plan. For the ornamentation of the town a new statue had just been cast. I forget of whom it was a statue. I only remember that in the essentials it was the usual sort of street statue, representing the usual sort of gentleman, with the usual stiff neck, riding the usual sort of horse — the horse that always walks on its hind legs, keeping its front paws for beating time. But in detail it possessed individuality. Instead of the usual sword or baton, the man was holding, stretched out in his hand, his own plumed hat; and the horse, instead of the usual waterfall for a tail, possessed a somewhat attenuated appendage that somehow appeared out of keeping with his ostentatious behaviour. One felt that a horse with a tail like that would not have pranced so much.

It stood in a small square not far from the farther end of the Karlsbrücke, but it stood there only temporarily. Before deciding finally where to fix it, the town authorities had resolved, very sensibly, to judge by practical test where it would look best. Accordingly, they had made three rough copies of the statue — mere wooden profiles, things that would not bear looking at closely, but which, viewed from a little distance, produced all the effect that was necessary. One of these they had set up at the approach to the Franz-Josefsbrücke, a second stood in the open space behind the theatre, and the third in the centre of the Wenzelsplatz.

"If George is not in the secret of this thing," said Harris — we were walking by ourselves for an hour, he having remained behind in the hotel to write a letter to his aunt — "if he has not observed these statues, then by their aid we will make a better and a thinner man of him, and that this very evening."

So during dinner we sounded him, judiciously; and finding him ignorant of the matter, we took him out, and led him by side-streets to the place where stood the real statue. George was for looking at it and passing on, as is his way with statues, but we insisted on his pulling up and viewing the thing conscientiously. We walked him round that statue four times, and showed it to him from every possible point of view. I think, on the whole, we rather bored him with the thing, but our object was to impress it upon him. We told him the history of the man who rode upon the horse, the name of the artist who had made the statue, how much it weighed, how much it measured. We worked that statue into his system. By the time we had done with him he knew more about that statue, for the time being, than he knew about anything else. We soaked him in that statue, and only let him go at last on the condition that he would come again with us in the morning, when we could all see it better, and for such purpose we saw to it that he made a note in his pocket-book of the place where the statue stood.

Then we accompanied him to his favourite beer hall, and sat beside him, telling him anecdotes of men who, unaccustomed to German beer, and drinking too much of it, had gone mad and developed homicidal mania; of men who had died young through drinking German beer; of lovers that German beer had been the means of parting for ever from beautiful girls.

At ten o'clock we started to walk back to the hotel. It was a stormy-looking night, with heavy clouds drifting over a light moon. Harris said:

"We won't go back the same way we came, we'll walk back by the river. It is lovely in the moonlight."

Harris told a sad history, as we walked, about a man he once knew, who is now in a home for harmless imbeciles. He said he recalled the story because it was on just such another night as this that he was walking with that man the very last time he ever saw the poor fellow. They were strolling down the Thames Embankment, Harris said, and the man frightened him then by persisting that he saw the statue of the Duke of Wellington at the corner of Westminster Bridge, when, as everybody knows, it stands in Piccadilly.

It was at this exact instant that we came in sight of the first of these wooden copies. It occupied the centre of a small, railed-in square a little above us on the opposite side of the way. George suddenly stood still and leant against the wall of the quay.

"What's the matter?" I said. "Feeling giddy?"

He said: "I do, a little. Let's rest here a moment."

He stood there with his eyes glued to the thing. He said, speaking huskily:

"Talking of statues, what always strikes me is how very much one statue is like another statue."

Harris said: "I cannot agree with you there — pictures, if you like. Some pictures are very like other pictures, but with a statue there is always something distinctive. Take that statue we saw early in the evening," continued Harris, "before we went into the concert hall. It represented a man sitting on a horse. In Prague you will see other statues of men on horses, but nothing at all like that one."

"Yes, they are," said George; "they are all alike. It's always the same horse, and it's always the same man. They are all exactly alike. It's idiotic nonsense to say they are not."

He appeared to be angry with Harris.

"What makes you think so?" I asked.

"What makes me think so?" retorted George, now turning upon me. "Why, look at that damned thing over there!"

I said: "What damned thing?"

"Why, that thing," said George: "look at it! There is the same horse with half a tail, standing on its hind legs; the same man without his hat; the same ——"

Harris said: "You are talking now about the statue we saw in the Ringplatz."

"No, I'm not," replied George: "I'm talking about the statue over there."

"What statue?" said Harris.

George looked at Harris; but Harris is a man who might, with care, have been a fair amateur actor. His face merely expressed friendly sorrow, mingled with alarm. Next, George turned his gaze on me. I endeavoured, so far as lay with me, to copy Harris's expression, adding to it on my own account a touch of reproof.

"Will you have a cab?" I said as kindly as I could to George. "I'll run and get one."

"What the devil do I want with a cab?" he answered ungraciously. "Can't you fellows understand a joke? It's like being out with a couple of confounded old women," saying which, he started off across the bridge, leaving us to follow.

"I am so glad that was only a joke of yours," said Harris, on

31

our overtaking him. "I knew a case of softening of the brain that began——"

"Oh, you're a silly ass!" said George, cutting him short. "You know everything."

He was really most unpleasant in his manner.

We took him round by the river side of the theatre. We told him it was the shortest way, and, as a matter of fact, it was. In the open space behind the theatre stood the second of these wooden apparitions. George looked at it, and again stood still.

"What's the matter?" said Harris kindly. "You are not ill, are you?"

"I don't believe this is the shortest way," said George.

"I assure you it is," persisted Harris.

"Well, I'm going the other," said George; and he turned and went: we, as before, following him.

Along the Ferdinand Strasse Harris and I talked about private lunatic asylums, which, Harris said, were not well managed in England. He said a friend of his, a patient in a lunatic asylum——

George said, interrupting: "You appear to have a large number of friends in lunatic asylums."

He said it in a most insulting tone, as though to imply that is where one would look for the majority of Harris's friends. But Harris did not get angry; he merely replied, quite mildly:

"Well, it really is extraordinary, when one comes to think of it, how many of them have gone that way sooner or later. I get quite nervous sometimes, now."

At the corner of the Wenzelplatz, Harris, who was a few steps ahead of us, paused.

"It's a fine street, isn't it? he said, sticking his hands in his pockets, and gazing up at it admiringly.

George and I followed suit. Two hundred yards away from us, in its very centre, was the third of these ghostly statues. I think it was the best of the three — the most like, the most deceptive. It stood boldly outlined against the wild sky: the horse on its hind legs, with its curiously attenuated tail; the man bare-headed, pointing with his plumed hat to the now entirely visible moon.

"I think, if you don't mind," said George — he spoke with

almost a pathetic ring in his voice, his aggressiveness had completely fallen from him— "that I will have that cab, if there's one handy."

"I thought you were looking queer," said Harris kindly. "It's your head, isn't it?"

"Perhaps it is," answered George.

"I have noticed it coming on," said Harris; "but I didn't like to say anything to you. You fancy you see things, don't you?"

"No, no; it isn't that," replied George, rather quickly. "I don't know what it is."

"I do," said Harris solemnly, "and I'll tell you. It's this German beer that you are drinking. I have known a case where a man——"

"Don't tell me about him just now," said George. "I dare say it's true, but somehow I don't feel I want to hear about him."

"You are not used to it," said Harris.

"I shall give it up from tonight," said George. "I think you must be right; it doesn't seem to agree with me."

We took him home, and saw him to bed. He was very gentle and quite grateful.

One evening later on, after a long day's ride, followed by a most satisfactory dinner, we started him on a big cigar, and, removing things from his reach, told him of this stratagem that for his good we had planned.

"How many copies of that statue did you say we saw?" asked George, after we had finished.

"Three," replied Harris.

"Only three?" said George. "Are you quite sure?"

"Positive," replied Harris. "Why?"

"Oh, nothing!" answered George.

But I don't think he quite believed Harris.

JAMES MATTHEW BARRIE

THE PERILS OF NOT SMOKING

When the Arcadians heard that I had signed an agreement to give up smoking they were first incredulous, then sarcastic, then angry. Instead of coming as usual to my room they went one night in a body to Pettigrew's, and there, as I afterwards discovered, a scheme for "saving me" was drawn up. So little did they understand the firmness of my character that they thought I had weakly yielded to the threats of the lady referred to in my first chapter, when, of course, I had only yielded to her arguments, and they agreed to make an appeal on my behalf to her. Pettigrew, as a married man himself, was appointed intercessor, and I understand that the others not only accompanied him to her door but waited in an alley until he came out. I never knew whether the reasoning brought to bear on the lady was of Pettigrew's devising or suggested by Jimmy and the others, but it was certainly unselfish of Pettigrew to lie so freely on my account. At the time, however, the plot enraged me, for the lady conceived the absurd idea that I had sent Pettigrew to her.

Undoubtedly it was a bold stroke. Pettigrew's scheme was to play upon his hostess's attachment for me by hinting to her that if I gave up smoking I would probably die. Finding her attentive rather than talkative, he soon dared to assure her that he himself loathed tobacco and only took it for his health.

"By the doctor's orders, mark you," he said, impressively, "Dr. Southwick, of Hyde Park."

She expressed polite surprise at this, and then Pettigrew, believing he had made an impression, told his story as concocted.

"My own case," he said, "is one much in point. I suffered lately from sore throat, accompanied by depression of spirits and loss of appetite. The ailment was so unusual with me that I thought it prudent to put myself in Dr. Southwick's hands. As far as possible I shall give you his exact words:

" 'When did you give up smoking?' he asked, abruptly, after examining my throat.

" 'Three months ago,' I replied, taken by surprise, 'but how did you know I had given it up?'

" 'Never mind how I knew,' he said, severely; 'I told you that, however much you might desire to do so, you were not to take to not smoking. This is how you carry out my directions.'

" 'Well,' I answered, sulkily, 'I have been feeling so healthy for the last two years that I thought I could indulge myself a little. You are aware how I abominate tobacco.'

" 'Quite so,' he said, 'and now you see the result of this miserable self-indulgence. Two years ago I prescribed tobacco for you, to be taken three times a day, and you yourself admit that it made a new man of you. Instead of feeling thankful, you complain of the brief unpleasantness that accompanies its consumption, and now in the teeth of my instructions you give it up. I must say the ways of patients are a constant marvel to me.'

" 'But how,' I asked, 'do you know that my reverting to the pleasant habit of not smoking is the cause of my present ailment?'

" 'Oh!' he said, 'you are not sure of that yourself, are you?'

" 'I thought,' I replied, 'there might be a doubt about it; though of course I have not forgotten what you told me two years ago.'

" 'It matters very little,' he said, 'whether you remember what I tell you if you do not follow my orders. But as for knowing that indulgence in not smokir is what has brought you to this state, how long is it since you noticed these symptoms?'

" 'I can hardly say,' I answered. 'Still I should be able to think back. I had my first sore throat this year the night I saw Mr. Irving at the Lyceum, and that was on my wife's birthday, the 3rd of October. How long ago is that?'

" 'Why, that is more than three months ago. Are you sure of the date?'

" 'Quite certain,' I told him; 'so you see I had my first sore throat before I risked not smoking again.'

" 'I don't understand this,' he said. 'Do you mean to say that in the beginning of May you were taking my prescription daily? You were not missing a day now and then — forgetting to order a new stock of cigars when the others were done, of flinging them away before they were half smoked? Patients do such things.'

" 'No, I assure you I compelled myself to smoke. At least —'

" 'At least what? Come, now, if I am to be of any service to you, there must be no reserve.'

" 'Well, now that I think of it, I was only smoking one cigar a day at that time.'

" 'Ah! we have it now,' he cried. 'One cigar a day, when I ordered you three. I might have guessed as much. When I tell non-smokers that they must smoke or I will not be answerable for the consequences, they entreat me to let them break themselves of the habit of not smoking gradually. One cigarette a day to begin with, they beg of me, promising to increase the dose by degrees. Why, man, one cigarette a day is poison; it is worse than not smoking.'

" 'But that is not what I did.'

" 'The idea is the same,' he said. 'Like the others, you make all this moan about giving up completely a habit you should never have acquired. For my own part, I cannot even understand where the subtle delights of not smoking come in. Compared with health, they are surely immaterial?'

" 'Of course, I admit that.'

" 'Then, if you admit it, why pamper yourself?'

" 'I suppose because one is weak in matters of habit. You have many cases like mine?'

" 'I have such cases every week,' he told me; 'indeed, it was having so many cases of the kind that made me a specialist in the subject. When I began practice I had not the least notion how common the non-tobacco throat, as I call it, is."

" 'But the disease has been known, has it not, for a long time?'

" 'Yes,' he said; 'but the cause has only been discovered recently. I could explain the malady to you scientifically, as many medical men would prefer to do; but you are better to have it in plain English.'

" 'Certainly; but I should like to know whether the symptoms in other cases have been in every way similar to mine.'

" 'They have doubtless differed in degree, but not otherwise,' he answered. 'For instance, you say your sore throat is accompanied by depression of spirits.'

" 'Yes; indeed the depression sometimes precedes the sore throat."

" 'Exactly. I presume, too, that you feel most depressed in the evening — say, immediately after dinner?'

" 'That is certainly the time I experience the depression most.'

" 'The result,' he said, 'if I may venture on somewhat delicate matters, is that your depression of spirits infects your wife and family, even your servants?'

" 'That is quite true,' I answered. 'Our home has by no means been so happy as formerly. When a man is out of spirits, I suppose, he tends to be brusque and undemonstrative to his wife, and to be easily irritated by his children. Certainly that has been the case with me of late.'

" 'Yes,' he exclaimed, 'and all because you have not carried out my directions. Men ought to see that they have no right to indulge in not smoking, if only for the sake of their wives and families. A bachelor has more excuse, perhaps; but think of the example you set your children in not making an effort to shake this self-indulgence off. In short, smoke for the sake of your wife and family if you won't smoke for the sake of your health.' "

I think this is pretty nearly the whole of Pettigrew's story, but I may add that he left the house in depression of spirits, and then infected Jimmy and the others with the same ailment, so that they should all have hurried in a cab to the house of Dr. Southwick.

"Honestly," Pettigrew said, "I don't think she believed a word I told her."

"If she had only been a man," Marriot sighed, "we could have got round her."

"How?" asked Pettigrew.

"Why, of course," said Marriot, "we could have sent her a tin of the Arcadia."

HECTOR HUGH MUNRO (SAKI)

REGINALD'S CHRISTMAS

They say (said Reginald) that there's nothing sadder than victory except a defeat. If you've ever stayed with dull people during what is alleged to be the festive season, you can probably revise that saying. I shall never forget putting in a Christmas at the Babwolds'. Mrs. Babwold is some relation of my father's — a sort of to-be-left-till-called-for cousin — and that was considered sufficient reason for my having to accept her invitation at about the sixth time of asking though why the sins of the fathers should be visited by the children — you won't find any notepaper in that drawer; that's where I keep old menus and first-night programmes.

Mrs. Babwold wears a rather solemn personality, and has never been known to smile, even when saying disagreeable things to her friends or making out the Stores list. She takes her pleasures sadly. A state elephant at a Durbar gives one a very similar impression. Her husband gardens in all weathers. When a man goes out in the pouring rain to brush caterpillars off rose trees, I generally imagine his life indoors leaves something to be desired; anyway, it must be very unsettling for the caterpillars.

Of course there were other people there. There was a Major Somebody who had shot things in Lapland, or somewhere of that sort; I forget what they were, but it wasn't for want of re-

39

minding. We had them cold with every meal almost, and he was continually giving us details of what they measured from tip to tip, as though he thought we were going to make them warmunderthings for the winter. I used to listen to him with a rapt attention that I thought rather suited me, and then one day I quite modestly gave the dimensions of an okapi I had shot in the Lincolnshire fens. The Major turned a beautiful Tyrian scarlet (I remember thinking at the time that I should like my bathroom hung in that colour), and I think that at that moment he almost found it in his heart to dislike me. Mrs. Babwold put on a first-aid-to-the-injured expression, and asked him why he didn't publish a book of his sporting reminiscences; it would be *so* interesting. She didn't remember till afterwards that he had given her two fat volumes on the subject, with his portrait and autograph as a frontispiece and an appendix on the habits of the Arctic mussel.

It was in the evening that we cast aside the cares and distraction of the day and really lived. Cards were thought to be too frivolous and empty a way of passing the time, so most of them played what they called a book game. You went out into the hall — to get an inspiration, I suppose — then you came in again with a muffler tied round your neck and looked silly, and the others were supposed to guess that you were "Wee MacGregor". I held out against the inanity as long as I decently could, but at last, in a lapse of good-nature, I consented to masquerade as a book, only I warned them that it would take some time to carry out. They waited for the best part of forty minutes while I went and played wineglass skittles with the page-boy in the pantry; you play it with a champagne cork, you know, and the one who knocks down the most glasses without breaking them wins. I won, with four unbroken out of seven; I think William suffered from over-anxiousness. They were rather mad in the drawing-room at my not having come back, and they weren't a bit pacified when I told them afterwards that I was "At the end of the passage".

"I never did like Kipling," was Mrs. Babwold's comment, when the situation dawned upon her. "I couldn't see anything clever in 'Earthworms out of Tuscany' — or is that by Darwin?"

Of course these games are very educational, but, personally, I prefer bridge.

On Christmas evening we were supposed to be specially festive in the Old English fashion. The hall was horribly draughty, but it seemed to be the proper place to revel in, and it was decorated with Japanese fans and Chinese lanterns, which gave it a very Old English effect. A young lady with a confidential voice favoured us with a long recitation about a little girl who died or did something equally hackneyed, and then the Major gave us a graphic account of a struggle he had with a wounded bear. I privately wished that the bears would win sometimes on these occasions; at least they wouldn't go vapouring about it afterward. Before we had time to recover our spirits, we were indulged with some thought-reading by a young man whom one knew instinctively had a good mother and an indifferent tailor — the sort of young man who talks unflaggingly through the thickest soup, and smooths his hair dubiously as though he thought it might hit back. The thought-reading was rather a success; he announced that the hostess was thinking about poetry, and she admitted that her mind was dwelling on one of Austin's odes. Which was near enough. I fancy she had been really wondering whether a scrag-end of mutton and some cold plum-pudding would do for the kitchen dinner next day. As a crowning dissipation, they all sat down to play progressive halma, with milk-chocolate for prizes. I've been carefully brought up, and I don't like to play games of skill for milk-chocolate, so I invented a headache and retired from the scene. I had been preceded a few minutes earlier by Miss Langshan-Smith, a rather formidable lady, who always got up at some uncomfortable hour in the morning, and gave you the impression that she had been in communication with most of the European Governments before breakfast. There was a paper pinned on her door with a signed request that she might be called particularly early on the morrow. Such an opportunity does not come twice in a lifetime. I covered up everything except the signature with another notice, to the effect that before these words should meet the eye she would have ended a misspent life, was sorry for the trouble she was giving, and would like a military funeral. A few minutes later I violently exploded an air-filled

41

paper-bag on the landing, and gave a stage moan that could have been heard in the cellars. Then I pursued my original intention and went to bed. The noise those people made in forcing open the good lady's door was positively indecorous; she resisted gallantly, but I believe they searched her for bullets for about a quarter of an hour, as if she had been a historic battlefield.

I hate travelling on Boxing Day, but one must occasionally do things that one dislikes.

THE RETICENCE OF LADY ANNE

Egbert came into the large, dimly lit drawing-room with the air of a man who is not certain whether he is entering a dove-cote or a bomb factory, and is prepared for either eventuality. The little domestic quarrel over the luncheon-table had not been fought to a definite finish, and the question was how for Lady Anne was in a mood to renew or forgo hostilities. Her pose in the arm-chair by the tea-table was rather elaborately rigid; in the gloom of a December afternoon Egbert's pince-nez did not materially help him to discern the expression of her face.

By way of breaking whatever ice might be floating on the surface he made a remark about a dim religious light. He or Lady Anne were accustomed to make that remark between 4:30 and 6 on winter and late autumn evenings; it was a part of their married life. There was no recognised rejoinder to it, and Lady Anne made none.

Don Tarquinio lay astretch on the Persian rug, basking in the fire-light with superb indifference to the possible ill-humour of Lady Anne. His pedigree was as flawlessly Persian as the rug, and his ruff was coming into the glory of its second winter. The page-boy, who had Renaissance tendencies, had christened him Don Tarquinio. Left to themselves, Egbert and Lady Anne would unfailingly have called him Fluff, but they were not obstinate.

Egbert poured himself out some tea. As the silence gave no sign of breaking on Lady Anne's initiative, he braced himself for another Yermak effort.

"My remark at lunch had a purely academic application," he announced; "you seem to put an unneccessarily personal significance into it."

Lady Anne maintained her defensive barrier of silence. The bullfinch lazily filled in the interval with an Air from *Iphigénie en Tauride*. Egbert recognized it immediately, because it was the only air the bullfinch whistled, and he had come to them with the reputation for whistling it. Both Egbert and Lady Anne would have preferred something from *The Yeoman of the Guard,* which was their favourite opera. In matters artistic they had a similarity of taste. They leaned towards the honest and explicit in art, a picture, for instance, that told its own story, with generous assistance from its title. A riderless war-horse with harness in obvious disarray, staggering into a courtyard full of pale swooning women, and marginally noted "Bad News," suggested to their minds a distinct interpretation of some military catastrophe. They could see what it was meant to convey, and explain it to friends of duller intelligence.

The silence continued. As a rule Lady Anne's displeasure became articulate and markedly voluble after four minutes of introductory muteness. Egbert seized the milk-jug and poured some of its contents into Don Tarquinio's saucer; as the saucer was already full to the brim an unsightly overflow was the result. Don Tarquinio looked on with a surprised interest that evanesced into elaborate unconsciousness when he was appealed to by Egbert to come and drink up some of the spilt matter. Don Tarquinio was prepared to play many roles in life, but a vacuum carpet-cleaner was not one of them.

"Don't you think we're being rather foolish?" said Egbert cheerfully.

If Lady Anne thought so she didn't say so.

"I dare say the fault has been partly on my side," continued Egbert, with evaporating cheerfulness. "After all, I'm only human, you know. You seem to forget that I'm only human."

He insisted on the point, as if there had been unfounded suggestions that he was built on Satyr lines, with goat continuations where the human left off.

The bullfinch recommenced its air from *Iphigénie en Tauride*. Egbert began to feel depressed. Lady Anne was not drinking her tea. Perhaps she was feeling unwell. But when Lady Anne felt unwell she was not wont to be reticent on the subject. "No one knows what I suffer from indigestion" was one of her favourite statements; but the lack of knowledge can only have been caused by defective listening; the amount of information available on the subject would have supplied material for a monograph.

Evidently Lady Anne was not feeling unwell.

Egbert began to think he was being unreasonably dealt with; naturally he began to make concessions.

"I dare say," he observed, taking as central a position on the hearth-rug as Don Tarquinio could be persuadad to concede him, "I may have been to blame. I am willing, if I can thereby restore things to a happier standpoint, to undertake to lead a better life."

He wondered vaguely how it would be possible. Temptations came to him, in middle age, tenatively and without insistence, like a neglected butcher-boy who asks for a Christmas box in February for no more hopeful reason than that he didn't get one in December. He had no more idea of succumbing to them than he had of purchasing the fish-knives and fur boas that ladies are impelled to sacrifice through the medium of advertisement columns during twelve months of the year. Still, there was something impressive in this unasked-for renunciation of possibly latent enormities.

Lady Anne showed no sign of being impressed.

Egbert looked at her nervously through his glasses. To get the worst of an argument with her was no new experience. To get the worst of a monologue was a humiliating novelty.

"I shall go and dress for dinner," he announced in a voice into which he intended some shade of sternness to creep.

At the door a final access of weakness impelled him to make a further appeal.

"Aren't we being very silly?"

"A fool," was Don Tarquinio's mental comment as the door closed on Egbert's retreat. Then he lifted his velvet fore-paws in the air and leapt lightly on to a bookshelf immediately under the bullfinch's cage. It was the first time he had seemed to notice the bird's existence, but he was carrying out a long-formed theory of action with the precision of mature delibera-tion. The bullfinch, who had fancied himself something of a despot, depressed himself of a sudden into a third of his nor-mal displacement; then he fell to a helpless wing-beating and shrill cheeping. He had cost twenty-seven shillings without the cage, but Lady Anne made no sign of interfering. She had been dead for two hours.

TEA

James Cushat-Prinkly was a young man who had always had a settled conviction that one of these days he would marry; up to the age of thirty-four he had done nothing to jus-tify that conviction. He liked and admired a great many women collectively and dispassionately without singling out one for especial matrimonial consideration, just as one might admire the Alps without feeling that one wanted any particu-lar peak as one's own private property. His lack of initiative in this matter aroused a certain amount of impatience among the sentimentally minded women-folk of his home circle; his mother, his sisters, an aunt-in-residence, and two or three intimate matronly friends regarded his dilatory approach to the married state with a disapproval that was far from being inarticulate. His most innocent flirtations were watched with the straining eagerness which a group of unexercised terriers concentrates on the slightest movements of a human being who may be reasonably considered likely to take them for a walk. No decent-souled mortal can long resist the pleading of several pairs of walk-beseeching dog-eyes; James Cushat-Prinkly was not sufficiently obstinate or indifferent to home influences to disregard the obviously expressed wish of his family that he should become enamoured of some nice marriageable girl, and when his Uncle Jules departed this life and bequeathed him a comfortable little legacy it really seemed the correct thing to do to set about discovering some one to share it with him. The process of discovery was carried on more by the force of suggestion and the weight of public opinion than by any initiative of his own; a clear working majority of his female relatives and the aforesaid matronly friends had pitched on Joan Sebastable as the most suitable young woman in his range of acquaintance to whom he might propose marriage, and James became gradually accustomed to the idea that he and Joan would go together through the prescribed stages of congratulations, present-receiving, Norwegian or Mediterranean hotels, and eventual domesticity. It was necessary, however, to ask the lady what she thought about the matter; the family had so far conducted and directed the flirtation with ability and discretion, but the actual proposal would have to be an individual effort.

Cushat-Prinkly walked across the Park towards the Sebastable residence in a frame of mind that was moderately complacent. As the thing was going to be done he was glad to feel that he was going to get it settled and off his mind that afternoon. Proposing marriage, even to a nice girl like Joan, was a rather irksome business, but one could not have a honeymoon in *Minorca* and a subsequent life of married happiness without such preliminary. He wondered what Minorca was really like as a place to stop in; in his mind's eye it was an island in perpetual half-mourning, with black or white *Minorca hens* running all over it. Probably it would not be a bit like that when one came to examine it. People who had been in Russia had told him that they did not remember having seen any *Muscovy ducks* there, so it was possible that there would be no Minorca fowls on the island.

Mediterranean musings were interrupted by the sound of a clock striking the half-hour. Half past four. A frown of dissatisfaction settled on his face. He would arrive at the Sebastable mansion just at the hour of afternoon tea. Joan would be seated at a low table, spread with an array of silver kettles and cream-jugs and delicate porcelain teacups, behind which her voice would tinkle pleasantly in a series of little friendly questions about weak or strong tea, how much, if any, sugar, milk, cream, and so forth. "Is it one lump? I forgot. You do take milk, don't you? Would you like some more hot water, if it's too strong?"

Cushat-Prinkly had read of such things in scores of novels, and hundreds of actual experiences had told him that they were true to life. Thousands of women, at this solemn afternoon hour, were sitting behind dainty porcelain and silver fittings, with their voices tinkling pleasantly in a cascade of solicitous little questions. Cushat-Prinkly detested the whole system of afternoon tea. According to his theory of life a woman should lie on a divan or couch, talking with incomparable charm or looking unutterable thoughts, or merely silent as a thing to be looked on, and from behind a silken curtain a small Nubian page should silently bring in a tray with cups and dainties, to be accepted silently, as a matter of course, without drawn-out chatter about cream and sugar and hot water. If one's soul was really enslaved at one's mistress's feet, how could one talk coherently about weakened tea? Cushat-Prinkly had never expounded his views on the subject to his mother; all her life she had been accustomed to tinkle pleasantly at tea-time behind dainty porcelain and silver, and if he had spoken to her about divans and Nubian pages she would have urged him to take a week's holiday at the seaside. Now, as he passed through a tangle of small streets that led indirectly to the elegant *Mayfair* terrace for which he was bound, a horror at the idea of confronting Joan Sebastable at her tea-table seized on him. A momentary deliverance presented itself; on one floor of a narrow little house at the noisier end of Esquimault Street lived Rhoda Ellam, a sort of remote cousin, who made a living by creating hats out of costly materials. The hats really looked as if they had come from Paris; the cheques she got for them unfortunately never looked as if they were going to Paris. However, Rhoda appeared to find life amusing and to have a fairly good time in spite of her straitened circumstances. Cushat-Prinkly decided to climb up to her floor and defer by half-a-hour or so the important business which lay before him; by spinning out his visit he could contrive to reach the Sebastable mansion after the last vestiges of dainty porcelain had been cleared away.

Rhoda welcomed him into a room that seemed to do duty as workshop, sitting-room, and kitchen combined, and to be wonderfully clean and comfortable at the same time.

"I'm having a picnic meal," she announced. "There's caviare in that jar at your elbow. Begin on that brown bread-and-butter while I cut some more. Find yourself a cup; the teapot is behind you. Now tell me about hundreds of things."

She made no other allusion to food, but talked amusingly and made her visitor talk amusingly too. At the same time she cut the bread-and-butter with a masterly skill and produced red pepper and sliced lemon, where so many women would merely have produced reasons and regrets for not having any. Cushat-Prinkly found that he was enjoying an excellent tea without having to answer as many questions about it as a Minister for Agriculture might be called on to reply to during an outbreak of cattle plague.

"And now tell me why you have come to see me," said Rhoda suddenly. "You arouse not merely my curiosity but my business instincts. I hope you've come about hats. I heard that you had come into a legacy the other day, and, of course, it struck me that it would be a beautiful and desirable thing for you to celebrate the event by buying brilliantly expensive hats for all your sisters. They may not have said anything about it, but I feel sure the same idea has occurred to them. Of course, with Goodwood on us, I am rather rushed just now, but in my business we're accustomed to that; we live in a series of rushes — like the infant Moses."

"I didn't come about hats," said her visitor. "In fact, I don't think I really came about anything. I was passing and I just thought I'd look in and see you. Since I've been sitting talking to you, however, a rather important idea has occurred to me. If you'll forget Goodwood for a moment and listen to me, I'll tell you what it is."

Some forty minutes later James Cushat-Prinkly returned to the bosom of his family, bearing an important piece of news.

"I'm engaged to be married," he announced.

A rapturous outbreak of congratulation and self-applause broke out.

"Ah, we knew! We saw it coming! We foretold it weeks ago!"

"I'll bet you didn't," said Cushat-Prinkly. "If any one had told me at lunch-time today that I was going to ask Rhoda Ellam to marry me and that she was going to accept me, I would have laughed at the idea."

The romantic suddenness of the affair in some measure compensated James's women-folk for the ruthless negation of all their patient effort and skilled diplomacy. It was rather trying to have to deflect their enthusiasm at a moment's notice from Joan Sebastable to Rhoda Ellam; but, after all, it was James's wife who was in question, and his tastes had some claim to be considered.

On a September afternoon of the same year, after the honeymoon in Minorca had ended, Cushat-Prinkly came into the drawing-room of his new house in Granchester Square. Rhoda was seated at a low table, behind a service of dainty porcelain and gleaming silver. There was a pleasant tinkling note in her voice as she handed him a cup.

"You like it weaker than that, don't you? Shall I put some more hot water to it? No?"

FILBOLD STUDGE, THE STORY OF
A MOUSE THAT
HELPED

"I want to marry your daughter," said Mark Spayley with faltering eagerness. "I am only an artist with an income of two hundred a year, and she is the daughter of an enormously wealthy man, so I suppose you will think my offer a piece of presumption."

Duncan Dullamy, the great company inflator, showed no outward sign of displeasure. As a matter of fact, he was secretly relieved at the prospect of finding even a two-hundred-a-year husband for his daughter Leonore. A crisis was rapidly rushing upon him, from which he knew he would emerge with neither money nor credit; all his recent ventures had fallen flat, and flattest of all had gone the wonderful new breakfast food, Pipenta, on the advertisement of which he had sunk such huge sums. It could scarcely be called a drug in the market; people bought drugs, but no one bought Pipenta.

"Would you marry Leonore if she were a poor man's daughter?" asked the man of phantom wealth.

"Yes," said Mark, widely avoiding the error of over-protestation. And to his astonishment Leonore's father not only gave his consent, but suggested a fairly early date for the wedding.

"I wish I could show my gratitude in some way," said Mark with genuine emotion. "I'm afraid it's rather like the mouse proposing to help the lion."

"Get people to buy that beastly muck," said Dullamy, nodding savagely at a poster of the despised Pipenta, "and you'll have done more than any of my agents have been able to accomplish."

"It wants a better name," said Mark reflectively, "and something distinctive in the poster line. Anyway, I'll have a shot at it."

Three weeks later the world was advised of the coming of a new breakfast food, heralded under the resounding name of "Filbold Studge." Spayley put forth no pictures of massive babies springing up with fungus-like rapidity under its forcing influence, or of representatives of the leading nations of the world scrambling with fatuous eagerness for its possession. One huge sombre poster depicted the Damned in Hell suffering a new torment from their inability to get at the Filbold Studge which elegant young fiends held in transparent bowls just beyond their reach. The scene was rendered even more gruesome by a subtle suggestion of the features of leading men and women of the day in the portrayal of the Lost Souls; prominent individuals of both political parties, Society hostesses, well-known dramatic authors and novelists, and distinguished aeroplanists were dimly recognizable in that doomed throng; noted lights of the musical-comedy stage flickered wanly in the shades of the Inferno, smiling still from force of habit, but with the fearsome smiling rage of baffled effort. The poster bore no fulsome allusions to the merits of the new breakfast food, but a single grim statement ran in bold letters along its base: "They cannot buy it now."

Spayley had grasped the fact that people will do things from a sense of duty which they would never attempt as a pleasure. There are thousands of respectable middle-class men who, if you found them unexpectedly in a Turkish bath, would explain in all sincerity that a doctor had ordered them to take Turkish baths; if you told them in return that you went there because you liked it, they would stare in pained wonder at the

51

frivolity of your motive. In the same way, whenever a massacre of Armenians is reported from Asia Minor, every one assumed that it has been carried out "under orders" from somewhere or another; no one seems to think that there are people who might like to kill their neighbours now and then.

And so it was with the new breakfast food. No one would have eaten Filbold Studge as a pleasure, but the grim austerity of its advertisement drove housewives in shoals to the grocers' shops to clamour for an immediate supply. In small kitchens solemn pig-tailed daughters helped depressed mothers to perform the primitive ritual of its preparation. On the breakfast-tables of cheerless parlours it was partaken of in silence. Once the womenfolk discovered that it was thoroughly unpalatable, their zeal in forcing it on their households knew no bounds. "You haven't eaten your Filbold Studge!" would be screamed at the appetiteless clerk as he hurried wearily from the breakfast-table, and his evening meal would be prefaced by a warmed-up mess which would be explained as "your Filbold Studge that you didn't eat this morning." Those strange fanatics who ostentatiously mortify themselves, inwardly and outwardly, with health biscuits and health garments, battened aggressively on the new food. Earnest spectacled young men devoured it on the steps of the *National Liberal Club*. A bishop who did not believe in a future state preached against the poster, and a peer's daughter died from eating too much of the compound. A further advertisement was obtained when an infantry regiment mutinied and shot its officers rather than eat the nauseous mess; fortunately, Lord Birrell of Blatherstone, who was War Minister at the moment, saved the situation by his happy epigram, that "Discipline to be effective must be optional."

Filbold Studge had become a household word, but Dullamy wisely realized that it was not necessarily the last word in breakfast dietary; its supremacy would be challenged as soon as some yet more unpalatable food should be put on the market. There might even be a reaction in favour of something tasty and appetizing, and the Puritan austerity of the moment might be banished from domestic cookery. At an opportune moment, therefore, he sold out his interests in the article which had brought him in colossal wealth at a critical juncture, and placed his financial reputation beyond the reach of cavil. As for Leonore, who was now an heiress on a far greater scale than ever before, he naturally found her something a vast deal higher in the husband market than a two-hundred-a-year poster designer. Mark Spayley, the brainmouse who had helped the financial lion with such untoward effect, was left to curse the day he produced the wonder-working poster.

"After all," said Clovis, meeting him shortly afterwards at his club, "you have this doubtful consolation, that *'tis not in mortals to countermand success.*"

MAX BEERBOHM

A GOOD PRINCE

I first saw him one morning of last summer, in the Green
Park. Though short, even insignificant, in stature and with an
obvious tendency to be obese, he had that unruffled, Olympian
air, which is so sure a sign of the Blood Royal. In a suit of
white linen he looked serenely cool, despite the heat. Perhaps
I should have thought him, had I not been versed in the *Almanach de Gotha*, a trifle older than he is. He did not raise his hat
in answer to my salute, but smiled most graciously and made
as though he would extend his hand to me, mistaking me,
I doubt not, for one of his friends. Forthwith, a member of his
suite said something to him in an undertone, whereat he
smiled again and took no further notice of me.

I do not wonder the people idolise him. His almost blame-
less life has been passed among them, nothing in it hidden
from their knowledge. When they look upon his dear present-
ment in the photographer's window — the shrewd, kindly eyes
under the high forehead, the sparse locks so carefully distributed — words of loyalty only and of admiration rise to
their lips. For of all princes in modern days he seems to fulfil
most perfectly the obligation of princely rank.

He might have been called in the heroic age, when princes
were judged according to their mastery of the sword or of the
bow, or have seemed, to those mediæval eyes that loved to see

54

a scholar's pate under the crown, an ignoramus. We are less exigent now. We do but ask of our princes that they should live among us, be often manifest to our eyes, set a perpetual example of a right life. We bid them be the ornaments of our State. Too often they do not attain to our ideal. They give, it may be, a half-hearted devotion to soldiering, or pursue pleasure merely — tales of their frivolity raising now and again the anger of a public swift to envy them their temptations. But against this admirable Prince no such charges can be made. Never (as yet, at least) has he cared to "play at soldiers." By no means has he shocked the Puritans. Though it is no secret that he prefers the society of ladies, not one breath of scandal has ever tinged his name. Of how many English princes could this be said, in days when Figaro, quill in hand, inclines his ear to every keyhole?

Upon one action that were well obliterated from his record I need not long insist. It seems that the wife of an aged ex-Premier came to have an audience and pay her respects. Hardly had she spoken when the Prince, in a fit of unreasoning displeasure, struck her a violent blow with his clenched fist. Had His Royal Highness not always stood so far aloof from political contention, it had been easier to find a motive for this unmannerly blow. The incident is deplorable, but it belongs, after all, to an earlier period of his life; and, were it not that no appreciation must rest upon the suppression of any scandal, I should not have referred to it. For the rest, I find no stain, so-ever faint, upon his life. The simplicity of his tastes is the more admirable for that he is known to care not at all for what may be reported in the newspapers. He has never touched a card, never entered a play-house. In no stud of racers has he indulged, preferring to the finest blood-horse ever bred a certain white and wooly lamb with a blue riband to its neck. This he is never tired of fondling. It is with him, like the roebuck of Henri Quatre, wherever he goes.

Suave and simple his life is! Narrow in range, it may be, but with every royal appurtenance of delight, for to him Love's happy favours are given and the tribute of glad homage, always, here and there and every other where. Round the flower-garden at Sandringham runs an old wall of red brick, streaked with ivy and topped infrequently with balls of stone. By its iron gates, that open to a vista of flowers, stand two kind policemen, guarding the Prince's procedure along that bright vista. As his perambulator rolls out of the gate of St. James's Palace, he stretches out his tiny hands to the scarlet sentinels. An obsequious retinue follows him over the lawns of the White Lodge, cooing and laughing, blowing kisses and praising him. Yet do not imagine his life has been all gaiety! The afflictions that befall royal personages always touch very poignantly the heart of the people, and it is not too much to say that all England watched by the cradle-side of Prince Edward in that dolorous hour, when first the little battlements rose about the rose-red roof of his mouth. I am glad to think that not one querulous word did His Royal Highness, in his great agony, utter. They only say that his loud, incessant cries bore testimony to the perfect lungs for which the House of Hanover is most justly famed. Irreiterate be the horror of that epoch!

As yet, when we know not even what his first words will be, it is too early to predict what verdict posterity will pass upon him. Already he has won the hearts of the people; but in the years which, it is to be hoped, still await him, he may accomplish more. *Attendons*! He stands alone among European princes — but, as yet, only with the aid of a chair.

AN INCIDENT

One afternoon in the early Spring of (I think) the year 1906, I took part, with Henry James, in an incident which afterwards seemed to me strangely and exactly like the basis of a short story written by himself— one of the many stories he wrote on the theme of an elderly and very eminent great writer in relation to an earnest young admirer and disciple.

I had been at a luncheon party given by Somerset Maugham at the Carlton Hotel, and I was on my way to my club, the Savile, which in those days was housed at the southern end of Piccadilly. A new monthly review had just been started, with a story in it by Henry James— a story entitled "The Velvet Glove." I was going straight to the Savile to read that story. There was a keen north-easterly wind blowing, and I was wearing a rather thin overcoat, and was therefore walking quickly. But I would have been speeding in any case, so eager was I to read that story. And then, half-way down the slope, I encountered a slowly ascending figure that seemed to me vaguely familiar. I must explain that hitherto it was only in drawing-rooms and dining-rooms that I had seen Henry James, and that his magnificently massive and shapely brow was what had always most impressed me there. Hence my momentary failure now to recognise him in a very large old top hat of which the brim came down almost to the level of his eyebrows. He, however, had identified *me* and he accosted me in the deeply ruminating manner that was his. He told me he had just come up to London from his home at Rye. He said he was "to all intents and purposes a country cousin," and he asked me whether there was any new exhibition of pictures for him to see. I was able to tell him that there was a very good one at the Grafton Galleries. He asked me, with much circumlocution, whether I would be inclined to act as his guide. I felt much honoured— and yet, to my great surprise, I heard myself saying instantly "Well, I'm afraid I can't. I have to be in Kensington at half-past three." "Ah," he said, "you young men, always entangled in webs of engagements, yes, yes..." and passed on up the slope.

What had prompted me to tell that fib? It wasn't merely the north-east wind and the thin overcoat and the prospect of having to walk slowly up that slope. It wasn't merely shyness and the fear that whatever I might have to say would seem cheap and tawdry to Henry James, that profoundly fastidious critic of men. Nor was it merely the presentiment that he would not share my admiration for that picture which was the outstanding one in the Grafton Galleries — young Augustus John's "Woman Smiling." It was mainly my aforesaid impatience to be reading "The Velvet Glove."

And here I was now in the Savile, reading it. It was, of course, a very good story, and yet, from time to time, I found my mind wandering away from it. It was not so characteristic, not so intensely Jamesian a story as James would have founded on the theme of what had just been happening between us — the theme of a disciple loyally — or unloyally? — preferring the Master's work to the Master.

RUDYARD KIPLING

Then it's collar 'im tight,
  In the name o' the Laws!
'Ustle 'im, shake 'im till 'e's sick,
  Wot, 'e *would*, would 'e? Well,
Then yer've got ter give 'im 'Ell,
An' it's trunch, trunch, truncheon does the trick.

POLICE STATION DITTIES.

I had spent Christmas Eve at the Club, listening to a grand pow-wow between certain of the choicer sons of Adam. Then Slushby had cut in. Slushby is one who writes to newspapers and is theirs obediently "HUMANITARIAN." When Slushby cuts in, men remember they have to be up early next morning.

Sharp round a corner on the way home, I collided with something firmer than the regulation pillar-box. I righted myself after the recoil and saw some stars that were very pretty indeed. Then I perceived the nature of the obstruction.

"Evening, Judlip," I said sweetly, when I had collected my hat from the gutter. "Have I broken the law, Judlip? If so, I'll go quiet."

"Time yer was in bed," grunted X, 36. "Yer Ma'll be lookin' out for yer."

This from the friend of my bosom! It hurt. Many were the night-beats I had been privileged to walk with Judlip, imbibing curious lore that made glad the civilian heart of me. Seven whole 8×5 inch note-books had I pitmanised to the brim with Judlip. And now to be repulsed as one of the uninitiated! It hurt horrid.

There is a thing called Dignity. Small boys sometimes stand on it. Then they have to be kicked. Then they get down, weeping. I don't stand on Dignity.

"What's wrong, Judlip?" I asked, more sweetly than ever. "Drawn a blank to-night?"

"Yuss. Drawn a blank blank blank. 'Aven't 'ad so much as a kick at a lorst dorg. Christmas Eve ain't wot it was." I felt for my note-book. "Lawd! I remembers the time when the drunks and disorderlies down this street was as thick as flies on a fly-paper. One just picked 'em orf with one's finger and thumb. A bloomin' battew, that's wot it wos."

"The night's yet young, Judlip," I insinuated, with a jerk of my thumb at the flaring windows of the "Rat and Blood Hound." At that moment the saloon-door swung open, emitting a man and woman who walked with linked arms and exceeding great care.

Judlip eyed them longingly as they tacked up the street. Then he sighed. Now, when Judlip sighs the sound is like unto that which issues from the vent of a Crosby boiler when the gauges are at 260° F.

"Come, Judlip!" I said. "Possess your soul in patience. You'll soon find some one to make an example of. Meanwhile"—I threw back my head and smacked my lips—"the usual, Judlip?"

In another minute I emerged through the swing-door, bearing a furtive glass of that same "usual," and nipped down the mews where my friend was wont to await these little tokens of esteem.

"To the Majesty of the Law, Judlip!"

When he had honoured the toast, I scooted back with the glass, leaving him wiping the beads off his beard-bristles. He was in his philosophic mood when I rejoined him at the corner.

"Wot am I?" he said, as we paced along. "A bloomin' cypher. Wot's the sarjint? 'E's got the Inspector over 'im. Over above the Inspector there's the Sooprintendent. Over above 'im's the old red-tape-masticatin' Yard. Over above that there's the 'Ome Sec. Wot's 'e? A cypher, like me. Why?" Judlip looked up at the stars. "Over above 'im's We Dunno Wot. Somethin' wot issues its horders an' regulations an' divisional injunctions, inscrootable like, but p'remptory; an' we 'as ter see as 'ow they're carried out, not arskin' no questions, but each man goin' about 'is dooty."

" 'Is dooty,' " said I, looking up from my note-book. "Yes, I've got that."

"Life ain't a bean-feast. It's a 'arsh reality. An' them as makes it a bean-feast 'as got to be 'arshly dealt with accordin'. That's wot the Force is put 'ere for from Above. Not as 'ow we ain't fallible. We makes our mistakes. An' when we makes 'em we sticks to 'em. For the honour o' thc Force. Which same is the jool Britannia wears on 'er bosom as a charm against hanarchy. That's wot the brarsted old Beaks don't understand. Yet remember Smithers of our Div.?"

I remembered Smithers — well. As fine, upstanding, square-toed, bullet-headed, clean-living a son of a gun as ever perjured himself in the box. There was nothing of the softy about Smithers. I took off my billicock to Smithers' memory.

"Sacrificed to public opinion? Yuss," said Judlip, pausing at a front door and flashing his 45 c.p. down the slot of a two-grade Yale. "Sacrificed to a parcel of screamin' old women wot ort ter 'ave gorn down on their knees an' thanked Gawd for such a protector. 'E'll be out in another 'alf year. Wot'll 'e do then, pore devil? Go a bust on 'is conduc' money an' throw in 'is lot with them same hexperts wot 'ad a 'oly terror of 'im." Then Judlip swore gently.

"What should you do, O Great One, if ever it were your duty to apprehend him?"

"Do? Why, yer blessed innocent, yer don't think I'd shirk a fair clean cop? Same time, I don't say as 'ow I wouldn't 'andle 'im tender like, for sake o' wot 'e wos. Likewise 'cos 'e'd be a stiff customer to tackle. Likewise 'cos——"

He had broken off, and was peering fixedly upwards at an angle of 85° across the moonlit street. "'Ullo!" he said in a hoarse whisper.

Striking an average between the direction of his eyes—for Judlip, when on the job, has a soul-stirring squint—I perceived some one in the act of emerging from a chimney-pot.

Judlip's voice clove the silence. "Wot are yer doin' hup there?"

The person addressed came to the edge of the parapet. I saw then that he had a hoary white beard, a red ulster with the hood up, and what looked like a sack over his shoulder. He said something or other in a voice like a concertina that has been left out in the rain.

"I dessay," answered my friend. "Just you come down, an' we'll see about that."

The old man nodded and smiled. Then—as I hope to be saved—he came floating gently down through the moonlight, with the sack over his shoulder and a young fir-tree clasped to his chest. He alighted in a friendly manner on the curb beside us.

Judlip was the first to recover himself. Out went his right arm, and the airman was slung round by the scruff of the neck, spilling his sack in the road. I made a bee-line for his shoulder-blades. Burglar or no burglar, he was the best airman out, and I was muchly desirous to know the precise nature of the apparatus under his ulster. A back-hander from Judlip's left caused me to hop quickly aside. The prisoner was squealing and whimpering. He didn't like the feel of Judlip's knuckles at his cervical vertebrae.

"Wot was yer doin' hup there?" asked Judlip tightening the grip.

"I'm S-Santa Claus, Sir. P-please, Sir, let me g-go."

"Hold him," I shouted. "He's a German!"

"It's my dooty ter caution yer that wotever yer say now may

be used in hevidence against yer, yer old sinner. Pick up that there sack, an' come along o' me."

The captive snivelled something about peace on earth, good will toward men.

"Yuss," said Judlip. "That's in the Noo Testament, ain't it? The Noo Testament contains some uncommon nice readin' for old gents an' young ladies. But it ain't included in the library o' the Force. We confine ourselves to the Old Testament — O.T., 'ot. An' 'ot you'll get it. Hup with that sack, an' quick march!"

I have seen worse attempts at a neck-wrench, but it was just not slippery enough for Judlip. And the kick that Judlip then let fly was a thing of beauty and a joy for ever.

"Frog's-march him!" I shrieked, dancing. "For the love of Heaven, frog's-march him!"

Trotting by Judlip's side to the Station, I reckoned it out that if Slushby had not been at the Club I should not have been here to see. Which shows that even Slushbys are put into this world for a purpose.

MAURICE BARING

KING LEAR'S DAUGHTER

Letter from Goneril, Daughter of King Lear,
to her sister Regan

I have writ my sister.

King Lear, Act I, Scene IV.

The Palace, November.

Dearest Regan,

I am sending you this letter by Oswald. We have been having the most trying time lately with Papa, and it ended today in
one of those scenes which are so painful to people like you and
me, who *hate* scenes. I am writing now to tell you all about it,
so that you may be prepared. This is what has happened.

When Papa came here he brought a hundred knights with
him, which is a great deal more than we could put up, and
some of them had to live in the village. The first thing that
happened was that they quarrelled with our people and refused to take orders from them, and whenever one told anyone
to do anything it was either — if it was one of Papa's men —
"not his place to do it"; or if it was one of our men, they said
that Papa's people made work impossible. For instance, only
the day before yesterday I found that blue vase which you
brought back from Dover for me on my last birthday broken

to bits. Of course I made a fuss, and Oswald declared that one of Papa's knights had knocked it over in a drunken brawl. I complained to Papa, who flew into a passion and said that his knights, and in fact all his retainers, were the most peaceful and courteous people in the world, and that it was my fault, as I was not treating him or them with the respect which they deserved. He even said that I was lacking in filial duty. I was determined to keep my temper, so I said nothing.

The day after this the chief steward and the housekeeper and both my maids came to me and said that they wished to give notice. I asked them why. They said they couldn't possibly live in a house where there were such "goings-on." I asked them what they meant. They refused to say, but they hinted that Papa's men were behaving not only in an insolent but in a positively outrageous manner to them. The steward said that Papa's knights were never sober, that they had entirely demoralised the household, and that life was simply not worth living in the house; it was *impossible* to get anything done, and they couldn't sleep at night for the noise.

I went to Papa and talked to him about it quite quietly, but no sooner had I mentioned the subject than he lost all self-control, and began to abuse me. I kept my temper as long as I could, but of course one is only human, and after I had borne his revilings for some time, which were monstrously unfair and untrue, I at last turned and said something about people of his age being trying. Upon which he said I was throwing up his old age at him, that I was a monster of ingratitude — and he began to cry. I cannot tell you how painful all this was to me. I did everything I could to soothe him and quiet him, but the truth is, ever since Papa has been here he has lost control of his wits. He suffers from the oddest kind of delusions. He thinks that for some reason he is being treated like a beggar; and although he has a hundred knights — a hundred, mind you! (a great deal more than we have) — in the house, who do nothing but eat and drink all day long, he says he is not being treated like a King! I do hate unfairness.

When he gave up the crown he said he was tired of affairs, and meant to have a long rest; but from the very moment that he handed over the management of affairs to us he never

64

stopped interfering, and was cross if he was not consulted about everything, and if his advice was not taken.

And what is still worse is this: ever since his last illness he has lost not only his memory but his control over language, so that often when he wants to say one thing he says just the opposite, and sometimes when he wishes to say some quite simple thing he uses *bad* language quite unconsciously. Of course we are used to this, and *we* don't mind, but I must say it is very awkward when strangers are here. For instance, the other day before quite a lot of people, quite unconsciously, he called me a dreadful name. Everybody was uncomfortable and tried not to laugh, but some people could not contain themselves. This sort of thing is constantly happening. So you will understand that Papa needs perpetual looking after and management. At the same time, the moment one suggests the slightest thing to him he boils over with rage.

But perhaps the most annoying thing which happened lately, or, at least, the thing which happens to annoy me most, is Papa's Fool. You know, darling, that I have always hated that kind of humour. He comes in just as one is sitting down to dinner, and beats one on the head with a hard, empty bladder, and sings utterly idiotic songs, which make me feel inclined to cry. The other day, when we had a lot of people here, just as we were sitting down in the banqueting-hall, Papa's Fool pulled my chair from behind me so that I fell sharply down on the floor. Papa shook with laughter, and said: "Well done, little Fool," and all the courtiers who were there, out of pure snobbishness, of course, laughed too. I call this not only very humiliating for me, but undignified in an old man and a king; of course Albany refused to interfere. Like all men and all husbands, he is an arrant coward.

However, the crisis came yesterday. I had got a bad headache, and was lying down in my room, when Papa came in from the hunt and sent Oswald to me, saying that he wished to speak to me. I said that I wasn't well, and that I was lying down — which was perfectly true — but that I would be down to dinner. When Oswald went to give my message Papa beat him, and one of his men threw him about the room and really hurt him, so that he has now got a large bruise on his forehead and a sprained ankle.

This was the climax. All our knights came to Albany and myself, and said that they would not stay with us a moment longer unless Papa exercised some sort of control over his men. I did not know what to do, but I knew the situation would have to be cleared up sooner or later. So I went to Papa and told him frankly that the situation was intolerable; that he must send away some of his people, and choose for the remainder men fitting to his age. The words were scarcely out of my mouth than he called me the most terrible names, ordered his horses to be saddled, and said that he would shake the dust from his feet and not stay a moment longer in this house. Albany tried to calm him, and begged him to stay, but he would not listen to a word, and said he would go and live with you.

So I am sending this by Oswald, that you may get it before Papa arrives and know how the matter stands. All I did was to suggest he should send away fifty of his men. Even fifty is a great deal, and puts us to any amount of inconvenience, and is a source of waste and extravagance — two things which I cannot bear. I am perfectly certain you will not be able to put up with his hundred knights any more than I was. And I beg you, my dearest Regan, to do your best to make Papa listen to sense. No one is fonder of him than I am. I think it would have been difficult to find a more dutiful daughter than I have always been. But there is a limit to all things, and one cannot have one's whole household turned into a pandemonium, and one's whole life into a series of wrangles, complaints, and brawls, simply because Papa in his old age is losing the control of his faculties. At the same time, I own that although I kept my temper for a long time, when it finally gave way I was perhaps a little sharp. I am not a saint, nor an angel, nor a lamb, but I do hate unfairness and injustice. It makes my blood boil. But I hope that you, with your angelic nature and your tact and your gentleness, will put everything right and make poor Papa listen to reason.

Let me hear at once what happens.

Your loving

GONERIL

P.S.—Another thing Papa does which is most exasperating is to throw up Cordelia at one every moment. He keeps on saying: "If only Cordelia were here," or "How unlike Cordelia!" And you will remember, darling, that when Cordelia was here Papa could not endure the sight of her. Her irritating trick of mumbling and never speaking up used to get terribly on his nerves. Of course, I thought he was even rather unfair on her, trying as she is. We had a letter from the French Court yesterday, saying that she is driving the poor King of France almost mad.

P.P.S.—It is wretched weather. The poor little ponies on the heath will have to be brought in.

THE REHEARSAL

SCENE.— *The Globe Theatre*, 1595. *On the stage the* AUTHOR, *the* PRODUCER *and the* STAGE MANAGER *are standing. A rehearsal of "Macbeth" is about to begin. Waiting in the wings are the actors who are playing the* WITCHES, BANQUO, MACDUFF, *etc. They are all men.*

THE STAGE MANAGER. We'd better begin with the last act.

THE PRODUCER. I think we'll begin with the first act. We've never done it all through yet.

THE STAGE MANAGER. Mr. Colman isn't here. It's no good doing the first act without Duncan.

THE PRODUCER. Where is Mr. Colman? Did you let him know about rehearsal?

THE STAGE MANAGER. I sent a messenger to his house in Gray's Inn.

THE FIRST WITCH. Mr. Colman is playing Psyche in a masque at Kenilworth. He won't be back until the day after to-morrow.

THE PRODUCER. That settles it. We'll begin with the fifth act.

THE FIRST WITCH. Then I suppose I can go.

THE SECOND WITCH. ⎱ And I suppose we
THE THIRD WITCH. ⎰ needn't wait.

THE STAGE MANAGER. Certainly not. We're going on to the fourth act as soon as we've done the fifth.

BANQUO. But I suppose you don't want me.

THE STAGE MANAGER. And what about your ghost entrance in Act IV? We must get the business right this time; besides, we'll do the second act if we've time. Now, Act V, Mr. Thomas and Mr. Bowles, please.

THE FIRST WITCH. Mr. Bowles can't come to-day. He told me to tell you. He's having a tooth pulled out.

THE STAGE MANAGER. Then will you read the waiting gentlewoman's part. Mr. Lyle. You can take this scrip.

[*The* FIRST WITCH *takes the scrip.*

Where is Mr. Thomas?

THE FIRST WITCH. He said he was coming.

THE STAGE MANAGER. We can't wait. I'll read his part. We'll leave out the beginning and just give Mr. Hughes his cue.

THE FIRST WITCH (*reading*). "Having no witness to confirm my speech."

THE STAGE MANAGER. Mr. Hughes.

THE FIRST WITCH. He was here a moment ago.

THE STAGE MANAGER (*louder*). Mr. Hughes.

Enter LADY MACBETH (MR. HUGHES, *a young man about* 24)

LADY MACBETH. Sorry. (*He comes on down some steps. L. C.*)

THE PRODUCER. That will never do, Mr. Hughes; there's no

necessity to say as if you were intoxicated, and you mustn't look at your feet.

LADY MACBETH. It's the steps. They're so rickety.

THE PRODUCER. We'll begin again from "speech."

[LADY MACBETH *comes on again. He looks straight in front of him and falls heavily on to the ground.*

I said those steps were to be mended yesterday.

[*The* FIRST WITCH *is convulsed with laughter.*

LADY MACBETH. There's nothing to laugh at.

THE PRODUCER. Are you hurt, Mr. Hughes?

LADY MACBETH. Not much. (*The steps are replaced by two supers.*)

THE PRODUCER. Now from "speech."

[MR. HUGHES *comes on again.*

THE PRODUCER. You must not hold the taper upside down.

LADY MACBETH. How can I rub my hands and hold a taper too? What's the use of the taper?

THE PRODUCER. You can rub the back of your hand. You needn't wash your hands in the air. That's better.

[*The dialogue between the* DOCTOR *and the* GENTLEWOMAN *proceeds until* LADY MACBETH'S *cue: "hour."*
Enter the DOCTOR (MR. THOMAS). *He waits R.*

LADY MACBETH. "Here's a damned spot."

THE STAGE MANAGER. No, no, Mr. Hughes, "Yet, here's a spot."

THE PRODUCER. Begin again from "hands."

GENTLEWOMAN. "It is an accustomed action with her, to seem thus washing her hands. I've known her to continue in this three-quarters of an hour."

LADY MACBETH. "Yet here's a damned spot."

THE STAGE MANAGER. It's not "damned" at all. That comes later.

LADY MACBETH. It's catchy. Couldn't I say "mark" instead of "spot" in the first line?

THE DOCTOR (*coming forward*). That would entirely spoil the effect of my "Hark!" You see "mark" rhymes with "Hark". It's impossible.

THE PRODUCER. Oh! It's you, Mr. Thomas. Will you go straight on. We'll do the whole scene over presently. Now from "hour."

LADY MACBETH. "Yes, here's a spot."

THE STAGE MANAGER. It's not "Yes," but "Yet," Mr. Hughes.

LADY MACBETH. "Yet here's a spot."

THE DOCTOR (*at the top of his voice*). "Hark!"

THE PRODUCER. Not so loud, Mr. Thomas, that would wake her up.

THE DOCTOR (*in a high falsetto.*) "Har-r-rk!" She spe-e-e-aks. I will ... set ... down."

THE PRODUCER. You needn't bleat that "speaks," Mr. Thomas, and the second part of that line is cut.

THE DOCTOR. It's not cut in my part. "Hark, she speaks."

LADY MACBETH. "Yet here's a spot."

THE STAGE MANAGER. No, Mr. Hughes; "out damned spot."

LADY MACBETH. Sorry.

THE PRODUCER. We must get that right. Now from "hour."

LADY MACBETH. "Yet here's a spot."

THE DOCTOR. "Hark! she speaks."

LADY MACBETH. "Get out, damned spot! Get out, I say! One, two, three, four: why there's plenty of time to do't. Oh! Hell! Fie, fie, my Lord! a soldier and a beard! What have we got to fear when none can call our murky power to swift account withal? You'd never have thought the old man had so much blood in him!"

THE AUTHOR. I don't think you've got those lines quite right yet, Mr. Hughes.

LADY MACBETH. What's wrong?

THE STAGE MANAGER. There's no "get." It's "one; two": and not "one, two, three, four." Then it's "Hell is murky." And there's no "plenty." And it's "a soldier and *afeared*," and not "a soldier and a *beard*."

THE AUTHOR. And after that you made two lines into rhymed verse.

MR. HUGHES. Yes, I know I did. I thought it wanted it.

THE PRODUCER. Please try to speak your lines as they are written, Mr. Hughes.

Enter Mr. Burbage, *who plays Macbeth.*

MR. BURBAGE. That scene doesn't go. Now don't you think Macbeth had better walk in his sleep instead of Lady Macbeth?

THE STAGE MANAGER. That's an idea.

THE PRODUCER. I think the whole scene might be cut. It's quite unnecessary.

LADY MACBETH. Then I shan't come on in the whole of the fifth act. If that scene's cut I shan't play at all.

THE STAGE MANAGER. We're thinking of transferring the scene to Macbeth. (*To the* AUTHOR.) It wouldn't need much altering. Would you mind rewriting that scene, Mr. Shakespeare? It wouldn't want much alteration. You'd have to change that line about Arabia. Instead of this "little hand," you might say: "All the perfumes of Arabia will not sweeten this horny hand." I'm not sure it isn't more effective.

THE AUTHOR. I'm afraid it might get a laugh.

MR. BURBAGE. Not if I play it.

THE AUTHOR. I think it's more likely that Lady Macbeth would walk in her sleep, but——

MR. BURBAGE. That doesn't signify. I can make a great hit in that scene.

LADY MACBETH. If you take that scene from me, I shan't play Juliet to-night.

THE STAGE MANAGER (*aside to* PRODUCER.) We can't possibly get another Juliet.

THE PRODUCER. On the whole, I think we must leave the scene as it is.

MR. BURBAGE. I've got nothing to do in the last act. What's the use of my coming to rehearsal when there's nothing for me to rehearse?

THE RRODUCER. Very well, Mr. Burbage. We'll go on to the Third Scene at once. We'll go through your scene again later, Mr. Hughes.

MR. BURBAGE. Before we do this scene there's a point I wish to settle. In Scene V, when Seyton tells me the Queen's dead, I say: "She should have died hereafter; there would have been a time for such a word"; and then the messenger enters. I should like a soliloquy here, about twenty or thirty lines, if possible in rhyme, in any case ending with a tag. I should like it to be about Lady Macbeth. Macbeth might have something touching to say about their happy domestic life, and the early days of their marriage. He might refer to their courtship. I must have something to make Macbeth sympathetic, otherwise the public won't stand it. He might say his better-half had left him, and then he might refer to her beauty. The speech might begin:

> O dearest chuck, it is unkind indeed
> To leave me in the midst of my sore need.

Or something of the kind. In any case it ought to rhyme. Could I have that written at once, and then we could rehearse it?

THE PRODUCER. Certainly, certainly, Mr. Burbage. Will you write it yourself, Mr. Shakespeare, or shall we get some one else to do it?

THE AUTHOR. I'll do it myself if some one will read my part.

THE PRODUCER. Let me see; I forget what is your part.

THE STAGE MANAGER. Mr. Shakespeare is playing Seyton. (*Aside.*) We cast him for Duncan, but he wasn't up to it.

THE PRODUCER. Mr. Kydd, will you read Mr. Shakespeare's part?

BANQUO. Certainly.

THE PRODUCER. Please let us have that speech, Mr. Shakespeare, as quickly as possible. (*Aside.*) Don't make it too long. Ten lines at the most.

THE AUTHOR (*aside.*) Is it absolutely necessary that it should rhyme?

THE PRODUCER. (*aside.*) No, of course not; that's Burbage's fad.

[*Exit the* AUTHOR *into the wings.*

MR. BURBAGE. I should like to go through the fight first.

THE PRODUCER. Very well, Mr. Burbage.

THE STAGE MANAGER. Macduff — Mr. Foote——

MACDUFF. I'm here.

MR. BURBAGE. I'll give you the cue:

72

"Why should I play the fool and like a Roman
Die on my sword, while there is life, there's hope;
The gashes are for them."

MACDUFF. "Turn, hell-hound, turn."

MR. BURBAGE. I don't think Macduff ought to call Macbeth a hell-hound.

THE PRODUCER. What do you suggest?

MR. BURBAGE. I should suggest: "False Monarch, turn." It's more dignified.

MACDUFF. I would rather say "hell-hound."

THE PRODUCER. Supposing we make it "King of Hell."

MR. BURBAGE. I don't think that would do.

THE PRODUCER. Then we must leave it for the present.

MACDUFF. "Turn, hell-hound, turn."

[*They begin to fight with wooden swords.*

THE STAGE MANAGER. You don't begin to fight till Macduff says "Give thee out."

MR. BURBAGE. I think we might run those two speeches into one, and I might say:

"Of all men I would have avoided thee,
But come on now, although my soul is charged
With blood of thine, I'll have no further words.
My voice is in my sword."

Then Macduff could say:

"O bloodier villain than terms can well express."

THE PRODUCER. We must consult the author about that.

MR. BURBAGE. We'll do the fencing without words first.

[*They begin to fight again,* MACDUFF *gives* MR. BUR-BAGE a *tremendous blow on the shoulder*

MR. BURBAGE. Oh! Oh! That's my rheumatic shoulder. Please be a little more careful, Mr. Foote. You know I've got no padding. I can't go on rehearsing now. I am very seriously hurt indeed.

MACDUFF. I'm sure I'm very sorry. It was entirely an accident.

MR. BURBAGE. I'm afraid I must go home. I don't feel up to it.

THE STAGE MANAGER. I'll send for some ointment. Please be

more careful, Mr. Foote. Couldn't you possibly see your way to take Scene III, Mr. Burbage?

MR. BURBAGE. I know Scene III backwards. However, I'll just run through my speech.

THE STAGE MANAGER. What? "This push will cheer me ever"?

MR. BURBAGE (*peevishly*). No, not that one. You know that's all right. That tricky speech about medicine. Give me the cue.

THE STAGE MANAGER. "That keep her from her rest."

MR. BURBAGE. "Cure her of that:
    Canst thou not minister to a sickly mind,
    Pull from the memory a booted sorrow,
    Rub out the troubles of the busy brain,
    And with a sweet and soothing antidote
    Clean the stiff bosom of that dangerous poison
    Which weighs upon the heart?"
There, you see, word-perfect. What did I say?

THE STAGE MANAGER. Yes, yes, Mr. Burbage. Here's Mr. Shakespeare.

THE AUTHOR. I've written that speech. Shall I read it?

THE PRODUCER. Please.

MR. SHAKESPEARE (*reads.*) "To-morrow, and to-morrow, and to-morrow
    Creeps in this petty pace from day to day,
    To the last syllable of recorded time;
    And all our yesterdays have lighted fools
    The way to dusty death. Out, out, brief candle!
    Life's but a walking shadow, a poor player
    That struts and frets his hour upon the stage,
    And then is heard no more; it is a tale
    Told by an idiot, full of sound and fury,
    Signifying nothing."

MR. BURBAGE. Well, you don't expect me to say that, I suppose. It's a third too short. There's not a single rhyme in it. It's got nothing to do with the situation, and it's an insult to the stage. "Struts and frets" indeed! I see there's nothing left for me but to throw up the part. You can get any one you please to play Macbeth. One thing is quite certain, I won't.

[*Exit* MR. BURBAGE *in a passion.*

74

THE STAGE MANAGER (*to the* AUTHOR.) Now you've done it.

THE AUTHOR (*to the* PRODUCER.) You said it needn't rhyme.

THE PRODUCER. It's Macduff. It was all your fault, Mr. Foote.

LADY MACBETH. Am I to wear a fair wig or a dark wig?

THE PRODUCER. Oh! I don't know.

THE AUTHOR. Dark, if you please. People are always saying I'm making portraits. So, if you're dark, nobody can say I meant the character for the Queen or for Mistress Mary Fytton.

THE STAGE MANAGER. It's no good going on now. It's all up—it's all up.

Curtain

EDMUND V. KNOX

THE PERFECT GUEST

On the hill opposite there is a tumulus; one sees it from the garden of the cottage; the sheep with their tinkling bells graze over it and around it. Little they think, as Lord Macaulay puts it, on those strong limbs that moulder deep below. Nor as a matter of fact do I think on them much at ordinary times. It was my brother Gregory who first made me do so.

"I think I'm coming down to spend the week-end with you," he said.

"Not if I know it," I answered, a little brusquely perhaps, but you must understand that Gregory is hardly the fellow to take a quiet hint.

"I suppose I'd better bring golf-clubs," he went on. "What kind of course is it?"

"Practically untouched since the Romans came," I responded cheerfully. "The pagan soil that Wilfred found, if you remember."

"Never mind," said Gregory: "It'll be good for a round or so yet. What else is there to do?"

In all the books on etiquette that I have read it is explained that the tactful host does not map out the day too precisely for his guest in advance; there seems to be no established code of honour preventing the tactless guest from mapping out the day too precisely for his host. I felt that Gregory was taking advantage of this.

"There are many primroses," I told him, "in the little hollows of the woods—primroses and violets. How will you like to go out and fill your hands with bunches of primroses and violets, Gregory?"

"One can bathe, I suppose," he continued meditatively. "Would you mind if I brought down my red-striped bathing-suit?"

"Not if you keep the bathroom door shut," I said.

"In the sea, I meant. You could run me down before break-fast in the car, if the weather's decent, couldn't you? It's not more than a mile away."

I looked rather anxiously at him.

"Feverish, I'm afraid," I said in a soothing voice, "feverish. Does the heart murmur at all, I wonder?"

Gregory puffed at his pipe.

"Are there any horses, by the way?" he asked suddenly.

I jumped.

"How do you mean, are there any horses?" I said.

"Can't we get a couple of horses to ride on?"

One might have supposed I was living on the pampas.

"I should think you could easily hire a couple of horses in Westingham and have them sent out. I should rather like a gallop in the morning over the downs."

"You weren't thinking of doing any shooting, were you?" I asked a little bitterly. "I noticed a lot of bullfinches on the downs the last time I was there."

"I'll see what I can arrange as we go through," said Gregory quietly. "After all, one must fill in the time somehow, you know. What time do we start? I'll drive if you like."

I was aroused next morning from my beauty sleep by the rattling of stones on my window. I jumped out of bed and trod on a pebble. Looking out of the window I observed a man holding an unoccupied horse and Gregory sitting on another. The first horse looked up at me with an indescribably unpleasant expression. I noticed that it had far more ridges on it than Gregory's.

The air struck chill. Far away I could perceive the cold shining sea beyond the gap in the downs. A thought occurred to me.

"You've not had your dip yet, Gregory," I shouted. "Why not have that while I get ready?"

There was always a chance, I reflected, that the man might get himself drowned.

"Don't be an ass," shouted Gregory cheerfully. "Hurry up and come down."

I began to shave.

"What you ought to do here," said Gregory after breakfast, "is to level away all this grass slope between you and the road and make a tennis-court — a hard tennis-court, I think."

He had eaten, I noticed, all the marmalade.

"There's a drain," I said coldly, "underneath that grass slope. At least I like to believe there is."

"Oh, nonsense!" he cried; "you needn't touch that. Come out with me now and I'll show you where to begin. We might make a start on it before we go to the links. Have you got any spades?"

"Having no spades —" I began, but Gregory was too quick for me. He had discovered the outhouse. Like a fool I had not locked it up. A moment later he had discovered two monstrous-looking instruments of torture inside. I took one and toyed with it. Owing to the unpleasant horse with the ridges I was already aching all — well, I was aching, anyhow. Gregory turned round and began to dig. It was then that gazing upwards from the garden to the hill, I let my fancy play lightly around the green tumulus. How many Romans, I fancied, how many Danes, how many other unwelcome intruders might not lie buried beneath its ancient soil? I wondered whether a little tumulus would not be a handsome addition to my own small garden. I looked at Gregory's strong limbs and thought. I lifted up my spade.

Then suddenly I checked myself. "The tactful host," I murmured, "does not map out the day too precisely for his guest in advance."

I began to help Gregory to dig.

PELHAM GRENVILLE WODEHOUSE

DO THRILLERS NEED HEROINES?

Whoever first got the idea that any one wants a beastly girl messing about and getting in the way when the automatics are popping I am at a loss to imagine. Nobody has a greater respect than myself for girls in their proper place — in the paddock at Ascot, fine: at Lord's during the luncheon interval of the Eton and Harrow match, capital: if I went to a night-club and found no girls there, I should be the first to complain: but what I do say is that they have no business in Lascar Joe's Underground Den at Limehouse on a busy evening. Apart from anything else, woman seems to me to lose her queenly dignity when she is being shoved into cupboards with a bag over her head. And, if there is one thing certain, it is that sooner or later something of that sort will be happening to the heroine of a thriller.

For, though beautiful, with large grey eyes and hair the colour of ripe corn, the heroine of the thriller is almost never a very intelligent girl. Indeed, it would scarcely be overstating it to say that her mentality is that of a cockroach — and not an ordinary cockroach, at that, but one which has been dropped on its head as a baby. She may have escaped death a dozen times. She may know perfectly well that the notorious Blackbird Gang is after her to secure the papers. The police may have warned her on no account to stir outside her house. But when a messenger calls at half-past two in the morning with an unsigned note saying "Come at once", she just snatches at her hat and goes. The messenger is a one-eyed Chinaman with a pock-marked face and an evil grin, so she trusts him immediately and, having accompanied him to the closed car with steel shutters over the windows, bowls off in it to ruined cottage in the swamp. And when the hero, at great risk and inconvenience to himself, comes to rescue her, she will have nothing to do with him because she has been told by a mulatto with half a nose that it was he who murdered her brother Jim.

This girl must go. We readers demand it. We know the publishers want a female in the story so that they can put her on the jacket with her hands clasped and a wild look of agony in her eyes, but nevertheless we stick to it that she must go. Better a jacket with only a masked man pushing a paper-knife into a millionaire in his library than this continued poisoning of sensational fiction with imbeciles like Myrtle or Gladys or Elaine or whatever her name may be.

What we all liked so much about Sherlock Holmes was his correct attitude in this matter of girls in mystery stories. True, he would sometimes permit them to call at Baker Street and tell him about the odd behaviour of their uncles or stepfathers ... in a pinch he might even allow them to marry Watson ... but once the story was under way they had to retire into the background and stay there. That was the spirit, and we want a little more of it nowadays.

The obvious person, of course, to rid us of these pests is the villain, and in fairness to a willing worker it cannot be denied that he does his best. He has the zeal, the enthusiasm — every quality, you would say, which is required for the task. And yet, for one reason or another, he always fails. Even when he has got the girl chained up in the cellar under the wharf with the water pouring through the grating we never in our hearts really expect the happy ending. Experience has taught us that we cannot rely on this man. He has let us down too often, and forfeited our confidence. We know him for what he is, a broken reed.

Broadly speaking, the trouble with every villain of a thriller is that he suffers from a fatal excess of ingenuity. When he was a boy, his parents must thoughtlessly have told him that he was clever, and it has absolutely spoiled him for effective work.

The ordinary man, when circumstances compel him to murder a female acquaintance, borrows a revolver and a few cartridges and does the thing in some odd five minutes of the day when he is not at the office or the pictures. He does not bother about art or technique or scientific methods. He just goes and does it.

But the villain cannot understand simplicity. A hundred times he manoeuvres the girl into a position where one good dig with a knife or a carefully directed pistol-shot would produce the happiest results, and then, poor ass, he goes and ruins it all by being too clever. It never occurs to him just to point a pistol at the heroine and fire it. If you told him the thing could be done that way, he would suspect you of pulling his leg. The only method he can imagine is to tie her in a chair, erect a tripod, place the revolver on it, tie a string to the trigger, pass the string along the walls till it rests on a hook, attach another string to it, pass this over a hook, tie a brick to the end of the second string and light a candle under it. He has got the thing reasoned out. The candle will burn the second string, the brick will fall, the weight will tighten the first string, thus pulling the trigger, and there you are.

Then somebody comes along and blows the candle out, and all the weary work to do over again.

Still, I suppose it is no use being angry with the poor fellows. They are doing their best according to their lights. It is simply that they are trying to tackle a highly specialised job without the requisite training. What the villain needs is to forget all he thinks he knows and go right back to the beginning and start learning the business from the bottom up. He requires careful schooling. And this is what he ought to be given at once if thrillers are to be purged of heroines.

The keynote of the curriculum of this School for Villains would be the inculcation of simplicity and directness. The pupil would receive at first what one might call a kindergarten education. For the greater part of his opening term he would confine himself to swatting flies. From this he would work up through the animal kingdom in easy stages till eventually he

81

arrived at heroines. By the time he had taken his degree, the Myrtles and Gladyses would be climbing trees and pulling them up after them to avoid the man, for by then he would be really dangerous.

The great difficulty, of course, would be to restrain and hold in check that infernal ingenuity of his. The average villain's natural impulse, if called upon to kill a fly, would be to saw away the supports of the floor, tie a string across the doorway, and then send the fly an anonymous letter urging it to come at once in order to hear of something to its advantage. The idea being that it would hurry to the room, trip over the string, fall on the floor, tumble into the depths, and break its neck.

That, to the villain's mind, is not merely the simplest, it is the only way of killing flies. And the hardest task facing his form-master would be to persuade him that excellent results may be obtained through the medium of a rolled-up "Daily Mail" gripped by the Football Coupon.

The maddening thing is that it is only when dealing with the heroine that he is so beastly clever. With anybody of his own sex he can be as straightforward as a medieval headsman. Give him a baronet and he will stick a knife in his back without a second thought. But the moment he finds himself up against a heroine he seems to go all to pieces, and we get all this stuff of suspending snakes from the chandelier and fooling about with bombs which can only be exploded by means of a gramophone record with an A in alt on it.

I have known a villain to sit the heroine on a keg of gunpowder and expect it to be struck by lightning. You can't run a business that way.

What these men have got to learn is that the best way of disposing of a girl with hair the colour of ripe corn is to hit that hair as hard as possible with a bit of gas-pipe. Buying tarantulas to put in her vanity-bag or little-known Asiatic poisons with which to smear her lipstick do no good whatever and only add to the overhead.

Let them master this fundamental truth, and then we shall see what we shall see.

82

JEEVES EXERTS THE OLD CEREBELLUM

CHAPTER 1

"Morning, Jeeves," I said.

"Good morning, sir," said Jeeves.

He put the good old cup of tea softly on the table by my bed, and I took a refreshing sip. Just right, as usual. Not too hot, not too sweet, not too weak, not too strong, not too much milk, and not a drop spilled in the saucer. A most amazing cove, Jeeves. So dashed competent in every respect. I've said it before, and I'll say it again. I mean to say, take just one small instance. Every other valet I've ever had used to barge into my room in the morning while I was still asleep, causing much misery: but Jeeves seems to know when I'm awake by a sort of telepathy. He always floats in with the cup exactly two minutes after I come to life. Makes a deuce of a lot of difference to a fellow's day.

"How's the weather, Jeeves?"

"Exceptionally clement, sir."

"Anything in the papers?"

"Some slight friction threatening in the Balkans, sir. Otherwise, nothing."

"I say, Jeeves, a man I met at the club last night told me to put my shirt on Privateer for the two o'clock race this afternoon. How about it?"

"I should not advocate it, sir. The stable is not sanguine."

That was enough for me. Jeeves knows. How, I couldn't say, but he knows. There was a time when I would laugh lightly, and go ahead, and lose my little all against his advice, but not now.

"Talking of shirts," I said, "have those mauve ones I ordered arrived yet?"

"Yes, sir. I sent them back."

"Sent them back?"

"Yes, sir. They would not have become you."

Well, I must say I'd thought fairly highly of those shirtings, but I bowed to superior knowledge. Weak? I don't know. Most fellows, no doubt, are all for having their valets confine their activities to creasing trousers and what not without trying to run the home; but it's different with Jeeves. Right from the first day he came to me, I have looked on him as a sort of guide, philosopher, and friend.

"Mr. Little rang up on the telephone a few moments ago, sir. I informed him that you were not yet awake."

"Did he leave a message?"

"No, sir. He mentioned that he had a matter of importance to discuss with you, but confided no details."

"Oh, well, I expect I shall be seeing him at the club."

"No doubt, sir."

I wasn't what you might call in a fever of impatience. Bingo Little is a chap I was at school with, and we see a lot of each other still. He's the nephew of old Mortimer Little, who retired from business recently with a goodish pile. (You've probably heard of Little's Liniment — It Limbers Up the Legs.) Bingo biffs about London on a pretty comfortable allowance given him by his uncle, and leads on the whole a fairly unclouded life. It wasn't likely that anything which he described as a matter of importance would turn out to be really so frightfully important. I took it that he had discovered some new brand of cigarette which he wanted me to try, or something like that, and didn't spoil my breakfast by worrying.

After breakfast I lit a cigarette and went to the open window to inspect the day. It certainly was one of the best and brightest.

"Jeeves," I said.

"Sir?" said Jeeves. He had been clearing away the breakfast things, but at the sound of the young master's voice cheesed it courteously.

"You were absolutely right about the weather. It is a juicy morning."

"Decidedly, sir."

"Spring and all that."

"Yes, sir."

"In the spring, Jeeves, a livelier iris gleams upon the burnished dove."

"So I have been informed, sir."

"Right ho! Then bring me my whangee, my yellowest shoes, and the old green Homburg. I'm going into the Park to do pastoral dances."

I don't know if you know that sort of feeling you get on these days round about the end of April and the beginning of May, when the sky's a light blue, with cotton-wool clouds, and there's a bit of a breeze blowing from the west? Kind of uplifted feeling. Romantic, if you know what I mean. I'm not much of a ladies' man, but on this particular morning it seemed to me that what I really wanted was some charming girl to buzz up and ask me to save her from assassins or something. So that it was a bit of an anti-climax when I merely ran into young Bingo Little, looking perfectly foul in a crimson satin tie decorated with horseshoes.

"Hallo, Bertie," said Bingo.

"My God, man!" I gargled. "The cravat! The gent's neckwear! Why? For what reason?"

"Oh, the tie?" He blushed. "I—er—I was given it."

He seemed embarrassed so I dropped the subject. We toddled along a bit, and sat down on a couple of chairs by the Serpentine.

"Jeeves tells me you want to talk to me about something," I said.

"Eh?" said Bingo, with a start. "Oh yes, yes. Yes."

I waited for him to unleash the topic of the day, but he didn't seem to want to get going. Conversation languished. He stared straight ahead of him in a glassy sort of manner.

"I say, Bertie," he said, after a pause of about an hour and a quarter.

"Hallo!"

"Do you like the name Mabel?"

"No."

"No?"

"No."

"You don't think there's a kind of music in the word, like the wind rustling gently through the tree-tops?"

"No."

He seemed disappointed for a moment; then cheered up.

"Of course, you wouldn't. You always were a fat-headed worm without any soul, weren't you?"

"Just as you say. Who is she? Tell me all."

For I realized now that poor old Bingo was going through it once again. Ever since I have known him — and we were at school together — he has been perpetually falling in love with someone, generally in the spring, which seems to act on him like magic. At school he had the finest collection of actresses' photographs of anyone of his time; and at Oxford his romantic nature was a byword.

"You'd better come along and meet her at lunch," he said, looking at his watch.

"A ripe suggestion," I said. "Where are you meeting her? At the Ritz?"

"Near the Ritz."

He was geographically accurate. About fifty yards east of the Ritz there is one of those blighted tea-and-bun shops you see dotted about all over London, and into this, if you'll believe me, young Bingo dived like a homing rabbit; and before I had time to say a word we were wedged in at a table, on the brink of a silent pool of coffee left there by an early luncher.

I'm bound to say I couldn't quite follow the development of the scenario. Bingo, while not absolutely rolling in the stuff, has always had a fair amount of the ready. Apart from what he got from his uncle, I knew that he had finished up the jumping season well on the right side of the ledger. Why, then, was he lunching the girl at this God-forsaken eatery? It couldn't be because he was hard up.

Just then the waitress arrived. Rather a pretty girl.

"Aren't we going to wait—?" I started to say to Bingo, thinking it somewhat thick that, in addition to asking a girl to lunch with him in a place like this, he should fling himself on the foodstuffs before she turned up, when I caught sight of his face, and stopped.

The man was goggling. His entire map was suffused with

a rich blush. He looked like the Soul's Awakening done in pink.

"Hallo, Mabel!" he said, with a sort of gulp.

"Hallo!" said the girl.

"Mabel," said Bingo, "this is Bertie Wooster, a pal of mine."

"Pleased to meet you," she said. "Nice morning."

"Fine," I said.

"You see I'm wearing the tie," said Bingo.

"It suits you beautiful," said the girl.

Personally, if anyone had told me that a tie like that suited me, I should have risen and struck them on the mazzard, regardless of their age and sex; but poor old Bingo simply got all flustered with gratification, and smirked in the most gruesome manner.

"Well, what's it going to be to-day?" asked the girl, introducing the business touch into the conversation.

Bingo studied the menu devoutly.

"I'll have a cup of cocoa, cold veal and ham pie, slice of fruit cake, and a macaroon. Same for you, Bertie?"

I gazed at the man, revolted. That he could have been a pal of mine all these years and think me capable of insulting the old tum with this sort of stuff cut me to the quick.

"Or how about a bit of hot steak-pudding, with a sparkling limado to wash it down?" said Bingo.

You know, the way love can change a fellow is really frightful to contemplate. This chappie before me, who spoke in that absolutely careless way of macaroons and limado, was the man I had seen in happier days telling the head-waiter at Claridge's exactly how he wanted the *chef* to prepare the *sole frite au gourmet aux champignons,* and saying he would jolly well sling it back if it wasn't just right. Ghastly! Ghastly!

A roll and butter and a small coffee seemed the only things on the list that hadn't been specially prepared by the nastier-minded members of the Borgia family for people they had a particular grudge against, so I chose them, and Mabel hopped it.

"Well?" said Bingo rapturously.

I took it that he wanted my opinion of the female poisoner who had just left us.

"Very nice," I said.

He seemed dissatisfied.

"You don't think she's the most wonderful girl you ever saw?" he said wistfully.

"Oh, absolutely!" I said, to appease the blighter. "Where did you meet her?"

"At a subscription dance at Camberwell."

"What on earth were you doing at a subscription dance at Camberwell?"

"Your man Jeeves asked me if I would buy a couple of tickets. It was in aid of some charity or other."

"Jeeves? I didn't know he went in for that sort of thing."

"Well, I suppose he has to relax a bit every now and then. Anyway, he was there, swinging a dashed efficient shoe. I hadn't meant to go at first, but I turned up for a lark. Oh, Bertie, think what I might have missed!"

"What might you have missed?" I asked, the old lemon being slightly clouded.

"Mabel, you chump. If I hadn't gone I shouldn't have met Mabel."

"Ah, ah!"

At this point Bingo fell into a species of trance, and only came out of it to wrap himself round the pie and macaroon.

"Bertie," he said, "I want your advice."

"Carry on."

"At least, not your advice, because that wouldn't be much good to anybody. I mean, you're a pretty consummate old ass, aren't you? Not that I want to hurt your feelings, of course."

"No, no, I see that."

"What I wish you would do is to put the whole thing to that fellow Jeeves of yours, and see what he suggests. You've often told me that he has helped other pals of yours out of messes. From what you tell me, he's by way of being the brains of the family."

"He's never let me down yet."

"Then put my case to him."

"What case?"

"My problem."

"What problem?"

"Why, you poor fish, my uncle, of course. What do you

think my uncle's going to say to all this? If I sprang it on him cold, he'd tie himself in knots on the hearthrug."

"One of these emotional johnnies, eh?"

"Somehow or other his mind has got to be prepared to receive the news. But how?"

"Ah!"

"That's a lot of help, that 'ah'! You see, I'm pretty well dependent on the old boy. If he cut off my allowance, I should be very much in the soup. So you put the whole binge to Jeeves and see if he can't scare up a happy ending somehow. Tell him my future is in his hands, and that, if the wedding bells ring out, he can rely on me, even unto half my kingdom. Well, call it ten quid. Jeeves would exert himself with ten quid on the horizon, what?"

"Undoubtedly," I said.

I wasn't in the least surprised at Bingo wanting to lug Jeeves into his private affairs like this. It was the first thing I would have thought of doing myself if I had been in any hole of any description. As I have frequently had occasion to observe, he is a bird of the ripest intellect, full of bright ideas. If anybody could fix things for poor old Bingo, he could.

I stated the case to him that night after dinner.

"Jeeves."

"Sir?"

"Are you busy just now?"

"No, sir."

"I mean, not doing anything in particular?"

"No, sir. It is my practice at this hour to read some improving book; but if you desire my services, this can easily be postponed, or, indeed, abandoned altogether."

"Well, I want your advice. It's about Mr. Little."

"Young Mr. Little, sir, or the elder Mr. Little, his uncle, who lived in Pounceby Gardens?"

Jeeves seemed to know everything. Most amazing thing. I'd been pally with Bingo practically all my life, and yet I didn't remember ever having heard that his uncle lived anywhere in particular.

"How did you know he lived in Pounceby Gardens?" I said.

"I am on terms of some intimacy with the elder Mr. Little's cook, sir. In fact, there is an understanding."

89

I'm bound to say that this gave me a bit of a start. Somehow I'd never thought of Jeeves going in for that sort of thing.

"Do you mean you're engaged?"

"It may be said to amount to that, sir."

"Well, well!"

"She is a remarkably excellent cook, sir," said Jeeves, as though he felt called on to give some explanation. "What was it you wished to ask me about Mr. Little?"

I sprang the details on him.

"And that's how the matter stands, Jeeves," I said. "I think we ought to rally round a trifle and help poor old Bingo put the thing through. Tell me about old Mr. Little. What sort of a chap is he?"

"A somewhat curious character, sir. Since retiring from business he has become a great recluse, and now devotes himself almost entirely to the pleasures of the table."

"Greedy hog, you mean?"

"I would not, perhaps, take the liberty of describing him in precisely those terms, sir. He is what is usually called a gourmet. Very particular about what he eats, and for that reason a high value on Miss Watson's services."

"The cook?"

"Yes, sir."

"Well, it looks to me as though our best plan would be to shoot young Bingo in on him after dinner one night. Melting mood, I mean to say, and all that."

"The difficulty, is, sir, that at the moment Mr. Little is on a diet, owing to an attack of gout."

"Things begin to look wobbly."

"No, sir, I fancy that the elder Mr. Little's misfortune may be turned to the younger Mr. Little's advantage. I was speaking only the other day to Mr. Little's valet, and he was telling me that it has become his principal duty to read to Mr. Little in the evenings. If I were in your place, sir, I should send young Mr. Little to read to his uncle."

"Nephew's devotion, you mean? Old man touched by kindly action, what?"

"Partly that, sir. But I would rely more on young Mr. Little's choice of literature."

"That's no good. Jolly old Bingo has a kins face, but when it comes to literature he stops at the *Sporting Times*."

"That difficulty may be overcome. I would be happy to select books for Mr. Little to read. Perhaps I might explain my idea further?"

"I can't say I quite grasp it yet."

"The method which I advocate is what, I believe, the advertisers call Direct Suggestion, sir, consisting as it does of driving an idea home by constant repetition. You may have had experience of the system?"

"You mean they keep on telling you that some soap or other is the best, and after a bit you come under the influence and charge round the corner and buy a cake?"

"Exactly, sir. The same method was the basis of all the most valuable propaganda during the recent war. I see no reason why it should not be adopted to bring about the desired result with regard to the subject's views on class distinctions. If young Mr. Little were to read day after day to his uncle a series of narratives in which marriage with young persons of an inferior social status was held up as both feasible and admirable, I fancy it would prepare the elder Mr. Little's mind for the reception of the information that his nephew wishes to marry a waitress in a tea-shop."

"*Are* there any books of that sort nowadays? The only ones I ever see mentioned in the papers are about married couples who find life grey, and can't stick each other at any price."

"Yes, sir, there are a great many, neglected by the reviewers but widely read. You have never encountered *All for Love*, by Rosie M. Banks?"

"No."

"Nor *A Red, Red Summer Rose*, by the same author?"

"No."

"I have an aunt, sir, who owns an almost complete set of Rosie M. Banks. I could easily borrow as many volumes as young Mr. Little might require. They make very light, attractive reading."

"Well, it's worth trying."

"I should certainly recommend the scheme, sir."

"All right, then. Toddle round to your aunt's to-morrow

and grab a couple of the fruitiest. We can but have a dash at it."

"Precisely, sir."

NO WEDDING BELLS FOR BINGO

CHAPTER 2

Bingo reported three days later that Rosie M. Banks was the goods and beyond a question the stuff to give the troops. Old Little had jibbed somewhat at first at the proposed change of literary diet, he not being much of a lad for fiction and having stuck hitherto exclusively to the heavier monthly reviews; but Bingo had got chapter one of *All for Love* past his guard before he knew what was happening, and after that there was nothing to it. Since then they had finished *A Red, Red Summer Rose, Madcap Myrtle* and *Only a Factory Girl,* and were half-way through *The Courtship of Lord Strathmorlick.*

Bingo told me all this in a husky voice over an egg beaten up in sherry. The only blot on the thing from his point of view was that it wasn't doing a bit of good to the old vocal cords, which were beginning to show signs of cracking under the strain. He had been looking his symptoms up in a medical dictionary, and he thought he had got "clergyman's throat". But against this you had to set the fast that he was making an undoubted hit in the right quarter, and also that after the evening's reading he always stayed on to dinner; and, from what he told me, the dinners turned out by old Little's cook had to be tasted to be believed. There were tears in the old blighter's eyes as he got on the subject of the clear soup. I suppose to a fellow who for weeks had been tackling macaroons and li-mado it must have been like Heaven.

Old Little wasn't able to give any practical assistance at these banquets, but Bingo said that he came to the table and had his whack of arrowroot, and sniffed the dishes, and told stories of *entrées* he had had in the past, and sketched out scenarios of what he was going to do to the bill of fare in the future, when the doctor put him in shape; so I suppose he enjoyed himself, too, in a way. Anyhow, things seemed to be buzzing along quite satisfactorily, and Bingo said he had got an idea which, he thought, was going to clinch the thing. He wouldn't tell me what it was, but he said it was a pippin.

"We make progress, Jeeves," I said.

"That is very satisfactory, sir."

"Mr. Little tells me that when he came to the big scene in *Only a Factory Girl,* his uncle gulped like a stricken bull-pup."

"Indeed, sir?"

"Where Lord Claude takes the girl in his arms, you know, and says—"

"I am familiar with the passage, sir. It is distinctly moving. It was a great favourite of my aunt's."

"I think we're on the right track."

"It would seem so, sir."

"In fact, this looks like being another of your successes. I've always said, and I always shall say, that for sheer brain, Jeeves, you stand alone. All the other great thinkers of the age are simply in the crowd, watching you go by."

"Thank you very much, sir. I endeavour to give satisfaction."

About a week after this, Bingo blew in with the news that his uncle's gout had ceased to trouble him, and that on the morrow he would be back at the old stand working away with knife and fork as before.

"And, by the way," said Bingo, "he wants you to lunch with him to-morrow."

"Me? Why me? He doesn't know I exist."

"O, yes, he does. I've told him about you."

"What have you told him?"

"Oh, various things. Anyhow, he wants to meet you. And take my tip, laddie—you go! I should think lunch tomorrow would be something special."

I don't know why it was, but even then it struck me that there was something dashed odd—almost sinister, if you know what I mean—about young Bingo's manner. The old egg had the air of one who has something up his sleeve.

"There is more in this than meets the eye," I said. "Why should your uncle ask a fellow to lunch whom he's never seen?"

"My dear old fathead, haven't I just said that I've been

telling him all about you — that you're my best pal — at school together, and all that sort of thing?"

"But even then — and another thing. Why are you so dashed keen on my going."

Bingo hesitated for a moment.

"Well, I told you I'd got an idea. This is it. I want you to spring the news on him. I haven't the nerve myself."

"What! I'm hanged if I do!"

"And you call yourself a pal of mine!"

"Yes, I know; but there are limits."

"Bertie," said Bingo reproachfully. "I saved your life once."

"When?"

"Didn't I? It must have been some other fellow, then. Well, anyway, we were boys together and all that. You can't let me down."

"Oh, all right," I said. "But, when you say you haven't nerve enough for any dashed thing in the world, you misjudge yourself. A fellow who —"

"Cheerio!" said young Bingo. "One-thirty to-morrow. Don't be late."

*

I'm bound to say that the more I contemplated the binge, the less I liked it. It was all very well for Bingo to say that I was slated for a magnificent lunch; but what good is the best possible lunch to a fellow if he is slung out into the street on his ear during the soup course? However, the word of a Wooster is his bond and all that sort of rot, so at one-thirty next day I tottered up the steps of No. 16, Pounceby Gardens, and punched the bell. And half a minute later I was up in the drawing room, shaking hands with the fattest man I have ever seen in my life.

The motto of the Little family was evidently "variety". Young Bingo is long and thin and hasn't had a superfluous ounce on him since we first met; but the uncle restored the average and a bit over. The hand which grasped mine wrapped it round and enfolded it till I began to wonder if I'd ever get it out without excavating machinery.

"Mr. Wooster, I am gratified—I am proud—I am honoured."

It seemed to me that young Bingo must have boosted me to some purpose.

"Oh, ah!" I said.

He stepped back a bit, still hanging on to the good right hand.

"You are very young to have accomplished so much!"

I couldn't follow the train of thought. The family, especially my Aunt Agatha, who has savaged me incessantly from childhood up, have always rather made a point of the fact that mine is a wasted life, and that, since I won the prize at my first school for the best collection of wild flowers made during the summer holidays, I haven't done a damn thing to land me on the nation's scroll of fame. I was wondering if he couldn't have got me mixed up with someone else, when the telephone-bell rang outside in the hall, and the maid came in to say that I was wanted. I buzzed down, and found it was young Bingo.

"Hallo!" said young Bingo. "So you've got there? Good man! I knew I could rely on you. I say, old crumpet, did my uncle seem pleased to see you?"

"Absolutely all over me. I can't make it out."

"Oh, that's all right. I just rang up to explain. The fact is, old man, I know you won't mind, but I told him that you were the author of those books I've been reading to him."

"What!"

"Yes, I said that 'Rosie M. Banks' was your pen-name, and you didn't want it generally known, because you were a modest, retiring sort of chap. He'll listen to you now. Absolutely hang on your words. A brightish idea, what? I doubt if Jeeves in person could have thought up a better one than that. Well, pitch it strong, old lad, and keep steadily before you the fact that I must have my allowance raised. I can't possibly marry on what I've got now. If this film is to end with the slow fade-out on the embrace, at least double is indicated. Well, that's that. Cheerio!"

And he rang off. At that moment the gong sounded, and the genial host came tumbling downstairs like the delivery of a ton of coals.

*

I always look back to that lunch with a sort of aching regret. It was the lunch of a lifetime, and I wasn't in a fit state to appreciate it. Subconsciously, if you know what I mean, I could see it was pretty special, but I had got the wind up to such a frightful extent over the ghastly situation in which young Bingo had landed me that its deeper meaning never really penetrated. Most of the time I might have been eating sawdust for all the good it did me.

Old Little struck the literary note right from the start.

"My nephew has probably told you that I have been making a close study of your books of late?" he began.

"Yes. He did mention it. How—er—how did you like the bally things?"

He gazed reverently at me.

"Mr. Wooster, I am not ashamed to say that the tears came into my eyes as I listened to them. It amazes me that a man as young as you can have been able to plumb human nature so surely to its depths; to play with so unerring a hand on the quivering heart-strings of your reader; to write novels so true, so human, so moving, so vital!"

"Oh, it's just a knack," I said.

The good old persp. was bedewing my forehead by this time in a pretty lavish manner. I don't know when I've been so rattled.

"Do you find the room a trifle warm?"

"Oh, no, no, rather not. Just right."

"Then it's the pepper. If my cook has a fault—which I am not prepared to admit—it is that she is inclined to stress the pepper a trifle in her made dishes. By the way, do you like her cooking?"

I was so relieved that we had got off the subject of my literary output that I shouted approval in a ringing baritone.

"I am delighted to hear it, Mr. Wooster. I may be prejudiced, but to my mind that woman is a genius."

"Absolutely!" I said.

"She has been with me seven years, and in all that time I have not known her guilty of a single lapse from the highest standard. Except once, in the winter of 1917, when a purist might have condemned a certain mayonnaise of hers as lacking in creaminess. But one must make allowances. There had been several air-raids about that time, and no doubt the poor woman was shaken. But nothing is perfect in this world, Mr. Wooster, and I have had my cross to bear. For seven years I have lived in constant apprehension lest some evilly-disposed person might lure her from my employment. To my certain knowledge she has received offers, lucrative offers, to accept service elsewhere. You may judge of my dismay, Mr. Wooster, when only this morning the bolt fell. She gave notice!"

"Good Lord!"

"Your consternation does credit, if I may say so, to the heart of the author of *A Red, Red Summer Rose*. But I am thankful to say the worst has not happened. The matter has been adjusted. Jane is not leaving me."

"Good egg!"

"Good egg, indeed — though the expression is not familiar to me. I do not remember having come across it in your books. And, speaking of your books, may I say that what has impressed me about them even more than the moving poignancy of the actual narrative, is your philosophy of life. If there were more men like you, Mr. Wooster, London would be a better place."

This was dead opposite to my Aunt Agatha's philosophy of life, she having always rather given me to understand that it is the presence in it of chappies like me that makes London more or less of a plague spot; but I let it go.

"Let me tell you, Mr. Wooster, that I appreciate your splendid defiance of the outworn fetishes of a purblind social system. I appreciate it! *You* are big enough to see that rank is but the guinea stamp and that, in the magnificent words of Lord Bletchmore in *Only a Factory Girl*, "Be her origin ne'er so humble, a good woman is the equal of the finest lady on earth!""

I sat up.

"I say! Do you think that?"

"I do, Mr. Wooster. I am ashamed to say that there was a time when I was, like other men, a slave to the idiotic

97

convention which we call Class Distinction. But, since I read your books —"

I might have known it. Jeeves had done it again.

"You think it's all right for a chappie in what you might call a certain social position to marry a girl of what you might describe as the lower classes?"

"Most assuredly I do, Mr. Wooster."

I took a deep breath, and slipped him the good news.

"Young Bingo — your nephew, you know — wants to marry a waitress," I said.

"I honour him for it," said old Little.

"You don't object?"

"On the contrary."

I took another deep breath and shifted to the sordid side of the business.

"I hope you won't think I'm butting in, don't you know," I said, "but — er — well, how about it?"

"I fear I do not quite follow you."

"Well, I mean to say, his allowance and all that. The money you're good enough to give him. He was rather hoping that you might see your way to jerking up the total a bit."

Old Little shook his head regretfully.

"I fear that can hardly be managed. You see, a man in my position is compelled to save every penny. I will gladly continue my nephew's existing allowance, but beyond that I cannot go. It would not be fair to my wife."

"What! But you're not married?"

"Not yet. But I propose to enter upon that holy state almost immediately. The lady who for years has cooked so well for me honoured me by accepting my hand this very morning." A cold gleam of triumph came into his eye. "Now let 'em try to get her away from me!" he muttered, defiantly.

*

"Young Mr. Little has been trying frequently during the afternoon to reach you on the telephone, sir," said Jeeves that night, when I got home.

"I'll bet he has," I said. I had sent poor old Bingo an outline of the situation by messenger-boy shortly after lunch.

"He seemed a trifle agitated."

"I don't wonder, Jeeves," I said, "so brace up and bite the bullet. I'm afraid I've bad news for you. That scheme of yours — reading those books to old Mr. Little and all that — has blown out a fuse."

"They did not soften him?"

"They did. That's the whole bally trouble. Jeeves, I'm sorry to say that *fiancée* of yours — Miss Watson, you know — the cook, you know — well, the long and the short of it is that she's chosen riches instead of honest worth, if you know what I mean."

"Sir?"

"She's handed you the mitten and gone and got engaged to old Mr. Little!"

"Indeed, sir?"

"You don't seem much upset."

"The fact is, sir, I had anticipated some such outcome."

I stared at him. "Then what on earth did you suggest the scheme for?"

"To tell you the truth, sir, I was not wholly averse from a severance of my relations with Miss Watson. In fact, I greatly desired it. I respect Miss Watson exceedingly, but I have seen for a long time that we were not suited. Now, the *other* young person with whom I have an understanding —"

"Great Scott, Jeeves! There isn't another?"

"Yes, sir."

"How long has this been going on?"

"For some weeks, sir. I was greatly attracted by her when I first met her at a subscription dance at Camberwell."

"My sainted aunt! Not —"

Jeeves inclined his head gravely.

"Yes, sir. By an odd coincidence it is the same young person that young Mr. Little — I have placed the cigarettes on the small table. Good night, sir."

THE LEVEL BUSINESS HEAD

"Another beaker of port, laddie?" urged Stanley Featherstonehaugh Ukridge, hospitably.

"Thanks."

"One more stoup of port for Mr. Corcoran, Baxter. You may bring the coffee, cigars and liqueurs to us in the library in about a quarter of an hour."

The butler filled my glass and melted away. I looked about me dizzily. We were seated in the spacious dining-room of Ukridge's Aunt Julia's house on Wimbledon Common. A magnificent banquet had wound its way to a fitting finish, and the whole thing seemed to me inexplicable.

"I don't understand this," I said. "How do I come to be sitting here, bursting with rich food paid for by your aunt?"

"Perfectly simple, laddie. I expressed a desire for your company tonight, and she at once consented."

"But why? She has never let you invite me here before. She can't stand me."

Ukridge sipped his port.

"Well, the fact of the matter is, Corky," he said, in a burst of confidence, "things have been occurring recently in the home which have resulted in what you might call the dawning of a new life as far as Aunt Julia and I are concerned. It is not too much to say that she now eats out of my hand and is less than the dust beneath my chariot wheels. I will tell you the story, for it will be of help to you in your journey through the world. It is a story which shows that, be the skies never so black,

100

nothing can harm a man provided that he has a level business head. Tempests may lour—"

"Get on with it. How did all this happen?"

Ukridge mused for awhile.

"I suppose the thing really started," he said, "when I pawned her brooch—"

"You pawned your aunt's brooch?"

"Yes."

"And that endeared you to her?"

"I will explain all that later. Meanwhile, let me begin at the beginning. Have you ever run across a man named Joe the Lawyer?"

"No."

"Stout fellow with a face like a haggis."

"I've never met him."

"Endeavour not to do so, Corky. I hate to speak ill of my fellow-man, but Joe the Lawyer is not honest."

"What does he do? Pawn people's brooches?"

Ukridge adjusted the ginger-beer wire that held his pince-nez to his flapping ears, and looked wounded.

"This is scarcely the tone I like to hear in an old friend, Corky. When I reach that point in my story, you will see that my pawning of Aunt Julia's brooch was a perfectly normal, straightforward matter of business. How else could I have bought half the dog?"

"Half what dog?"

"Didn't I tell you about the dog?"

"No."

"I must have done. It's the nub of the whole affair."

"Well, you didn't."

"I'm getting this story all wrong," said Ukridge. "I'm confusing you. Let me begin right at the beginning."

This bloke, Joe the Lawyer (said Ukridge), is a bookmaker with whom I have had transactions from time to time, but until the afternoon when this story starts we had never become in any way intimate. Occasionally I would win a couple of quid off him and he would send me a cheque, or he would win a couple of quid off me and I would go round to his office to ask him to wait till Wednesday week; but we had never mingled socially, as you might say, until this afternoon I'm speaking of, when I happened to look in at the Bedford Street Bodega and found him there, and he asked me to have a glass of the old tawny.

Well, laddie, you know as well as I do that there are moments when a glass of the old tawny makes all the difference; so I assented with a good deal of heartiness.

"Fine day," I said.

"Yes," said this bloke. "Do you want to make a large fortune?"

"Yes."

"Then listen," said this bloke. "You know the Waterloo Cup. Listen, I've taken over as a bad debt from a client the dog that's going to win the Waterloo Cup. This dog has been kept dark, but you can take it from me it's going to win the Waterloo Cup. And then what? Well, then it's going to fetch something. It's going to be valuable. It's going to have a price. It's going to be worth money. Listen. How would you like to buy a half-share in that dog?"

"Very much."

"Then it's yours."

"But I haven't any money."

"You mean to say you can't raise fifty quid?"

"I can't raise five."

"Gawblimey!" said the bloke.

And looking at me in a despairing sort of way, like a father whose favourite son has hurt his finest feelings, he finished his old tawny and pushed out into Bedford Street. And I went home.

Well, as you may imagine, I brooded not a little on my way back to Wimbledon. The one thing nobody can say of me, Corky, is that I lack the spacious outlook that wins to wealth. I know a good thing when I see one. This was a good thing, and I recognized it as such. But how to acquire the necessary capital was the point. Always my stumbling-block, that has been. I wish I had a shilling for every time I've failed to become millionaire through lack of the necessary capital.

What sources of revenue had I, I asked myself. George Tupper, if tactfully approached, is generally good for a fiver; and you, no doubt, had it been a matter of a few shillings or half a sovereign, would gladly have leaped into the breach. But fifty quid! A large sum, laddie. It wanted thinking over, and I devoted the whole force of my intelligence to the problem.

Oddly enough, the one source of supply that had never presented itself to me was my Aunt Julia. As you know, she has warped and peculiar ideas about money. For some reason or other she will never give me a cent. And yet it was my Aunt Julia who solved my problem. There is a destiny in these matters, Corky, a sort of fate.

When I got back to Wimbledon, I found her loking after her packing; for she was off next morning on one of those lecture tours she goes in for.

"Stanley," she said to me, "I nearly forgot. I want you to look in at Murgatroyd's in Bond Street tomorrow and get my diamond brooch. They are re-setting it. Bring it back and put it in my bureau drawer. Here is the key. Lock the drawer and send the key to me by registered post."

And so, you see, everything was most satisfactorily settled. Long before my aunt came back the Waterloo Cup would be run for, and I should have acquired vast affluence. All I had to do was to have a duplicate key made, so that I could put the brooch in the drawer when I had redeemed it. I could see no flaw in the scheme of things. I saw her off at Euston, sauntered round to Murgatroyd's, collected the brooch, sauntered off to the pawnbroker's, put the brooch up the spout, and walked out, for the first time in many weeks in a sound financial position. I rang up Joe the Lawyer on the phone, closed the deal about the dog, and there I was, with my foot on the ladder of Fortune.

But in this world, Corky, you never know. That is the thing I always try to impress on every young fellow starting out in life — that you never know. It was about two days later that the butler came to me in the garden and said a gentleman wished to speak to me on the phone.

I shall always remember that moment. It was a lovely, still evening, and I was sitting in the garden under a leafy tree, thinking beautiful thoughts. The sun was setting in a blaze of gold and crimson; the little birds were chirping their heads off; and I was half-way through the whisky and soda of a lifetime. I recollect that, an instant before Baxter came out to fetch me,

I had just been thinking how peaceful and wonderful and perfect the world was.

I went to the phone.

"Hullo!" said a voice.

It was Joe the Lawyer. And Baxter had said it was a gentleman.

"Are you there?" said this bloke Joe.

"Yes."

"Listen."

"What?"

"Listen. You know that dog I said was going to win the Waterloo Cup?"

"Yes."

"Well, he isn't."

"Why not?"

"Because he's dead."

I don't mind telling you, Corky, that I reeled. Yes, your old friend reeled.

"Dead!"

"Dead."

"You don't mean dead?"

"Yes."

"Then what about my fifty pounds?"

"I keep that."

"What!"

"Of course I keep it. Once a sale's gone through, it's gone through. I know my law. That's why the boys call me Joe the Lawyer. But I'll tell you what I'll do. You send me a letter, releasing all rights in that dog, and I'll give you a fiver. I'll be robbing myself, but I'm like that... Big-hearted old Joe, I am, and that's all there is about it."

"What did the dog die of?"

"Pneumonia."

"I don't believe he's dead at all."

"You don't believe my word?"

"No."

"Well, you come round to my stable and see for yourself."

So I went round and viewed the remains. There was no doubt about it, the dog had handed in his dinner-pail. So I wrote the letter, got my fiver, and came back to Wimbledon to try and rebuild my shattered life. Because you can readily see, Corky, that I was up against it in no uncertain manner. Aunt Julia would be back before long, and would want to see her brooch; and though I'm her own flesh and blood, and I shouldn't be surprised if she had dandled me on her knee when I was a child, I couldn't picture her bearing with anything like Christian fortitude the news that I had pawned it in order to buy a half-share in a dead dog.

And the very next morning in blew Miss Angelica Vining, the poetess.

She was a gaunt sort of toothy female who had come to lunch once or twice while I had been staying in my aunt's house. A great pal of my aunt's.

"Good morning," she said, beaming. "What a heavenly day! One could almost fancy oneself out in the country, couldn't one? Even at so short a distance from the heart of the City one seems to sense in the air a freshness which one cannot get in London, can one? I've come for your aunt's brooch."

I braced myself up with a hand on the piano.

"You've what?" I said.

"Tonight is the dance of the Pen and Ink Club, and I wired to your aunt to ask if I might borrow her brooch, and she has written to say that I may. It's in her bureau."

"Which is, most unfortunately, locked."

"Your aunt sent me the key. I have it in my bag."

She opened her bag, Corky, and at this moment my guardian angel, who had been lying down on his job pretty considerably for the last week or so, showed a sudden flash of speed. The door was open, and through it at this juncture there trickled one of my aunt's Pekes. You will recollect my aunt's Pekes. I pinched them once, to start a Dog College.

This animal gazed at the female, and the female went off like a soda-water bottle.

"Oh, the sweet thing!" she bubbled.

She put the bag down and swooped on the dog. He tried to side-step, but she had him.

"Oh, the tweetums!" she cried.

And, her back being turned, Corky, I nipped to the bag, found the key, trousered it, and back to position one.

Presently she came to the surface again.

"Now I really must hurry away," she said. "I will just get the brooch and scurry." She fumbled in her bag. "Oh, dear! I've lost the key."

"Too bad," I said. "Still," I went on, thinking it might be all for the best, "what does a girl need jewellery for? The greatest jewel a girl can possess is her youth, her beauty."

It went well, but not quite well enough.

"No," she said, "I must have the brooch. I've set my heart on it. We must break the lock."

"I couldn' t dream of such a thing." I said firmly. "I am in a position of trust. I cannot break up my aunt's furniture."

"Oh, but——"

"No."

Well, laddie, there ensued a pretty painful scene. Hell hath no fury like a woman scorned, and not many like a woman who wants a brooch and isn't allowed to get it. The atmosphere, when we parted, was full of strain.

"I shall write to Miss Ukridge and tell her exactly what has happened," said the poetess, pausing at the front door.

She then shoved off, leaving me limp and agitated. These things take it out of a fellow.

Something, I perceived, had got to be done, and done swiftly. From some source I had to raise fifty quid. But where could I turn? My credit, Corky — and I tell you this frankly, as an old friend — is not good. No, it is not good. In all the world there seemed to be but one man who might be induced to let me have fifty quid at a pinch, and that was Joe the Lawyer. I don't say I was relying on him, mind you. But it seemed to me that, if there was a spark of human feeling in his bosom, he might, after a good deal of eloquence, be persuaded to help an old business colleague out of a very tight place.

At any rate, he was the only relief in sight, so I rang up his office; and, finding that he would be at the Lewes Races next day, I took an early train there.

Well, Corky, I might have known. It stands to reason that, if a man has a spark of human feeling in his bosom, he does not become a bookie. I stood beside this bloke, Joe the Lawyer from the start of the two o'clock race to the finish of the four-thirty, watching him rake in huge sums from mugs of every description until his satchel was simply bursting with cash; but when I asked him for the loan of a measly fifty pounds he didn't even begin to look like parting.

You cannot fathom the psychology of these blighters, Corky. If you will believe me, the chief reason why he would not lend me this paltry sum appeared to be a fear of what people would say if they heard about it.

"Lend you fifty quid?" he said, in a sort of stunned way. "Who, me? Silly I'd look, wouldn't I, lending you fifty quid!"

"But you don't mind looking silly."

"Having all the boys saying I was a soft-hearted fool."

"A man of your stamp doesn't care what fellows like that say," I urged. "You're too big. You can't afford to despise them."

"Well, I can't afford to lend any fifty quid. I'd never hear the last of it."

I simply can't understand this terror of public opinion. Morbid, I call it. I told him I would keep the thing a dead secret — and, if he thought it safer, not even give him a line in writing to acknowledge the debt; but no, there was no tempting him.

"I'll tell you what I will do," he said.

"Twenty quid?"

"No, not twenty quid. Nor ten quid, either. Nor five quid. Nor one quid. But I'll give you a lift back as far as Sandown in my car tomorrow, that's what I'll do."

From the way he spoke, you would have thought he was doing me the best turn one man had ever done another. I was strongly inclined to reject his offer with contempt. The only thing that decided me to accept was the thought that, if he had as good a day at Sandown as he had had at Lewes, his better nature might after all assert itself even at the eleventh hour. I mean to say, even a bookie must have a melting mood occasionally; and if one came to Joe the Lawyer, I wanted to be on the spot.

"Start from here at eleven, sharp. If you aren't ready, I'll go without you."

This conversation, Corky, had taken place in the saloon bar of the Coach and Horses at Lewes; and, having said these few words, the bloke Joe popped off. I stayed on to have one more,

107

feeling the need of it after the breakdown of the business negotiations; and the fellow behind the bar got chatty.

"That was Joe the Lawyer just went out, wasn't it?" he said. He chuckled. "He's wide, that man is."

I wasn't much in the mood to pass the time discussing a fellow who wouldn't let an old business friend have an insignificant sum like fifty quid, so I just nodded.

"Heard the latest about him?"

"No."

"He's wide, Joe is. He had a dog that was entered for the Waterloo Cup, and it died."

"I know."

"Well, I bet you don't know what he did. Some of the lads were in here just now, talking about it. He raffled that dog."

"How do you mean, raffled it?"

"Put it up for a raffle at twenty pounds a ticket."

"But it was dead."

"Certainly it was dead. But he didn't tell them that. That's where he was wide."

"But how could he raffle a dead dog?"

"Why couldn't he raffle a dead dog? Nobody knew it was dead."

"How about the man who drew the winning ticket?"

"Ah! Well, he had to tell him, of course. He just handed him his money back. And there he was, a couple of hundred quid in hand. He's wide, Joe is."

Have you ever experienced, Corky, that horrible sensation of having all your ideals totter and melt away, leaving you in a world of hideous blackness where it seems impossible to trust your fellow man an inch? What do you mean, my aunt must often have felt that way? I resent these slurs, Corky. Whenever I have had occasion to pinch anything from my aunt, it has always been with the most scrupulous motives, with the object of collecting a little ready cash in order to lay the foundations of a vast fortune.

This was an entirely different matter. This fiend in human shape had had no thought but of self. Not content with getting fifty quid out of me and sticking to it like glue, he had deliberately tricked me into accepting five pounds for all rights in

108

a dead dog which he knew was shortly about to bring him in a couple of hundred. Was it fair? Was it just?

And the terrible part of the whole thing was that there seemed nothing that I could do about it. I couldn't even reproach him. At least, I could — but a fat lot of help that would have been. All I could do was to save my train-fare home by accepting a lift in his car.

I am bound to say, Corky — and this will show you how a man's moral outlook may deteriorate through contact with fellows of this stamp — I am bound to say that there were moments during the night when I toyed with the thought of taking a dip into that satchel of his, should the opportunity occur during the journey. But I dismissed the plan as unworthy of me. Whatever the injuries I had sustained, my hands at least, please heaven, should be clean. Besides, it seemed very improbable that an opportunity would occur.

And, sure enough, I noticed next morning, when we started out, that he kept the satchel wedged in between him and the side of the car, entirely out of my reach. He was that sort of man.

How strange it is, Corky, that in this world we seem fated never to be able to enjoy life to the full! No doubt it is all for a purpose, and is intended to make us more spiritual and fit us for the life to come; but it is a nuisance. Take my case. I am particularly fond of motoring; and circumstances have so ordered themselves that it is only occasionally that I am able to get a ride. And here I was, bowling along the high road on an ideal motoring day, and totally unable to enjoy the experience.

For there are certain conditions, laddie, under which the heart cannot rejoice. How could I revel in the present when the past was an agony to contemplate and the future as black as ink? Every time I tried not to let my mind dwell on the way this man beside me had done me down, it skidded off into the future and dwelt on the interview which must so soon take place between me and my aunt. So the fact that it was a lovely day and that I was getting a ride for nothing practically escaped me.

We buzzed on through the pleasant countryside. The sun shone in the sky: birds tootled in the hedgerows: the engine of the two-seater hummed smoothly.

And then, fairly suddenly, I became aware that the engine was not humming so smoothly. It had begun to knock. And then there was a sizzling noise, and steam began to creep out of the top of the radiator-cap.

Joe made one or two remarks concerning the man at the hotel who had forgotten to put water in the radiator.

"You can get some at that cottage," I said.

There was a cottage down the road, standing by itself in a lot of trees. Joe pulled up the car and got down.

"I'll stay here and look after your satchel," I said. There was no sense in not being civil and obliging.

"No, you won't. I'll take it with me."

"It will hamper you if you're going to carry a pail of water."

"I'd look silly leaving my satchel with you, wouldn't I?"

I don't know which distressed me the more, his sickening want of ordinary trust or his absurd respect for appearances.

The man seemed to go through the world in a restless fear lest some action of his might make him look silly.

And he couldn't possibly have looked sillier than he did about two minutes later.

This cottage, Corky, was separated from the road by iron railings with a gate in them. The bloke Joe shoved this gate open and went into the front garden. And he was just starting to move round in the direction of the back door when round the corner of the house there suddenly came trotting a dog.

Joe stopped, and the dog stopped. They stood there for a moment, drinking each other in.

"Ger-r-r!" said Joe.

Now, mind you, there was absolutely nothing about this dog to inspire alarm. Certainly it was on the large side and had rather a rolling eye; but I could see at a glance that it was just one of those friendly mongrels which your man of the world greets with a cheerful chirrup and prods in the ribs without a second thought. But Joe seemed ill at ease.

The dog came a step closer. I think he wanted to smell Joe, though I could have told him, as a friend, that there was neither profit nor pleasure to be derived from such a course.

"Gerroutofit!" said Joe.

The dog edged forward. Then, in a tentative sort of way, he barked. And Joe seemed to lose his head completely. Instead

110

of trying to conciliate the animal, he picked up a stone and threw it.

Well, you simply can't do that sort of thing to a dog you don't know in his own garden.

It was the satchel that saved Joe. It shows the lengths to which fear will drive a man, Corky; and if I hadn't seen it with my own eyes I wouldn't have believed it. But it's the truth that as that dog came leaping up in a business-like way that it did me good to watch, Joe the Lawyer, having given one look over his shoulder at the gate and decided that he couldn't make it, uttered a piercing cry and flung considerably over two hundred quid in bank-notes at the animal. The satchel took him low down on the chest, got entangled in his legs, and held him up. And while he was trying to unscramble himself, Joe nipped to the gate and slammed it behind him.

It was only then that he seemed to realize what a perfect chump he had made of himself.

"Gawblimey!" said Joe.

The dog left the satchel and came to the gate. He shoved his nose as far through the bars as he could manage, and made a noise like a saxophone.

"Now you've done it," I said.

And so he had, and I was glad, Corky. It pleased me sincerely to find a man who prided himself on his acumen capable of such perfectly cloth-headed behaviour. Here was this blighter, admired by all — provided they didn't have business dealings with him — for his wideness, breaking down lamentably in the first crisis where he was called upon to show a little ordinary intelligence. He had allowed himself to be out-generalled by a humble unit of the animal kingdom, and I had no sympathy for him.

However, I didn't say so. One must be diplomatic. I had not altogether given up hope of floating that loan, and anything in the nature of frivolous comment would, I felt, have the worst effect on the negotiations.

"What'll I do?" said Joe, after a few general remarks.

"Better shout," I suggested.

So he shouted. But nothing happened. The fact is, these bookies are never in very good voice after a day at the races, and he was handicapped by a certain roopiness. Besides, the owner of the cottage was evidently one of those blokes who plough the fields and scatter the good seed o'er the land, and he seemed to be out somewhere ploughing and scattering now.

Joe began to get emotional.

"Gawblimey!" he said, with tears in his voice. "This is a nice thing! Here I am, late already, and if I don't get to Sandown in time for the first race it's going to mean hundreds of pounds out of my pocket."

You will scarcely credit it, Corky, but this was the first moment that aspect of the affair had presented itself to me. His words opened up an entirely new train of thought. Naturally, I now perceived, mugs being what they are, every race a bookie misses means so much dead loss to him. Sandown was crowded with potential losers, all waiting to hand their money over to Joe; and if he was not there, what would happen? They had to give their money to someone, so they would hand it over to one of his trade rivals. I felt as if a sudden bright light had flashed upon me.

"Look here," I said, "if you will lend me fifty quid, I'll go in and get that satchel for you. I'm not afraid of a dog."

He did not answer. He cocked an eye at me; then he cocked an eye at the satchel. I could see he was weighing the proposition. But at this moment the luck went against me. The dog, getting a bit bored, gave a sniff and trotted back round the corner of the house. And no sooner had he disappeared than Joe, feeling that now was the time, popped through the gate and galloped for the satchel.

Well, Corky, you know me. Alert. Resourceful. There was a stick lying in the road, and a leap for it and grab it was with me the work of a moment. I rattled it energetically along the railings. And back came old Colonel Dog as if I had pulled him at the end of a rope. It was an occasion when Joe had to move quick, and he did so. He had perhaps a foot to spare, or it may have been eight inches.

He was a good deal annoyed, and for a while spoke freely of this and that.

"Fifty quid," I said, when there was a lull.

He looked at me. Then he nodded. I don't say he nodded genially, but he nodded. And I opened the gate and went in.

The dog bounded at me, barking; but I knew that was all

swank, and I told him so. I bent down and slapped my tummy, and the dog shoved his paws on my shoulders and licked my face. Then I took his head and waggled it sideways once or twice, and he took my hand in his mouth and gnawed it slightly. Then I rolled him over and began punching his chest; and then, when these civilities were finished, I got up and looked round for the satchel.

It was gone. And there was that blot on the human race, Joe the Lawyer, standing outside, fondling it as if it were a baby. Not that a man like that would fondle a baby, of course. Much more likely to kick it in the face and break open its money-box. But what I mean is, he'd dashed in when my back was turned and collared the satchel.

I had a grim foreboding that our little deal was off, but I displayed a cheerful exterior.

"In large notes," I said.

"Eh?" said the bloke Joe.

"I'd rather have my fifty quid in large notes. They take up less room in the pocket."

"What fifty quid?"

"The fifty quid you were going to give me for getting the satchel."

He gaped.

"Well I'll be blowed!" he said. "I like that! Who got the satchel, you or me?"

"I soothed the dog."

"If you like to waste your time playing with dogs, that's your business. I'd look silly, wouldn't I, giving you fifty quid for playing with dogs? But, if you like doing it, you go on playing with him while I step down the road and get some water from one of those other cottages."

Black-hearted. That, Corky, is the only adjective. It seemed to me at that moment as though this bloke Joe had allowed me to peer into his soul; and it was like looking into a dark cellar on a moonless night.

"Here, I say——" I began, but he had gone.

How long I stood there I don't know. But, though it seemed a lifetime, it couldn't really have been long, for Joe didn't come back with the water; and a faint hope began to steal over me that he had found another dog at one of the other cottages and was now being bitten to the bone. And then I heard footsteps.

I looked round. A cove was approaching.

"Is this your cottage?" I asked.

He was a rural-looking sort of cove, with a full beard and corduroy trousers with string tied round the knees. He came up and stood gazing at the car. Then he looked at me, and then at the car again.

"Ah?" he said. A bit deaf he seemed to be.

"Is this your cottage?"

"Ah."

"We stopped here to get some water."

He said he hadn't got a daughter. I said I never said he had.

"Water!"

"Ah."

"But there was nobody in. So the man with me went down the road."

"Ah," said the cove.

"He was frightened by your dog."

"Ah?"

"By your dog."

"Buy my dog?"

"Yes."

"You can have him for five shillings."

Now, as I said before, Corky, you know me. You know that the reason why one of these days I shall make an enormous fortune and retire to spend the evening of my life in affluence is that I have that strange knack, which is given to so few men, of seizing opportunity when it calls. An ordinary mutton-headed fellow like you — I use the expression without any intention of offence — would, undoubtedly, at this juncture, have raised his voice a trifle and explained to this bearded cove that the intricacies of the English language had led him into a pardonable error.

But did I? No, I did not. For, even as he spoke, an idea exploded in my brain like a bomb.

"Done!" I cried.

"Ah?"

"Here's your five bob. Whistle to the dog."

He whistled, and the dog came running up. And, having

114

massaged his ribs awhile, I picked him up and shoved him inside the car and banged the door. And then I saw Joe the Lawyer plodding up the road slopping water from a big pail.

"I got it," he said.

He went round and unscrewed the cap of the radiator and
was starting to pour the water in, when the dog barked. Joe
looked up, saw him, and dropped the pail — happily over his
trousers.

"Who put that dog in the car?" he said.

"I did. I've bought him."

"Then you can damn' well take him out."

"But I'm bringing him home with me."

"Not in my car."

"Well, then," I said, "I'll sell him to you, and you can do
what you like about him."

He exhibited a good deal of impatience.

"I don't want to buy any dogs."

"Nor did I, till you talked me into it. And I don't see what
you have to complain of. This dog's alive. The one you sold
me was dead."

"What do you want for him?"

"A hundred pounds."

He staggered somewhat. "A hundred pounds?"

"That's all. Don't let the boys hear of it, or they'll think me
silly."

He spoke for awhile.

"A hundred and fifty," I said. "The market's rising."

"Now, listen, listen, listen!" said the bloke Joe.

"I'll tell you what I'll do," I said. "And this is a firm offer.
One hundred pounds, if paid within the minute. After that the
price will go up."

Corky, old horse, I have in my time extracted various sums
of money from various people, and some of them have given
cheerfully of their abundance and others have unbelted in
a manner that you might call wry. But never in the whole of
my career have I beheld a fellow human being cough up in
quite the spirit that this bloke Joe the Lawyer did. He was
a short-necked man, and there was one moment when
I thought his blood-pressure was going to be too much for
him. He turned a rather vivid shade of maroon, and his lips

trembled as if he were praying. But in the end he dipped into the satchel and counted out the money.

"Thanks," I said. "Well, good-bye."

He seemed to be waiting for something.

"Good-bye," I said again. "I don't want to hurt your feelings, laddie, but I must decline to continue in your society. We are nearing civilization now, and at any moment some friend of mine might see me in your car, which would jeopardize my social prestige. I will walk to the nearest railway station."

"But, gawblimey——"

"Now what?"

"Aren't you going to take that dog out of the car?" he said, specifying what sort of a dog it was in his opinion. He also added a few remarks in a derogatory spirit about myself.

"Me?" I said. "Why? I simply sold him to you. My part in the transaction is ended."

"But how'm I going to get to Sandown if I can't get into my car?"

"Why do you want to get to Sandown?"

"If I'm late, it means hundreds of pounds out of my pocket."

"Ah?" I said. "Then, of course, you'll be willing to pay large sums to anyone who helps you to get there. I don't mind lending you a hand, if it's made worth my while. Removing dogs from cars is highly specialized work, and I'll have to insist on specialist's prices. Shall we say fifty quid for the job?"

He yammered a good deal, but I cut him short.

"Take it or leave it," I said. "It's all the same to me."

Whereupon he produced the stipulated sum, and I opened the door and hauled the dog out. And Joe got in without a word and drove off. And that, Corky, is the last I have seen of the man. Nor do I wish to see him again. He is slippery, Corky. Not honest. A man to avoid.

I took the dog back to the cottage, and bellowed for the bearded cove.

"I sha'n't want this, after all," I said. "You can have him."

"Ah?"

"I don't want this dog."

"Ah! Well, you won't get your five shillings back."

"God bless you, my merry peasant," I said, slapping the

116

cove genially abaft the collar-stud. "Keep it with my blessing. I toss such sums to the birds."

And he said "Ah" and pushed off; and I toddled along to see if I could find a station. And I sang, Corky, old boy. Yes, laddie, your old friend, as he strode through those country lanes, trilled like a bally linnet.

Next day I looked in at the pawnbroker's, shelled out the requisite cash, recovered the brooch, and bunged it back into the bureau drawer.

And on the following morning my aunt turned up in a taxi and, having paid it its legal fare, backed me into the library and fixed me with a burning eye.

"Stanley," she said.

"Say on, Aunt Julia," I said.

"Stanley, Miss Vining tells me you refused to allow her to obtain my diamond brooch."

"Quite right, Aunt Julia. She wanted to break open your bureau drawer, but I would have none of it."

"Shall I tell you why?"

"It was because she had lost the key."

"I am not referring to that, as you know very well. Shall I tell you why you would not let her break open the drawer."

"Because I respected your property too much."

"Indeed? I incline to think that it was because you knew the brooch was not there."

"I don't understand."

"I, on the contrary, did — the moment I received Miss Vining's letter. I saw it all. You pawned that brooch, Stanley! I know you so well."

I drew myself up.

"You cannot know me very well, Aunt Julia," I said coldly, "if you think that of me. And allow me to say, while on this subject, that your suspicions are unworthy of an aunt."

"Never mind what they're unworthy of. Open that drawer."

"Break it open?"

"Break it open."

"With a poker?"

"With anything you please. But opened it shall be, now, and in my presence."

I gazed at her haughtily.

"Aunt Julia," I said, "let us get this thing straight. You wish me to take a poker or some other blunt instrument and smash that bureau?"

"I do."

"Think well."

"I have done all the thinking necessary."

"So be it!" I said.

So I took the poker, and I set about that bureau as probably no bureau has ever been set about since carpentry first began. And there, gleaming in the ruins, was the brooch.

"Aunt Julia," I said, "a little trust, a little confidence, a little faith, and this might have been avoided."

She gulped pretty freely.

"Stanley," she said at last, "I wronged you."

"You did."

"I — I — well, I'm sorry."

"You may well be, Aunt Julia," I said.

And, pursuing my advantage, I ground the woman into apologetic pulp beneath what practically amounted to an iron heel. And in that condition, Corky, she still remains. How long it will last one cannot say, but for the time being I am the blue-eyed boy and I have only to give utterance to my lightest whim to have her jump six feet to fulfil it. So, when I said I wanted to ask you to dinner here tonight, she practically smiled. Let us go into the library, old horse, and trifle with the cigars. They are some special ones I had sent up from that place in Piccadilly.

ALLAN PATRICK HERBERT

LITERATURE

Well Trix dear, what do you think, I've become a *professional* girl, well really, my dear, Mum's got so tiresome about this *boring* marriage business and even Dad's beginning to wear a *martyrish* look, and really I believe if I'm not blighted in matrimony in another fortnight they'll *lock* the front door on me one night, and anyhow as Mr. Haddock said in these days economic thingummy is the *sole* criterion or something for a girl of spirit, don't you agree, so I made up my mind to be *Nature's* economic girl and earn some degrading lucre somehow, well, I thought it wouldn't be *too* prohibitive because as Mr. Haddock said England may be going to the dogs and democracy and everything but thank Heaven we're all snobs still and if Lady Topsy Trout can't find a niche in the façade of industry who *can* darling?

Well Mr. Haddock thought I might perhaps carve a bit of a niche in the *writing* profession because from what I can make out nearly all the writing is done by Society nowadays, it seems you start with advertising a face-cream and by degrees you become a gossip-writer, like Little Lord Fatface (my dear they say his ads. for "Reduce-It-In-The-Home" were *too* exquisite) well my dear I'm in luck because it seems there's the *most* venomous face-cream war going on between "Queen Cream" and "Skindew", you see Skindew have just made a *capacious*

119

splash with that Stage Star series and Queen Cream were *just* preparing to retaliate with a Mayfair Flowers series when Mr. Haddock happened to mention *me*, and lo and behold your Topsy's the very *first* of the Mayfair Flowers, with a column and a half about How I Keep My Beauty, my dear you can say what you like but it *is* rather a thrill this writing and I can't *tell* you what they're paying me, and *masses* of Queen Cream for life for nothing, of course. I'd never *heard* of the stuff before, I *always* use Skindew, but the *most* efficient Queen Cream young woman came to see me with a sniff and my dear a skin like a *sponge*, the *most* deceptive ad. for a cream you can imagine and it's just as well they don't photograph *her*, well she read out all the most *litterary* bits she'd written and simply *all* I had to do was to sign it, I must say Beauty and Queen Cream seem to be a whole-time job from what I seem to have written, my dear it's cream before meals and cream after meals and cream between meals and really the actual meals seem to be the *only* parts of the day I don't spend *creaming*, well it all came out in *The Glass* and next morning the telephone *never* stopped ringing, because my dear simply *everyone* read my article and they *adored* the photograph all except the *inconsequent* Mr. Haddock who said it looked like The Vamp Reformed, so I shan't give *him* one.

But my dear I haven't told you, the *most* fanatical thing happened, *Parker, you* know, my flat-footed maid, well my dear I asked her what she thought of the picture and she said it was sweetly pretty but she was a *wee* bit *difficile* I asked her what she thought, and the same night she gave notice, my dear I couldn't *imagine* why and you'll *never* guess, but Mum talked to her and it seems she didn't approve of me writing about Queen Cream when I've used nothing but Skindew since I left the Kindergarten, because she said it was *deceiving the public*, my dear wasn't it *perfectly* sweet, the *ideas* they have! well of course Mum talked her over but I still feel the old thing does a girl's hair more in sorrow than in anger, however, *much* more important, the next day my dear an *editor* or something rang up from *Undies, the divinest* paper, well I went to see him in the *most* insanitary office, but it seems he was *throbbed* about my article and he was *too* congenial, and they want me to try and do the Mayfair Maiden's page when Hermione Tarver goes to

India, well my dear you must say it's *rather* gratifying when you realise I've only just begun, mustn't you darling, they want me to do it as near as possible in the same style as Little Lord Fatface, which is a *tiny* bit lowering perhaps because really my dear *all* he does is to write down the names of *all* the people he met yesterday and fill in from *Who's Who* and my dear if I can't write as well as he does I shall just give up writing, anyhow I've just been practising, what d'you think of this: —

AN EX-OXONIAN.

I met Lord Birkenhead in the Park yesterday. He was smoking a cigar. His daughter Pamela was with him. The Secretary of State for India has two daughters, both girls. "F.E." was at Wadham.

STICK-NAMES.

Mention of "F.E." reminds me that Lord Danver is known to his intimate friends as "Bubbles." The nickname was a childish corruption of his first name, which is Charles. These nursery soubriquets often stick to a man through life.

WAR-HERO.

"Bubbles" owns four thousand acres and is a good shot. He belongs to the Marlborough Club. When I saw him at Hurlingham yesterday he had just had a spill. He was smiling at his mishap. His brother is the Admiral, who fought at Jutland.

PROVING THE RULE.

There are not many cases of twins marrying brothers. Lord Mouldsworth's daughters are no exception to the rule, for their fiancés are not related. Both girls are fond of sport. Helena plays golf. They are beautiful.

One day this week Lord Mouldsworth was dining with his family at a famous restaurant. He seemed to be enjoying his oysters. I asked him if he had found any pearls. "Two," he replied, and smilingly indicated his winsome daughters. He is a yachtsman. The Countess keeps white mice.

Not so bad d'you think darling, as a *matter* of fact Mr. Haddock helped me the *flimsiest* bit but he will *not* take it seriously and he does make the *most* naughty suggestions, but I do think that's *just* the kind of simple *sedative* stuff that all those *unfortunate* creatures in Whitechapel are *starving* for on a Sunday morning don't you, well anyhow I'm fairly *launched* on the litterary career and I *do* think it does everybody good if a girl mixes with the life of the people a bit and strikes out her own economic what-not don't you, so if Mr. Haddock won't help me I shall go *straight* to that *brainy* Queen Cream woman with the sniff, farewell Trix, your *only* Topsy.

ENGAGED

Trix darling I've come to the conclusion that I'm a *born* misogamist, well my dear what with the New Year I've been thinking *too* deeply about marriage and everything and I do think that perhaps *some* girls' destinies are *definitely* celibatic don't you, and if so it's *quite* sterile to shut the old eyes to it, well my dear here I am twenty-one already and not a *tinkle* from the village bells, though really my dear I *am* one of the rages of the city and when I think of the *platoons* of poor fish who merely *flounder* in my wake, not to speak of what I call the *rather* eligible danglers, but my dear the *utter* fallacy is that *whenever* I begin the *gentlest* heart-beat about a man he *merely* evaporates but the ones that go soupy about me are nearly always *absolutely* dispensable, my dear I find it *too* prohibitive to take the masculine gender seriously when it begins to *flabbify* don't you, on the other hand of course my *only* Patrick went off to India without so much as a parting wireless, and ever since the Park episode my *poor* Sweet has *dwindled* back into a walking Plato, my *unique* Nick *shuns* me, and my *unimpeachable* Wog does nothing but tell me about his *latest* proposal to the *noxious* Margery, my dear that *deluded* youth has been dangling from the *cradle*, and I do think Margery Pooks is perfectly *unclassified* don't you?

And of course Mr. Haddock is a *chronic* enigma, well there you are my dear, either the male merely *gravitates* at me or he *merely* gallops away, but always the wrong ones, my dear it's *too* inequitable, because my dear the *rows* of men who've *departed* to India and everywhere *just* as I was beginning to think they were *rather* tolerable, really darling in my humble way I'm *quite* populating the Empire, because my dear I do seem to have a gift for *dissipating* the flower of our youth to the four corners and everything while I *rally* about me a *complete* herd of the most *toxic* scions of the upper classes, and my dear I do think some of our aristocracy are *perfectly* unvaccinated, so it's all a little *morbid* you must admit and what with one thing and another and everything I might just as well decide on misogamy and have done with it, because my dear from what I see of marriage it's the *most* hypothetical of all human proceedings, well look at the *Featherlegs* who do nothing but *impeach* each other in public, and *look* at the Merridews who do nothing but *venerate* each other in public and really I don't know *which* is the most emetical, you know my dear I *can't* bear these *varicose* emotions, and besides I *rather* fancy that perhaps my real destiny is just to be the *world's* ray of sunshine, not anybody *particular's* darling but utterly communal, well what I mean is that I *rather* see myself *drifting* radiantly from *life* to *life*, my dear a sort of *universal* electric butterfly, well I should *flit* in at the Featherlegs and make the moribund

Featherleg see that *after* all there is something in life worth living for, my dear *too* spiritual and everything of *course* but when I flut away the *poor* lamb would be *utterly* reconciled to existence and Hattie F. and then I should merely *waft* in and out of the *Merridew* ménage and *shake* up that *sedimentary* man till he saw that *after* all there *is* something worth looking at besides his *totally* oval and methylated *wife*, my dear it would do the pair of them a *mountain* of good and my dear think what you like but *doing good* would be the *dominant* note of my *whole* policy and I do think there's something *rather* valid about the idea don't you darling?

Because my dear there's *no* doubt that married life *is* definitely a *dungeon*, and unless it gets *continual* rays of sunshine from the *outer* world well the whole thing becomes *too* unhygienic and fungy, and I do think that perhaps it's the *duty* of a really *unusual* ray of sunshine to keep herself available for *general* sweetness instead of wasting herself on a desert husband if you see what I mean, so I shall just *float* about the world *brightening* the lives of *despairing* widowers and suicidal City men, my dear *quite* fairy-like, and of course what's so remunerative one would keep the old figure for perfectly *ever*, and I *rather* see myself as the *most* heavenly old maid don't you darling, my dear the *nation's* godmother, *always* doing tapestry *cushion-covers* over the fire at house-parties, and my dear saying *sagacious* things about *Life* and everything, and of course my dear the *Young* would worship me because I should be *too* advanced and understanding about the *Young* and my dear always help the *Young* to marry each other *whatever* their *foul* parents said, and my dear the *most* blossomy nieces would cluster at my knee and say *Wasn't* there ever a *Man* in your life Aunt Topsy, and I shall say Well darlings I did meet a man once only the letter wasn't delivered and we *drifted* apart and everything, and p'raps I shall tell them how my *poor* Sweet took me to the greyhounds once, only of course by that time it will all sound *too* fragrant and Victorian, and I shall drop *two* tears on to my tapestry p'raps.

But my dear the *real* reason of all this philosophication is that I'm expecting Mr. Haddock ANY minute, my dear he *rang* up this morning and said he had a *rather* serious proposal to make and my dear I'm in a *virginal* dither from floor to ceiling, because my dear well Mr. Haddock has *never* yet turned oozy like most of them, he's *always* been a sort of *salubrious* background, and my dear if he does turn oozy I'm not *sure* that I can bear it, on the *other* hand darling it *isn't* like him and if he *should* suggest anything in a *disarming* way I've a *gnawing* fear my dear that I *may* have a moment of *girlish* abandon and utterly forget about misogamy and everything, because my dear with *all* his faults, O snakes here he is, pray for me darling.

Later.— Well my dear I'll tell you what happened, he didn't ooze a *fraction*, my dear *too* restrained, but he made the *longest* speech about my arresting *qualities*, well he said that I might be the *tiniest* bit superficial on the *top*, but he knew perfectly well that *deep* down I was *utterly* fundamental, my dear heart of gold and everything, because he said that he didn't care *what* these *fermented* centenarians said, *my* type of Modern Girl was the *penultimate* flower of *evolution*, which is what I've *always* thought haven't you darling, well he said that what he was going to propose might p'raps seem strange to a girl of my position and everything, and my dear I was just working up for *acute* emotion-trouble, my dear I felt like a *blanc-mange*, when he said the *fact* was he'd just been adopted for a *Parliamentary* Candidate and he wanted me to be a sort of extra-special super-Private *Secretary*, my dear *too* flattering, of course he'll have some plebeian creature to do the typing and everything *menial* but he wants somebody *rather* Cadogan to help in the *policy* department and *fascinate* the electors because it seems it's the *most* industrial neighbourhood, *Burbleton* or somewhere, my dear *too* democratic, but he says they're *all* snobs and adore Beauty, and he says he *rather* thinks I have a *flair* for politics, and he's *quite* sure that when it comes to it I shall have some perfectly *strategic* ideas, and it seems there may be a bye-election *quite* soon so we're to go down for weekends and *nurse* the constituency, my dear it's *rather* a throb *isn't* it, well of course after the first shock I said I'd do *anything* because my litterary career does seem to be *procrastinating* somewhat and I do think a girl ought to do *something* for her principles and the country and everything, of course it isn't *quite* what I expected but it never *is* with men *is* it darling and anyhow it's *quite* compatible with *utter* misogamy so farewell my sister soul, your *single* but nevertheless *secretarial* little Topsy.

THE WASH

I woke like a log, one eye at a time. Dimly I perceived beside my bed the night-nurse, a basin of water in one hand, a thermometer in the other.

"Do you feel like a little wash now?" she said brightly.

"No, Nurse, I do not," I said, and I went to sleep again.

When I re-woke (as the films say) there was a thermometer in my mouth and the night-nurse had "captured" (as the poets say) one of my hands.

"You know very well," I said, taking out the thermometer, "that my pulse and my temperature are always the same. I am very well. All that I need is sleep, and this is the hour of all hours in the day when I sleep the best. And if I am not to sleep I will not be washed."

"You must be washed," she said, "before the doctor comes."

"I am quite clean enough for a doctor," I said. "I will be washed at noon, when I stop sleeping."

"You will be washed now," she said, and, untucking all my snug bed-clothes, she piled them in a disorderly and draughty heap on my legs.

"This is barbarous," I said.

"Shut the eyes," said the night-nurse, and scrubbed my face with a hard rubber sponge.

"It is extraordinary," I said. "Whenever the doctor comes he inquires if I have slept well; when Sister comes in she asks anxiously how I slept; last night you gave me, yourself, *two* different preparations or drugs to make me sleep. One would think that the whole establishment had no other aim than to make me sleep; all the resources of medicine have been mobilised to make me sleep. Yet when I do sleep, or rather when at last I drop into a fitful doze, I am immediately woken up. And for what purpose? To be washed!"

"Quite a martyr, aren't you?" she said. "Now the hands."

"The hands do not want washing," I said. "Wash the hands if you must; but you will have no assistance from me."

She dropped the hands into a basin of boiling water.

"I should have thought that you, at least, Nurse, would have seen the futility of these proceedings," I said. "That sleeping draught you gave me was wholly ineffective. All night I tossed upon my sleepless couch, counting the hours, and every quarter reviling the punctual clanging of your local clock. Before five, I know, I did not sleep a wink. About six I may have dropped off. And no sooner do I drop off than you wake me with thermometers and soap."

"You have been sleeping like a log since ten o'clock," she said. "Now the legs."

"I deny it," I said. "What time is it now?"

"It's half past seven," she said, "and I'm late."

"Do you realise," I said, "that when I am in full health I do not begin to *think* of washing till about nine, and even then it does not always happen? Yet now, when I am extraordinarily ill and cruelly deprived of my appendix, I am expected to endure this distasteful ordeal at daybreak."

"You're lucky," she said; "at some places they wash the bodies at six."

"No one shall wash *this* body at six," I said.

"Can you lift that leg?"

"I can not," I said; "I am very ill."

She went out of the room, and I went to sleep again.

She came back with Nurse Andrews. They woke me up again and seized the right leg. They soaped the right leg and sponged it with a cruel sponge. They put the right foot in a basin, poured methylated spirit over heel and sprinkled powder

127

over the whole. Then they unveiled the left leg and started on that. Meanwhile the maid came in and did the grate, leaving the door open.

"Do you have many deaths in this hospital?" I said.

"Not so many," said the night-nurse.

"Well, one of these days you will have an Abdominal dying of ablutions. Just because I have no appendix," I said, "you think you can humiliate and torment me how you like. And there's another extraordinary thing I've discovered. I have been lying in this bed for a fortnight, Nurse, with no tobacco, no alcohol, no late nights, no night-clubs nor dances, nor the pernicious society of your sex, Nurse. I have not so much as eaten a sweet. I have lived, in fact, a life of abstinence and virtue, gazing at flowers, reading good books and eating little but vitamins. And if there is anything in what the reformers of this world tell us, I should wake each morning as fresh as a lark, Nurse. As soon as my eyes are open, I should have all my faculties alert and buoyant, ready for anything. Well, they are not, Nurse, I am not fresh. I wake each morning feeling like an old piece of blotting-paper, as other men do. I wake fuddled and suicidal and quarrelsome and hog-like, as usual. I wake like chewed string. I wake as I might wake after a week's debauch."

"If you will turn him over, Nurse Andrews," she said, "I will do the back."

"You will kindly leave the back alone," I said. "And I will not be talked about as if I were something in a butcher's shop. I am a living soul, with aspirations and a future life, and you are not to keep speaking of *the back* and *the leg* — as if I were so many joints of beef."

Neither of the ministering angels took any notice of this protest, so I resumed the main argument.

"There is this further consideration," I said. "So far (touching wood) I have made a most rapid recovery from the mutilations of the doctors. The wound is not septic, the tongue is clean, and, if all goes well, as you have told me, I shall escape from your clutches in record time. In fact, Nurse (making every allowance for the skill and attention of the medical and nursing professions) the conclusion is that, in order to be healthy and especially before an operation, a man should

128

constantly absorb in enormous quantities all those poisons which modern civilisation has made available, for this it is my habit to do, and you see the result; but you will find that long after I leave you the teetotallers and vegetarians and non-smokers will be stretched upon their beds about this hospital, feebly complaining and constantly ringing the bell. Which is the worst case here, Nurse?"

"The Abdominal in Number 9," she said.

"An archdeacon, I believe. A non-smoker?"

"Yes."

"And a teetotaller?"

"Yes."

"Well, there you are," I said.

"Now the teeth," she answered.

I washed the teeth under protest, for this is a thing I hate to do before ladies. I then shaved by numbers and lay back exhausted. They then began the painful and fatiguing process which is known as making the patient comfortable. This took a quarter-of-an-hour. I am condemned for some reason to sit upon an air-cushion, and while one is being washed one slides to the bottom of the bed. The two good women with heroic efforts hauled me up into a sitting position, but left the air-cushion behind. While the air-cushion was being placed in position, I slid down the bed again; it seemed to be a downhill bed. They heaved me on to the air-cushion, reviling me alternately for exerting myself too much and for making myself too heavy. When I was enthroned on the air-cushion at the right elevation the air-cushion was not central, and while the air-cushion was being centralised I slid down the bed again. When both the body and the air-cushion were right the pillows were wrong, and while the pillows were being put right, I did an avalanche, air-cushion and all. And all the time, with little anecdotes about abdominal cases they had known, the thoughtless women made me laugh, which hurts more than anything.

"Are you comfortable *now*?" said the night-nurse at last.

"I am not," I said. "But I would rather live on in discomfort than perish of exhaustion in a position of ease. I do not feel nearly so well. For a whole hour, Nurse, I have had worry and hard work, and all this before breakfast. When a man is in health, Nurse, a man takes great care of himself before breakfast, husbands his strength, nurses his soul and does as little as possible. But here upon a bed of sickness he does the equivalent of about two hours' hard labour before breakfast. It's extraordinary. And speaking of breakfast, Nurse — well, what about breakfast?"

The night-nurse arranged upon the table a number of nasty-looking steel instruments.

"The doctor is coming before breakfast," she said, "to take your stitches out. And," she added wickedly, "I hope it hurts."

NAT GUBBINS

A VISIT TO WALES

"Bore da i chwi"...

Which is Welsh for "Good morning to you". And to which you should reply, if you know any Welsh:

"Beth? y chwi uma?" Which means, "What? You here?"

And where, also a very high proportion of the population is named Jones, which can cause a certain amount of confusion and bewilderment at social gatherings.

"Oh, Mr. Gubbins."

"Mr. Jones?"

"Allow me to introduce you to a friend of mine, Mr. Jones."

"It is indeed a pleasure to meet you, Mr. Gubbins."

"It is indeed a pleasure to meet *you*, Mr. Jones."

"And Mr. Gubbins."

"Mr. Jones?"

"Here is another friend of mine, Mr. Jones."

"A pleasure to meet you, Mr. Jones."

"And well now, and look who's come. Mr. Gubbins, you must meet a very, very old friend of mine, Mr. Jones."

"How do you do, Mr. Jones?"

"Very well, Mr. Gubbins."

"And we have by here the guest of the evening."

"Not Mr. Jones?"

"Mr. Jones himself."

9*

Wales and the Welsh people have always held a high place in my affections, which are few and not lightly given. The only thing I have to say against them is that they prefer to talk Welsh in their pubs, which leaves me out in the cold, listening to uproarious laughter at jokes which might be against myself.

It may be for this reason that I bought a fourpenny pamphlet called "Welsh in a Week", and described as "a rapid method of learning Welsh by means of conversation."

But I found the whole thing too difficult, and soon became absorbed in the adventures of a Mr. J. (not a Mr. Jones by any chance?) whose story is told in the English-Welsh dialogue written for the instruction of the student.

We first meet Mr. J. in the train. To his first question: "Is there any room?" the reply from the other passenger is, "There is plenty of room here."

They soon get into amiable and courteous conversation.

"Are you going far?"

"I am going to Wales."

"Do we change carriages on the journey?"

"I think so. No, I don't think so."

"What is the name of the next station?"

"The next station is——"

(He evidently doesn't know or can't pronounce it.)

"Do we pass through——?"

"No, we leave it on the left, on the right."

"They are slackening speed. The train is going very fast."

"We are close by. We are a long way off."

"We have almost arrived."

"Do you know of a good hotel?"

"I should go to the Queen's, if I were you."

At the Queen's Hotel Mr. J. is received so warmly that he begins to throw his weight about.

"Good morning to you," he says rather coldly to the reception clerk.

"Good morning, sir."

"Can you give me a bed?"

"With great pleasure."

Evidently this is a most exceptional hotel. Mr. J., who seems a bit of a bully, then issues a series of sharp orders which, as we shall see, sets the whole staff against him.

"What is the number of my room?" barks Mr. J.

"Number Eleven."

"Show me the way. Take my bag up."

"Where is the waiter?"

The waiter appears.

"Can you speak English?" asks Mr. J.

"I understand a little, but cannot speak it."

"Do you understand me?"

"No. I do not unterstand you."

This jolts Mr. J. who probably fancies his English (and French too), for his next question is:

"Have you a table d'hôte?"

The waiter stares blankly at him, and no doubt Mr. J. has to repeat the question in Welsh:

"A ces gennych ginio cyhoeddus?"

The waiter understands this all right, but he already hates the pompous Mr. J. With an evil smile, he leads him to a table, with nothing on it but a tablecloth, and retires to the kitchen to discuss the new guest with the staff.

Let alone and unattended before his blank tablecloth, Mr. J. begins to mutter to himself:

"At what time do we eat today?"

"When do we have lunch?"

"What price is it?"

"What time is it?"

But nobody takes any notice, and we next hear him shouting at the top of his voice:

"Be so good as to bring me a knife."

"Be so good as to bring me a spoon."

"Be so good as to bring me a glass."

After letting him sweat a bit, the waiter appears at last and asks sneeringly:

"What can I offer you?"

And poor Mr. J., humbled by now, dare not ask for his grand table d'hôte, but says, in a crushed voice:

"I wish to have tea, with bread and butter and cold meat."

"Would you like some beer?" asks the wine waiter, not thinking him fit to look at the wine list.

"Thank you. I prefer water," says Mr. J. with quiet dignity.

A strange thing happens after this. Either the cold meat is uneatable or they don't bring it to Mr. J. at all.

Anyway, his next sentences are: "Let us have breakfast. Is breakfast ready?" And he is soon yelling for eggs.

"Bring me an egg," he roars.

"Bring me two eggs."

"Give us some boiled eggs."

Except for suppressed giggles in the kitchen, there is complete silence, and Mr. J. gives it up.

Desperate and lonely, he then goes to the office and asks: "Is there a letter for me?"

This is a silly question, because he has only just arrived, and the hotel clerk, once so amiable, ignores it.

"Have you notepaper, envelopes, pen and ink?" he asks. "What day of the month is it? Where is the post office? Is there anything to be seen here? What churches are to be seen in this neighbourhood? What public buildings are to be seen in this neighbourhood? How far away are they?"

"About forty to sixty miles," answers the maddened clerk, slamming his ledger and going off in a huff.

Driven into the street by the cold hostility of the hotel staff, the unhappy Mr. J. thinks he will call on somebody, although he appears to be a stranger in the district.

Hailing a passer-by, he says: "Excuse me, but is there not a Mr. J. living somewhere here?"

In a place half full of Mr. J.'s this question causes some amusement and the passer-by invites his friends to listen. Our Mr. J. is soon surrounded by a jeering crowd.

"Yes," says the passer-by, "there is a person of that name living here."

"Can you tell me where he lives?" asks the simple Mr. J. "Am I going in the right direction?"

"No. You are quite wrong."

"Which way, then, ought I to go?"

"You will come to a cross-road," says somebody.

"Then you can't miss it," says somebody else.

"Take the first turning to the left."

"Turn to the right," shouts a bystander.

"Ask at the first house you come to."

"Follow this path. It will take you there."

"On which side is it?" asks Mr. J.

"On this side," they shout.

"On the other side."

"Many thanks," says Mr. J., going in the wrong direction, amid shouts of laughter.

In the next chapter Mr. J. chums up with somebody.

"How do you do today?" asks his chum. "When did you arrive?"

"Yesterday, today, last night," answers Mr. J. (Evidently the place is getting him down.)

"How's your father?"

This old music-hall crack is too much for Mr. J. As you follow his adventures through the book you can see that he is slowly going mad.

Leaving his chum, he rushes wildly round the shops buying hats, collars, shirts, stockings, shoes, a pound of tea, a pound and a half of sugar, and half a pound of butter.

"Where shall I send it?" asks the shopkeeper.

"I will call for it on my way back."

"You had better let me send it," insists the shopkeeper.

"I want my hair cut," answers Mr. J.

Which seems to clinch the matter.

Romance, of a sort, comes to Mr. J. in the last chapter but one. Mr. J. takes a walk with somebody. And if Mr. J. is true to type, it is the hotel chambermaid.

"Will you come for a walk?"

"Willingly."

(She takes a second look at Mr. J. and changes her mind.)

"No, I do not think I can."

"It will be pleasant walking." (Satanic, Mr. J.)

"Are you ready to start?"

"I am waiting for you."

"Which way shall we go?"

"Whichever way you like."

"Let us go across the fields." (Steady, Mr. J.)

"Isn't the grass wet?"

"We can keep to the path."

"Let us walk through the wood." (Whoa, Mr. J.)

"How far shall we go?"

"We will not go very far."

"I must not be long away."

"We will turn back soon."

"Let us return the nearest way."

Well, that's the end of his rather futile attempt to be a ladies' man, and in the next chapter he is back in the hotel, fed up, frustrated, and far from home.

He makes a quick decision.

"What time does the first train start in the morning?" he asks the clerk.

The clerk doesn't answer.

"Let me have the bill," he snaps.

The clerk shows some speed over this.

"Here is your bill, sir," he says in a glad, ringing voice.

"Call me at eight o'clock," says Mr. J. stumping off to bed.

"Good night, sir."

Ffarwel. A thauth bletserus, Mr. J., bach.

(Translation: Farewell. And a pleasant journey, Mr. J., dear.)

JOHN B. MORTON

THE CASE OF JULIETTE MILTON

A Mrs. Webcross writes to me as follows:

Dear Sir,

I have seen it stated in the "Cardiff Bugle" that the fairies now appearing at the foot of Knockfierna in County Limerick are the celebrated red-headed dwarfs who have made Mr. Justice Cocklecarrot's life a hell. This is not so. The twelve little gentlemen are at present my lodgers, and I have no complaint to make of them, apart from a tendency to bawl for second helpings of meat (which are not included in our board), and a readiness to flirt with my pretty boarder in the most outrageous manner. In the term "flirting" I include ear-pinching, eye-rolling, lip-smacking, nudging, giggling, and even, upon occasion, sudden embracing in the passages. But my object in writing to you, sir, is to put it on record that neither I nor the late Mr. Webcross has ever harboured fairies, either knowingly or unknowingly.

Believe me, sir,

Yours respectfully,

(Mrs.) Lottie Webcross.

The Twelve Dwarfs

Dear Sir,

We, the undersigned dwarfs, desire to bestow our heartiest approval upon the wise and timely letter of our dear and revered landlady, Madame Webcross. We are not Little People in the fairy-tale sense of the words. We are merely small in the human sense of the word. As to flirtation, when you are as small as we are, and red-haired into the bargain, you have to take your fun where you find it. Full many a furtive kiss changes hands, or rather mouths, without Church and State rocking on their foundations, and if there is a jollier pastime for a spare moment in a corridor than the tweaking of some alluring ear, we, the undersigned dwarfs, would be glad to hear of it. Evil be to him who thinks evil, say we. Horseplay is no more out of place in a humble boarding-house than in the gilded mansions of the great, and a loving heart is just as likely to beat beneath the ready-made waistcoat of a lodger as beneath the braided and double-breasted garment of a loftier Lothario. All this we say, well knowing that one of our number, Churm Rincewind, is even at this moment encircling with adventurous right arm the provocative waist of Juliette, the sylph-like diseuse who, after bringing down two houses a night at the Old Victoria in Oldham has, bird-of-passage-like, made her temporary nest in No. 8, adjoining the linen cupboard.

We are, sir,
The Twelve Dwarfs.

The Pretty Boarder Replies

Dear Sir,

As the "pretty boarder" referred to by Mrs. Webcross in her letter to you, I should like to take this opportunity of denying the statement made by a dwarf of the name of Churm Rincewind to the effect that he put his arm round my waist. All that happened was this. Mr. Rincewind put a small ladder against me while I was reading a letter. He mounted the ladder and kissed the tip of my right ear. Thinking he was crazy I pushed him away, and he fell from the ladder and hurt his wrist. I understand he is claiming damages. The whole incident is too foolish to be taken seriously. One does not expect to have ladders put against one in respectable boarding-houses, nor to see a grinning face on the top rung.

Yours truly,
Juliette Milton.

I learn that the red-bearded dwarf, Churm Rincewind, who fell from a small folding ladder on the third-floor landing of Sea View boarding-house, Chelsea, while kissing the ear of Miss Juliette Milton, is bringing an action for damages. The case will come up for hearing shortly. The judge will be Mr. Justice Cocklecarrot. Miss Milton said yesterday, "The whole affair is too ludicrous to discuss. My solictor tells me that there has never before been a case of a small man planting a ladder against a lady, and then bringing an action because he is pushed away and hurts his wrist."

The nearest approach to such a case was when a man-about-town tried to throw a brass curtain-ring over the head of one of the giraffe-necked women from Burma. He mounted a ladder to get a better aim.

Mrs: Webcross Gives Evidence

The hearing began yesterday, before Mr. Justice Cocklecarrot (with full jury), of the case in which Mr. Churm Rincewind, a red-bearded dwarf about town, seeks to recover damages for an injury to his wrist, sustained when he fell from a ladder which he had mounted for the purpose of kissing the ear of a young lady boarder at Sea View, Chelsea (proprietress, Mrs. Webcross). Mr. Tinklebury Snapdriver was for the defence, Mr. Graham Gooseboote for the prosecution.

Mr. Gooseboote: You are Hermione Webcross, proprietress of the boarding-house known as Sea View?

Mrs. Webcross: I object, m'lud.

Cocklecarrot: What — to the boarding-house?

Mrs. Webcross: It is not "known as" Sea View. It *is* Sea View.

Mr. Gooseboote: And what sea, may one ask, does it view? The Pacific?

Mrs. Webcross: Properly speaking, there is no view of the sea, as we overlook Delton and Mackworth's Cycle Accessories. But the name was handed down by my late mother, Clara Webcross, Sea View.

Mr. Gooseboote: Very well. Now, Mrs. Webcross, do you encourage your male boarders to make overtures to your female boarders?

Mrs. Webcross: Certainly not. My house is not a co-educational roadhouse.

Mr. Gooseboote: Then how do you explain the fact that one of your boarders, a lady, was kissed on the ear from the top rung of a small ladder in broad daylight?

Mrs. Webcross: It was the exception that proves the rule. It might happen to anyone.

(The court then rose for drinks.)

Juliette Cross-Examined

Miss Juliette Milton, dressed in a four-piece gabardine of moire tussore with green revers and crotted manchlets, was cross-examined yesterday by Mr. Gooseboote.

Mr. Gooseboote: I suggest that you yourself helped to place the ladder up which your assailant climbed.

Miss Milton: No. I can get plenty of kissing without having to act as a sort of builder's mate.

Mr. Gooseboote: No doubt, no doubt. Er — did you in any way extend your ear, in order to make the dwarf's pleasant task easier?

Miss Milton: I am an actress, not a contortionist. I cannot move my ears at will.

Mr. Gooseboote: Not even a fraction of an inch, in order to avoid an unorthodox salutation?

Cocklecarrot: May we see this ladder?

Mr. Snapdriver. Certainly, m'lud. It is here. It shall be passed up to you.

Mr. Gooseboote: With your ludship's permission, I would like to try an experiment.

Cocklecarrot: With the ladder and the lady's ear? Fire ahead. I'm sure the whole court envies you.

(The court then rose for more drinks.)

Mr. Gooseboote was half-way up the ladder, which he had leaned against Miss Juliette Milton, and was already stooping to her ear, when a cry rang out.

Rincewind: M'worship, I object. Why should the learned counsel be allowed to do with impunity what I am being prosecuted for doing without impunity?

Cocklecarrot: It is in the interests of justice.

Miss Milton (blushing): Not entirely, I hope.

Mr. Gooseboote (beaming at her): No, of course, not entirely. There is the human element.

Cocklecarrot: That element, Mr. Gooseboote, must be strongly controlled in a court of law. The present experiment with an ear should be scientific, cold, detached. Meaning no slight to the — er — quite obvious charms of the lady.

Miss Milton: Thank you, m'lud. You are all most kind. It is so difficult for a lonely girl —

Rincewind: In every reconstruction of a crime that I can remember it was the accused who was given the leading part.

Cocklecarrot: There is no question of a crime in this case. It is no crime to — er — fondle such an ear.

Rincewind: Then why am I here?

Mr. Snapdriver: To claim damages, you fool, for a sprained wrist.

(The court then went rushing out for drinks.)

In Court

Mr. Gooseboote: Now, Mr. Rincewind —
Rincewind: Sir. Yours to command.

Cocklecarrot: Please, please, Mr. Rincewind.

Rincewind. With pleasure, m'ludship.

Cocklecarrot: Please do not speak until you are questioned.

Rincewind: I was under the impression that I *was* being questioned.

Cocklecarrot: Oh, very well. But try not to interrupt or to waste the time of the court. Pray proceed, Mr. Gooseboote.

Gooseboote: Now, Mr. Rincewind, how do you account for the fact that you fell from the ladder without Miss Milton pushing you?

Rincewind: Emotion.

Gooseboote: What do you mean — emotion?

Rincewind: It is difficult to balance on a ladder while including in dalliance and gallantry, as you probably know.

Gooseboote: The experience has not yet come my way.

Rincewind: Live in hope, cully, live in hope.

(The court then rose as one man and dashed madly for the canteen.)

Mr. Snapdriver. I put it to you, Mr. Rincewind —

Rincewind: Put away.

Snapdriver: What?

Rincewind: I said "put away".

Snapdriver: Put away what?

Rincewind: That's what you were going to tell us.

Cocklecarrot: Come, come. This is ludicrous. Mr. Rincewind, you must endeavour to refrain from interruption.

Rincewind: Your wish is law, Big Chief.

Cocklecarrot: Would that it were.

Rincewind: Were what?

Cocklecarrot: Law.

Rincewind: Oh.

Snapdriver: Now, I put it to you, Mr. Rince —

Rincewind: Now we're coming to it.

Snapdriver: M'lud, this is impossible.

Rincewind: He's losing his nerve.

Cocklecarrot: I shall have to fine you for contempt.

Rincewind: All the dough in the world wouldn't pay for my contempt of this court, not meaning any offence.

(Sensation. The court is cleared.)

Sensational Disclosure

Cocklecarrot: This case seems to have got out of hand. We are here to consider the claim for damages of little Mr. Rincewind, who fell from a ladder while kissing the ear of the plaintiff, Miss Juliette Milton. Mr. Gooseboote, learned counsel for the defence, has repeated Mr. Rincewind's experiment with success. Mr. Snapdriver, learned counsel for the prosecution, now demands to follow suit. Well, if we are all going to reconstruct the case so realistically, we shall be here for weeks. But I cannot for the life of me see what these experiments, dangerously pleasant in themselves, can possibly prove. Miss Milton, did you push Mr. Rincewind off the ladder?

Miss Milton: No.

Cocklecarrot: Then you encouraged his advances?

Miss Milton: Certainly not. He is so small. I did not see him until he kissed me.

Cocklecarrot: Do you ask me to believe that you did not notice that you had a ladder leaning against you.

Miss Milton: Of course, I noticed it, you bl — m'lud.

Cocklecarrot: Then why did you leave it there?

Miss Milton: Must I answer?

Cocklecarrot: Of course you must.

Miss Milton (shyly): I thought it might be someone else coming up it.

(Sensation.)

Cocklecarrot Sums Up

Mr. Justice Cocklecarrot said "As it seems quite impossible to conduct in a normal manner any case in which these little gentlemen are involved, I suppose I may as well make a kind of summing-up. If the jury think that Mr. Rincewind was pushed from the ladder, they will consider his claim for damages reasonable. If, however, they are satisfied that he was not pushed but fell, as it were, of his own volition, their duty is clear. One thing that has struck me as odd about the case—apart from the interludes of lunacy which we have all deplored—is the fact that Miss Milton awaited the marauder, calmly allowing a ladder to be laid against her, as though she were a wall. She must have heard the approaching steps of this little bravo, and descried his face as it was advanced menacingly towards the goal of his unlawful whim—I refer to the perilously beautiful ear of the defendant. Now, Mrs. Webcross has assured us that ladder-gallantry is not part of the everyday life at her boarding establishment, yet Miss Milton expressed no surprise when she felt the ladder against her body, nor when she saw this little gentleman's moon-face gazing up at her. I am puzzled; and I am bound to add that the two learned counsel have merely confused the issue by their prodigious display of idiocy and incompetence. I will end on that note. It is for the jury to make what they can of all this nonsense."

THE THUNDERBOLT

Within a few weeks everybody will be talking about "Thunderbolt" Footle, the new discovery of that greatest of British boxing promoters, Scrubby Botulos.

Mr. Botulos said yesterday, in an interview, "Here, at last, is the genuine article. He's very handsome, dresses well, and has a number of good books at his lodgings. I have worked out a preliminary programme. I'm going to fix a fight with someone not too good. The Thunderbolt will win, and we shall then have no difficulty in getting him on to the films. During the making of his first film he will become more or less engaged to an actress — or, better, to a society girl. That will keep his name before the public, and there will be no need to tire him with too much fighting. The idea of calling him Thunderbolt before he has done any fighting is to get the public to realize how good he's going to be."

Mr. Botulos then distributed photographs of the new world-beater, showing his enormous muscles, which, said Mr. Botulos, "are harder than iron, and bigger too".

I understand that a fifteen-round contest has been fixed up between "Thunderbolt" Footle and "Slugger" Faxafloi, the man-eater from Iceland. It will take place some time within the next year, if Footle's theatrical and film and concert engagements permit. Footle said yesterday, "I shall not train much. I don't have to. My dancing keeps me fit. And, anyway, one blow will finish the fight. He won't know what hit him."

It is rumoured that Footle is engaged to be married to Miss Mae West. But he said yesterday, "We're just good pals." Miss Mae West said, "Where does he get that stuff about being good?" Meanwhile the Thunderbolt is being sued for breach of promise by a friend of his publicity manager, Joe Bulgetti.

Mr. Billy ("Haunch") Venison, the boxing critic, said yesterday, "It's difficult to say much about the Thunderbolt till we've seen him fight. He'll have to fight somebody sooner or later. That yarn about how he can smash through a six-foot wall with his bare fist doesn't impress me. It is told of every British heavyweight. I know that wall. It's a cardboard one, kept in the training quarters and photographed with a hole in it."

"I SHALL WIN" ("Thunderbolt" Footle)

The Thunderbolt's manager, Scrubby Botulos, announced yesterday that the fight between his man and Faxafloi will have to take place very soon, because the film and cabaret people are not inclined to give good contracts to an unknown boxer. "The pooblic," he said, "was not interested in a singer or a dancer until he will be have won a fight or two. What we was have got to get is that our man Footle shall have been proved to be a champion."

145

Footle said: "The fight's as good as over. He won't know about it until the hospital surgeon brings him round. He won't know what hit him. I'll just give him one jab. He needn't bother to come into the ring. I'll just knock him through the ropes. You may say that I shall win easily by a knock-out in the first second of the fight."

The boxing critic, Billy ("Haunch") Venison, said: "It's difficult to say anything until one has seen the fighters at work. I think that Footle should win unless Faxafloi proves too much for him. The same may be said of Faxafloi, only vice, of course, versa."

Asked by his publicity manager whether the newspapers were to be informed that he had a deadly right or a deadly left, the Thunderbolt said, "Everything about me is deadly. I'm dynamite from head to foot. He won't know what hit him."

Faxafloi said, "I shall win. He'll never know what hit him. I've got a load of dynamite in each fist."

Informed of this, Footle said, "I shall win. I've got more dynamite in my little finger than he'll ever have in his whole body. He won't know what hit him."

Informed of this, Faxafloi said, "I won't have to hit him. Just a flick. I'm dynamite. He'll never know what hit him."

Asked what his tactics would be, Footle said, "I won't need any. Just a tap and he'll be in the doctor's hands for a year. I'm made of dynamite. He won't know what hit him."

It was announced at Footle's headquarters today that the Thunderbolt had strained his throat while fulfilling a crooning engagement at a cabaret. But he was out in the afternoon, skipping and being photographed. Later he dislocated his thumb with a savage blow at the punchball, which bounded back, struck him on the head, and knocked him down.

"He is a real fighter," said Scrubby Botulos. "He doesn't seem to know the meaning of defence, he's so aggressive."

The Thunderbolt said, "I shall win. He won't even guess what hit him."

"Even if he did guess he wouldn't believe it," sneered an onlooker.

Mrs. Dietrich, when asked if she would attend a film with the Thunderbolt, said, "You can say we are just pals. I hope to meet him soon." Joan Crawford, when asked if there was anything in the rumour of her affection for Footle, said, "I have never met him, but we are just good pals." Constance Bennett said, "I've never heard of him. We are just pals, that's all."

"Thunderbolt" Footle, Britain's new heavyweight boxer, has signed a contract to appear as Faust in Gounod's opera. A daily paper has acquired the rights of *The Story of my Fights,* which will not be published until he has done some fighting. Meanwhile, he is still training for his fight with Faxafloi, the mystery heavyweight from Iceland. Owing to the calls upon him for making gramophone records and being photographed at parties, the Thunderbolt will probably have training quarters in a large flat off Piccadilly. Tomorrow he is skipping in Hyde Park for United International Films, Ltd. It is hoped that before his training is over he will appear at the first night of a new film with Mrs. Dietrich.

"Thunderbolt" Footle was knocked out four times yesterday, once by each of his sparring partners. His trainer said, "Thunderbolt wasn't really trying, and he wasn't ready, and the sun was in his eyes. You can tell what he's made of by what he said when he came to in his dressing-room. He said, 'He'll never know what hit him. I'm dynamite. That's what I am. Dynamite'."

Rumour is still coupling Footle's name with that of Miss Mae West. "You may say we're just pals," he said yesterday.

Asked what his tactics would be in the fight with Faxafloi, he said, "I won't need any. I shall just come out of my corner like a whirlwind on the stroke of the bell. One blow will finish it." At last Britain seems to have a champion.

Faxafloi appears to be a grim young man. He can't croon, doesn't like dancing, and doesn't want to be an actor. "In fact, all he can do is fight," said his trainer.

The fifteen-round contest between "Thunderbolt" Footle and Ring Faxafloi, the Iceland Wizard, will take place on Monday night. The hour has been changed from nine-thirty to eight-thirty, because the Thunderbolt has a cabaret engagement later in the evening. Footle said yesterday, "I shall win. He won't know what hit him. Then I'm ready for Louis, Schmeling, Baer, Farr, one at a time or all together. I'm set for the championship, and you may say that I consider it an honour to bring glory to British boxing."

Scrubby Botulos said, "I'll be surprised if that Icelander even gets out of his corner to begin the fight." And "Haunch" Venison, the boxing critic, said, "The fellow with the most dynamite in his fists is going to win. It's always been my experience that, in a heavy-weight fight, the winner is the one that can put the other fellow down for the count. If I had to hazard a guess, I should say this fight will be no exception to that rule."

England is talking of nothing but the forthcoming big fight tonight at Burlington House. Has Britain at last found a native champion? Will this, Footle's first fight, put him at one bound in the forefront, etc., etc., etc.?

A round-by-round description of the fight will be broadcast, the running commentary being in the capable and experienced hands of Mr. Guy Babblebotham and Mr. Hardleigh A. Mouse. ("Slop" of the *Sporting Chance*.)

Footle took things quietly yesterday, to avoid becoming stale. He lay in bed and read Upchurch's *Pragmatism and the Endocrine Gland,* while his publicity manager wrote thousands of telegrams wishing him good luck, signed by such celebrities as Rabindranath Tagore ("Sock him, feller!"), Mae West ("May victory smile upon you!"), Gabriele d'Annunzio ("Atta Thunder-bolt!"), the League Council ("Geneva is with you, cully"), the Southern Railway ("May the decenter man win"), and Rear-Admiral Sir Ewart Hodgson ("Lots Road is watching you").

Hardly had my little pen come trippingly off the paper at the end of that last sentence, when a news agency message was handed to me by my assistant under-secretary.

The fight is postponed! Not enough people have bought seats. Lack of interest is attributed to the fact that Footle has not become engaged to any actress. So, in order to lose as little time as possible, the publicity manager has got him engaged to that tiresome old-stager, Boubou Flaring. As I write this, they are being photographed together. He is saying, "Boubou is just swell," and she is replying, "Thunderbolt's a great guy." And already seats are being bought like hot cakes. So it is unlikely that the postponement will be for more than a day or two.

Tonight the British hope, Footle, will meet the Iceland Man-Eater, Faxafloi, in a fifteen-round contest at Burlington House at 9.30. The running commentary by Mr. Guy Babblebotham and Mr. Hardleigh A. Mouse will be broadcast.

Footle is said to have developed a curious back-hand swing which will prove deadly. He said this morning, "I shall win. Probably a knock-out in round one. I'm dynamite." Faxafloi said, "I shall just rub him into the floor with my heel."

"Haunch" Venison, the boxing critic, said, "If you ask me, I should say that the man who can hit hardest, stand up longest, and prove himself a winner will win the fight. If it doesn't end in a knock-out there will probably be a decision on points. A dead-heat is hardly likely. Nor is a draw without a verdict. Both men will have to box. And the result—well—wait and see." We are now taking you over to Burlington House to listen to the big fight between "Thunderbolt" Footle and Faxafloi... Mr. Babblebotham and Mr. Hardleigh A. Mouse are going to describe the fight for you... Well, here we are. Burlington House is packed. I don't think I've ever seen such a crowd, have you, Mouse? No. Ah! You hear that cheering? Somebody's just come in. I think it's the French Ambassador, isn't it, Mouse?.. No. I think it's Jack Hobbs... Oh. Right. And here's—surely it's—isn't it Lady Cabstanleigh, Mouse?.. No. It's two bankers... Oh. Right. The ring is filled with famous boxers, and the referee is introducing them. I can see Louis, Schmeling, Neusel, Ford, Farr, Max Baer, J. H. Lewis, Wilde, Dempsey, Tunney, Beckett, Carpentier, Harvey, Thil... Hullo! What's happened? Oh, you heard that roaring. Footle has arrived, but he can't get into the ring owing to the mob of famous boxers. And here comes Faxafloi now. They'll have to clear the ring...

Footle looks magnificent in his blue dressing-gown with golden dragons on it. Faxafloi is wearing a green dressing-gown with red spots. He looks very fit. I'm sure we all want to see a sporting fight, but that doesn't prevent us from wanting to see a British victory. I think they both look pretty fit, don't you, Mouse?... Of course they do. Why wouldn't they?... Er— I've just heard that Lord Towcher is somewhere among the audience... Now, we'll be off soon. The gloves are on, and the referee is just making his little speech to the two men. Faxafloi looks very cool. Footle is grinning, and he is evidently the idol of the crowd... There goes the bell for the first round...

Footle has rushed from his corner like an express train. No wonder they call him "Thunderbolt". Faxafloi looks puzzled. Footle was in such a hurry to get at his man that he apparently had no time to aim a blow at him when he came within striking distance. Faxafloi has sidestepped and Footle has crashed into the ropes. Ah! He's coming back. He's certainly doing all the attacking so far. Full of spirit. Hullo! He's slipped. He's down. He's up again. He's a bit dazed, and has aimed a wild blow in the air. Faxafloi is at the other side of the ring talking to his seconds. He seems amused. Don't know why. Footle's coming for him again. What spirit! He's still doing all the attacking. If one of those blows connects! Now they're face to face. The bell just saved Faxafloi from one of those terrible swinging punches.

Round II.— Footle's changed his tactics. He's more cautious. Neither man has landed a blow so far, but if the fighting spirit counts for anything, the first round was Footle's. Hullo! Faxafloi has moved forward. He's hit Footle hard under the chin. Footle's down. One — two — three — four — five — six — seven — eight — nine — ten. Out! Faxafloi wins. The crowd is going mad. Booing, hissing, screaming. The verdict is evidently unpopular. But I must say I think Faxafloi won without a doubt. Don't you, Mouse?... I think so. Oh yes. But it was rotten luck on Footle... He's come to. Phugh! He's in a rage, kicking and scratching. Faxafloi came over to shake hands, but Footle shouted something at him, and then burst into tears. The crowd is cheering him for his plucky effort... We are now taking you over to Morecombe Bay Casino to hear Squelch Rongero's Band...

In his dressing-room Footle said, "I wasn't feeling well at the start. The lights were in my eyes, and I thought he was going to foul me. I'm confident that I was the better man. It wasn't his blow that knocked me out, it was the impact of my head on the floor of the ring. I'm ready for Louis or Schmeling now. I wasn't fairly beaten. I won the first round on points. I think I slipped just before he hit me in the second round. I was just going to hit him with all my might when it happened. I wasn't well, and my gloves weren't put on properly. I had him beat, then I slipped up. I don't think he hit me at all. My shoes were slippery, and the floor was dangerously slippery, too. I think I won on points."

DOMENIC B. WYNDHAM LEWIS

THE CASE OF THE VILLAGE BLACKSMITH

The Smithy at St. Mary Cray, in Kent, which (they say) inspired Mr. Longfellow, that poet, to verse, is about to disappear in the rebuilding of the High Street. The chestnut tree was destroyed some time ago. As for the poem, I recited it the other day to a man who thought it was the work of Mr. Drinkwater. Hence, I think, it is only right to celebrate the passing of the smithy by some brief appreciation of the Poet and his Message. The more awful literary reviews will probably follow my example shortly; but I doubt if you will understand a word of it. In any case I doubt if they will tell the real story of the Village Blacksmith; which is all the more reason why we should nip in before them now with some exclusive facts which we owe to the research work of Professor Bodger.

It is well known that Mr. Longfellow was first induced to visit the village by Eliza Cook, the poetess, with whom he was very friendly; and no doubt when he passed the forge and saw the honest blacksmith the poet's first thought was "How he perspires!" and his second, "I must make a poem about this." Next day the poet passed in the morning, and observed that the honest fellow had just begun making a horseshoe; and at evening Mr. Longfellow returned and found that the task was finished.

"Something attempted, I see," said the poet heartily. "And something done."

"Ay, ay, sir," returned the honest blacksmith, touching his forelock respectfully. "It do earn a night's repose."

Mr. Longfellow, struck by this thought, paced slowly home. In the morning the idea for a new poem was practically roughed out; and he said as much to his hostess at breakfast.

"Nothing indelicate, Wadsworth, I hope?" said Miss Eliza Cook, smoothing her black bombazine gown with a nervous hand.

"Certainly not," said Mr. Longfellow sharply. "Why?"

"You will remember," said Miss Eliza Cook, blushing faintly, "that I had to take exception to one stanza of your 'Wreck of the Hesperus,' in which you dwelt so regrettably on the physical charms of the skipp—"

"No sugar, thank you," said the poet coldly.

"I am also," said the lady, averting her gaze, "thinking of your 'Excelsior!' where—correct me, Wadsworth, if I am wrong—a young female is so far lost to modesty and propriety as to invite a passing stranger of the male sex to lay his head upon her breast." And Miss Eliza Cook, a warm wave of colour rushing over her neck, hid her head behind the tea-urn.

"Allow me," said Mr. Longfellow, coughing, "to recite to you a little of my poem." Whereupon, taking a paper from his pocket, the poet began:

> "Under the spreading chestnut tree
> The village smithy stands—"

reading slowly and enunciating each syllable with the greatest care, while Miss Eliza Cook beat time with a teaspoon. She listened with rapt attention, only interrupting to beg him to alter.

> "His brow is wet with honest sweat"
> "Thought it transpires he oft perspires"

which (as she justly observed) was equally euphonious and more genteel. Mr. Longfellow politely agreed, and pretended to alter the line in pencil.

"Otherwise," said Miss Eliza Cook, "it is a poem of great beauty and profound philosophy, and entirely free from anything objectionable or licentious. Its influence on English poetry will, I think, be incalculable."

"Baby," said Mr. Longfellow simply, "you said it."

He stayed in England a few weeks longer, hoping to be asked to become Poet Laureate, and then went home to America.

As for William Bashing — known in the village as Honest William — the blacksmith, he continued in his modest way to set an example to his fellow men. Toiling, rejoicing, sorrowing, onward through life he went; each morning saw one task (and no more) begun, each evening saw its close. He was, however, no longer compelled in church on Sunday mornings to wipe away his tear with a hard, rough hand, for a wealthy sympathiser supplied him with handkerchiefs for that purpose; and although his daughter's habit of singing high and shrill above the rest of the choir lost her many friends in the village, it brought many visitors. As the Vicar observed, in the wonderful scheme of Providence there is no evil without some attendant good.

There came to the village one day, when public interest in Honest William seemed to be slackening, a gentleman with an American accent, who walked briskly to the forge and held a short conversation with its pious occupant.

"What's it worth?" said Honest William at length.

"Loud sobs," replied the American gentleman, "two and a half per, sales above 1,000. Soft sobs, one per, sales above 5,000. Twice a Sunday. Double if you mention the poem. Get that?"

Honest William stretched out a large and sinewy hand.

The American gentleman's contribution was in pamphlet form, and ran:

You Have Heard the Village Blacksmith Sob.
Now Buy the Poem.
Say "Henry Wadsworth Longfellow" to Your Bookseller.
It's Worth it.

I admit that it has not the pep, the zip, the punch, the verve of modern specimens. But you must remember that publicity was practically in its infancy then. It served its purpose, at any rate, and Mr. Bashing was able to retire much sooner than he expected.

VICTOR SAWDON PRITCHETT

OEDIPUS COMPLEX

"Good morning, Mr. P," said Mr. Pollfax, rinsing and drying his hands after the last patient. "How's Mr. P?" I was always Mr. P until I sat in the chair and he switched the lamp on and had my mouth open. Then I got a peerage.

"That's fine, my lord," said Mr. Pollfax, having a look inside.

Dogged, with its slight suggestion of doggish, was the word for Mr. Pollfax. He was a short man, jaunty, hair going thin, with jaunty buttocks and a sway to his walk. He had two lines, from habitual grinning, cut deep from the nostrils, and scores of lesser lines like the fine hair of a bird's nest round his egg-blue eyes. There was something innocent, heroic and determined about Mr. Pollfax, something of the English Tommy in tin hat and full pack going up the line. He suggested in a quiet way — war.

He was the best dentist I ever had. He got you into the chair, turned on the light, tapped around a bit with a thing like a spoon and then, dropping his white-coated arm to his side, told you a story. Several more stories followed in his flat Somerset voice, when he had your mouth jacked up. And then, removing the towel and with a final "Rinse that lot out," he finished with the strangest story of all and let you go. A month or so later the bill came in. "Mr. Pollfax presents his compli-

ments," and across the bottom of it, in his hand, "Be good."
I have never known a dentist like Mr. Pollfax.

"Open, my lord," said Mr. Pollfax. "Let's see what sort of
life his Lordship has been leading. Still smoking that filthy
pipe, I see. I shall have to do some cleaning up."

He tapped around and then dropped his arm. A look of an-
xiety came into his face. "Did I tell you that one about the girl
who went to the Punch and Judy show? No? Nor the one
about the engine-driver who was put on sentry duty in Syria?
You're sure? When did I see you last? What was the last one
I told you? That sounds like last April? Lord, you *have* been
letting things go. Well," said Mr. Pollfax, tipping back my
head and squirting something on to a tooth, "we'll have a go
at that root at the back. It's not doing you any good. It was
like this. There was a girl sitting on the beach at Barmouth
with her young man watching a Punch and Judy show...."
(Closer and closer came Mr. Pollfax's head, lower and
lower went his voice.)

He took an instrument and began chipping his way through
the tooth and the tale.

"Not bad, eh?" he said, stepping back with a sudden shout
of laughter.

"Ah," I mouthed.

"All right, my lord," said Mr. Pollfax, withdrawing the instrument and relapsing into his dead professional manner.
"Spit that lot out."

He began again.

There was just that root, Mr. Pollfax was saying. It was no
good there. There was nothing else wrong; he'd have it out in
a couple of shakes.

"Though, my lord," he said, "you did grow it about as far
back in your throat as you could, didn't you, trying to make it
as difficult as you could for Mr. Pollfax? What we'll do first of
all is to give it a dose of something."

He swivelled the dish of instruments towards me and gave
a tilt to the lamp. I remembered that lamp because once the
bulb had exploded, sending glass all over the room. It was fortunate, Mr. Pollfax said at the time, that it had blown the
other way and none of it had hit me, for someone might have
brought a case for damages against someone—which remind-

ed him of the story of the honeymoon couple who went to a small hotel in Aberdeen....

"Now," said Mr. Pollfax, dipping things in little pots and coming to me with an injection needle; "open wide, keep dead still. I was reading Freud the other day. There's a man. Oedipus complex? Ever read about that? Don't move, don't breathe, you'll feel a prick, but for God's sake don't jump. I don't want it to break in your gum. I've never had one break yet, touch wood, but they're thin, and if it broke off you'd be in a nursing-home three weeks and Mr. Pollfax would be down your throat looking for it. The trouble about these little bits of wire is they move a bit farther into the system every time you swallow."

"There now," said Mr. Pollfax.

"Feel anything? Feel it prick?" he said. "Fine."

He went to a cupboard and picked out the instrument of extraction and then stood, working it up and down like a gardener's secateurs in his hand. He studied my face. He was a clean-shaven man and looked like a priest in his white coat.

"Some of the stories you hear!" exclaimed Mr. Pollfax. "And some of the songs. I mean where I come from. 'The Lot that Lily Lost in the Lottery' — know that one? Is your skin beginning to tingle, do you feel it on the tip of your tongue yet? That's fine, my lord. I'll sing it to you."

Mr. Pollfax began to sing. He'd give it another minute, he said, when he'd done with Lily; he'd just give me the chorus of "The Night Uncle's Waistcoat Caught Fire."

"Tra la la," sang Mr. Pollfax.

"I bet," said Mr. Pollfax sadistically, "one side of his lordship's face has gone dead and his tongue feels like a pincushion."

"Blah," I said.

"I think," he said, "we'll begin."

So Mr. Pollfax moved round to the side of me, got a grip on my shoulders and began to press on the instrument in my mouth. Pressing and drawing firmly, he worked upon the root. Then he paused and increased the pressure. He seemed to be hanging from a crowbar fixed to my jaw. Nothing happened. He withdrew.

"The Great Flood begins," said Mr. Pollfax, putting a tube in my mouth and taking another weapon from the tray.

The operation began again. Mr. Pollfax now seemed to hang and swing on the crowbar. It was not successful.

"Dug himself in, has he?" muttered Mr. Pollfax. He had a look at his instruments. "You can spit, my lord," he said.

Mr. Pollfax now seized me with great determination, hung, swung, pressed and tugged with increased energy.

"It's no good you thinking you're going to stay in," said Mr. Pollfax in mid-air, muttering to the root. But the instrument slipped and a piece of tooth broke off as he spoke.

"So that's the game is it?" said Mr. Pollfax, withdrawing. "Good rinse, my lord, while Mr. Pollfax considers the position."

He was breathing hard.

Oh well, he said, there were more ways than one of killing a cat. He'd get the drill on it. There were two Jews standing outside Buckingham Palace when a policeman came by, he said, coming at me with the drill which made a whistling noise like a fishing line as he drew it through. The tube gargled in my mouth. I was looking, as I always did at Mr. Pollfax's, at the cowls busily twirling on the chimneys opposite. Wind or no wind, these cowls always seemed to be twirling round. Two metal cowls on two yellow chimneys. I always remember them.

"Spit, my lord," said Mr. Pollfax, changing to a coarser drill. "Sorry, old man, if it slipped, but Mr. Pollfax is not to be beaten."

The drill whirred again, skidding and whining; the cowls twirled on the chimneys, Mr. Pollfax's knuckles were on my nose. What he was trying to do, he said, was to get a purchase.

Mr. Pollfax's movements got quicker. He hung up the drill, he tapped impatiently on the tray, looking for something. He came at me with something like a button-hook. He got it in. He levered like a signalman changing points.

"I'm just digging," he said. Another piece of tooth broke off.

Mr. Pollfax stared when he heard it go and drew back.

"Mr. Pollfax is in a dilemma," he said.

Well, he'd try the other side. Down came the drill again.

There were beads of sweat on his brow. His breath was shorter.

"You see," exclaimed Mr. Pollfax suddenly and loudly, looking angrily up at his clock. "I'm fighting against time. Keep that head this way, hold the mouth. That's right. Sorry, my lord, I've got to bash you about, but time's against me."

"Why, damn this root," said Mr. Pollfax, hanging up again. "It's wearing out my drill. We'll have to saw. Mr. Pollfax *is* up against it."

His face was red now, he was gasping and his eyes were glittering. A troubled and emotional look came over Mr. Pollfax's face.

"I've been up against it in my time," exclaimed Mr. Pollfax forcefully between his teeth. "You heard me mention the Oedipus complex to you?"

"Blah," I managed.

"I started well by ruining my father. I took every penny he had. That's a good start, isn't it?" he said, speaking very rapidly. "Then I got married. Perfectly happy marriage, but I went and bust it up. I went off with a French girl and her husband shot at us out in the car one day. I was with that girl eighteen months and she broke her back in a railway accident and I sat with her six months watching her die. Six ruddy months. I've been through it. Then my mother died and my father was going to marry again, a girl young enough to be his daughter. I went up and took that girl off him, ran off to Hungary with her, married her and we've got seven children. Perfect happiness at last. I've been through the mill," said Mr. Pollfax, relaxing his chin and shining a torch down my mouth, "but I've come out in the end."

"A good rinse, my noble lord," said Mr. Pollfax.

"The oldest's fourteen," he said, getting the saw. "Clever girl. Very clever with her hands."

He seized me again. Did I feel anything? Well, thank God for that, said Mr. Pollfax. Here we'd been forty minutes with this damned root.

"And I bet you're thinking why didn't Mr. Pollfax let sleeping dogs lie, like the telephone operator said. Did I tell you that one about the telephone operator? That gum of yours is going to be sore."

He was standing legs apart, chin trembling, eyes blinking, hacking with the button-hook, like a wrestler putting on a headlock.

"Mr. Pollfax with his back against the wall," he said, between his teeth.

"Mr. Pollfax making a last-minute stand," he hissed.

"On the burning deck!" he gasped.

"Whence," he added, "all but he had fled."

"Spit," he said. "And now let's have another look." He wiped his brow. "Don't say anything. Keep dead still. For God's sake don't let it hear you. My lords, ladies and gentlemen, pray silence for Mr. Pollfax. It's coming, isn't it. No, it isn't. It is. It is. There," he cried, holding a fragment in his fingers.

He stood gravely to attention.

> *"And his chief beside,*
> *Smiling the boy fell dead,"*

said Mr. Pollfax. "A good and final spit, my lord and prince."

JOHN COLLIER

THE FROG PRINCE

Two young men were discussing life. Said the richer of them to the poorer, "Paul, you had better marry my sister."

"That is a very strange thing to say," said Paul, "considering I have told you all about my debts."

"I am not wordly," replied Henry Vanhomry. "I should prefer my sister to marry a clean, decent, and kindly fellow like yourself, than some rich but blasé roué, cynic, near-man, sub-man, or half-man."

"I'm certainly not blasé," said Paul. "On the other hand, I had not the pleasure of meeting your family when I was in Boston."

"I am very fond of my sister," said Henry, "in a way."

"How delightful! No doubt she was a mother to you when you were small. A little mother!"

"No. No. She is ten years younger than I am, only twenty-eight, in fact."

"Aha! She would have come into her fortune just in the rockiest year of our financial history."

"Fortunately it is well invested, and yields her an income of forty thousand dollars."

"An objection occurs to me. We are men of the world, Henry. If we were of the other sex, we might also make mistakes. Fond as I am of children —"

"That would be a matter entirely for you to decide."

"Henry, your sister sounds charming. Tell me more about her. She is not by any chance a *teeny* little woman?" And Paul held his hand some thirty inches from the floor.

"Quite the reverse."

"*Quite* the reverse, eh?"

"My dear Paul, I do not mean that she is six feet four."

"Six feet three, perhaps?"

"And a half. But perhaps I should tell you she is rather plump. Disproportionately so, in fact."

"Upon my word! I hope she is good-tempered."

"Angelically. You should hear her petting her dolls."

"Pardon me, Henry, but is she at all — backward?"

"A matter of opinion. She reads and writes admirably."

"How delightful. We could correspond, if I happened to be away."

"I will be frank with you, Paul: her letters to famous boxers are quite amazingly expressive, though by no means perfect in orthography."

"Henry, she is capable of hero worships; she has an affectionate nature."

"Almost embarrassingly so. It appears from these letters of hers, which we censor, that she would make a devoted wife. However, my family are old-fashioned, and the boxers are cowardly brutes. I should like to see her married."

"But, as yet, if I understand you, she is pure as the driven snow? Charming!"

"Hers has been a cloistered girlhood. Yet there is something romantic in her nature which causes me alarm. Supposing one of the boxers responded. He might not treat her politely."

"I, on the other hand, would write her the most devoted letters, and bow, with old-world courtesy, whenever we met. Hm! All I fear, to be perfectly candid, is that a certain confounded coldness, a defect of my nature, might be a cause of pain, dissatisfaction, or longing."

"Well, my dear Paul, that is hardly a matter for me to speculate upon. I can only remind you that faint heart never won fair lady."

"Very well, Henry. I will at least come with you and see your sister."

163

"I am afraid I cannot accompany you. You forget that I am off to Europe next week. However, I'll give you a letter of introduction to the family."

All this being arranged, our good Paul took leave of his friend, and after walking about for a little with an air of distraction, he paid a visit to the apartment of another friend of his.

"My dear Olga," he said, after a time, "I'm afraid I have some very ridiculous news for you. I am going to be poor no longer."

"Tell me only one thing, Paul. Is she beautiful?"

"Not very, it seems. I have not seen her, but she is over six feet three, and disproportionately fat."

"My poor Paul! She is simply bound to have hair on her face. What will become of you?"

"Besides all this, she is not very bright, I hear."

"And, now I come to think of it, what will become of me?"

"She has forty thousand a year, my dear Olga."

"Paul, we women are given to incredible follies when we are jealous. I might refuse everything. I find myself capable of jealousy."

"But, on the other hand, are you, or am I, capable of living any longer without a little of that forty thousand a year?"

"Or some other."

"But what other, my dear Olga? Where is another forty thousand?"

"It is true, Paul. Am I right in believing that your gigantic bride-to-be is mentally nine years, or is it twelve years, old?"

"Seven, I should think, by all that Henry told me of her. She has an exuberant innocence. She writes to boxers, but caresses dolls."

"Really? That is very interesting. Dolls are so featureless. Now, is there any great hurry, Paul? I have still that bracelet you found at Palm Beach. It would provide us with a few last weeks together."

"I was going to suggest, as a matter of fact, that it should be my present to the bride, for I like to do things in good style. However, something may turn up. I admit that I love you."

"You shall promise me not to go near Boston for at least a month. I shall be busy, I have decided to wear my hair short, but at least we shall meet at week-ends. In between, you may say farewell to all your bachelor life."

"Yes, that is true, Olga. I shall have to do that, I suppose."

Everything being agreed, this young couple spent the next month or so as Olga had suggested, and at the end of it, she saw him off to Boston, with a restraint that he found almost too admirable.

He arrived at Boston, presented his letter of introduction, and was very well received by old Mrs. Vanhomry.

They got on admirably. "You are still a bachelor?" she asked.

"I cannot," he replied, "bring myself to regard the modern girl as a true mate. Those clipped locks, that flat masculine figure, that hardness, that ultra-sophistication! Where are the curves, the innocence, the warmheartedness of yesteryear? But why am I telling you all this—?"

"You would have liked our dear Ethel. Such a big, healthy, affectionate, old-fashioned girl! You must meet her, and her fiancé. Perhaps you will come to the wedding?"

"Nothing could be more delightful. Unfortunately, I have to return to New York almost immediately."

On his return, Paul called at once on Olga, but found that her flat was locked up. She had left no address; you may depend he sought her everywhere.

He saw in the papers an account of the wedding of Miss Vanhomry to a Mr. Colefax: it appeared that the happy pair were on their way to the Ritz-Carlton.

"I really must go and sit in the lobby," said he, "and console myself with a peep at the disadvantages attached to that forty thousand a year."

Very well, he sat in the lobby. Before very long, he saw the enormous form of what was evidently the happy bride crossing from the elevator.

"Upon my word!" he thought. "There is a great deal to be said for the simple life after all. One at least preserves one's individuality."

He peered about for the husband. At last he saw a sensitive face in the neighbourhood of the bride's hips. "That must be the husband," he said. "Very charming! Very charming indeed! But surely I have seen him before."

In order to make sure, he edged closer, and was amazed to find that this husband was none other than his own Olga, in male attire.

He at once applied for a private interview. "My dear Olga, this is a very pretty trick you have played on me. And what can your bride — *soi-disant* — think of it all?"

"You must regard the matter rationally, my dear Paul."

"I am so afraid there may be a scandal. You have no idea what spiteful tongues might make of it."

"You underestimate the innocence of my wife, whose dolls, as I suspected, were very ordinary dolls. And you must admit, Paul, that if either of us is to be in this position, I at least offer less grounds for jealousy. You had better be my secretary."

Paul submitted with a good grace, and for a long time enjoyed his occupation very tolerably. Fortunately, Henry Vanhomry remained in Europe.

On one occasion there was a dinner party at the Colefax home, and a few of the male guests, with Paul the friendly secretary, and dapper little Mr. Colefax, remained smoking together long after the gigantic bride had retired to bed. The conversation turned on women, a subject which the so-called Mr. Colefax enjoyed more than his secretary. They talked of attractions.

"My wife," said this charming impostor, "is disarmingly simple: why try to disguise it? Nevertheless, she has an amazing personality buried, as it were, beneath her *naïveté*. I am convinced it is there, I sense it, and yet I could hardly find an example to describe. How do you account for that?"

"It is very simple, my dear Colefax," said a very eminent doctor. "Your wife, if I may say so, owes her adorable simplicity, as she does her admirably robust physique, to a little glandular maladjustment, which (always supposing you should desire what professionally we should regard as an improvement) could easily be put right. Who knows what she is like underneath?"

"It would certainly be interesting to find out," said her false husband, intrigued.

"She might be slim, vivacious, a positive butterfly," continued the doctor.

"It would be like carving out ambergris from a whale," observed a well-known adventurer who was present.

"Or opening a neolithic barrow," added an eminent archaeologist.

"Or undressing an Eskimo girl at Christmas," put in a notorious Don Juan.

"You might find more than you bargain for," observed Paul, overcome by an inexplicable foreboding.

He spoke too late. Everyone was desperately keen on the experiment.

"You must bring your dear wife to a little home that I have in Paris," said the doctor, "where I have every facility for the treatment."

"We shall come at once. You, Paul, had better remain behind, to deal with everything we shall have to leave unsettled."

Paul, therefore, was left. Ethel and her spouse went on the next boat to Paris, accompanied by the doctor, and, as a matter of fact, by the adventurer, the archaeologist, and the Don Juan as well.

My Dear Paul,

You will be amazed at the result of our experiment, and possibly a little disconcerted, though you were always a connoisseur of poetic justice. Under the treatment Ethel has lost no less than a hundred pounds. The removal of this prodigious quantity of blubber has left her exposed as a lean, agile, witty, and very handsome man. "How absurd that I should have been called Ethel so long!" he observed to me when first he was apprised of this transformation. In order to put him at his ease, I replied at once, "No more absurd than that I should have been called your husband." After all, the cat was, so to speak, out of the bag, and there was nothing else to do.

He took it extremely well, saying with a smile, "We must make the punishment fit the crime." On my part, I was not long in promising never to deceive him again.

We are remaining on this side to avoid gossip, for the situation has a ludicrous side which we might find painful. But not nearly so ludicrous or painful, my dear Paul, as it might have proved, in all the circumstances, had you had your original wish.

Once more,

OLGA

VARIATION ON A THEME

A young man, with a bowler hat, cane, flaxen mustache, and blue suit, was looking at a gorilla in a zoo. All about him were cages floored with squares of desert. On these yellow flats, like precise false statements of equatorial latitudes, lay the shadows of bars. There were nutshells, banana skins, fading lettuce; there were the cries of birds who believed themselves mewed up because they were mad, the obeisances of giraffes, the yawns of lions. In an imitation of moon crags, mountain goats bore about ignobly eyes that were pieces of moon. The elephants, grey in a humidity of grass and dung, shifted from one foot to another. Jurassic days, it seemed, would quite definitely never be here again. Mice, moving with the speed of a nervous twitch, were bold in the freedom of a catastrophe of values.

Perceiving that they were alone, the gorilla adressed the young man in an imitation of the American accent, which he affected for reasons of his own. "Pal, you look a decent sort of guy. Get me a suit like yours, only larger, a bowler hat, and a cane. I guess I can do without the mustache. I want to get out of here. I got ambitions."

The young man was greatly taken aback to hear a gorilla speak. However, common sense reminded him that he was in a city in which many creatures enjoyed that faculty, whom, at first sight, or at any hearing, one would hardly credit with sufficient intelligence to have attained it. He therefore recovered from his wonder, but, having a nice sense of distinctions, he replied to the gorilla, "I do not see that I can do that, for the place for a gorilla is either a cage or the Congo. In the society of men you would be like a fish out of water, a bull in a china shop, or a round peg in a square hole. You would be a cause of embarrassment, and would therefore yourself be embarrassed. You would be treated as an alien, disdained on account of your complexion, and slighted because of your facial angle."

The gorilla was very much mortified by this reply, for he was extremely vain. "Here," he said, "you don't want to say that sort of thing. I'm a writer. Write you anything you like. I've written a novel."

"That alters the situation entirely!" cried the young man with enthusiasm. "I am a novelist myself, and am always ready to lend a hand to a struggling fellow author. Tell me one thing only, and my services are yours. Have you genius?"

"Yes," said the gorilla, "I certainly have."

"In that case," said the young man, "I shall bring you suit, hat, cane, shoes, and body-linen at this hour tomorrow. I will also bring you a file, and you will find me awaiting you under the large chestnut tree by the West Gate, at the hour of dusk."

The gorilla had not expected the file. As a matter of fact, he had asked for the outfit, not for purposes of escape, but in order to cut a figure before the public. He was rather like one of those prisoners who wrote from old Spain, and who were more interested in what they got in than in how they got out. However, he hated to waste anything, so, having received the file, he put it to such use as enabled him to join his benefactor under the dark and summer tree.

The young man, intoxicated by his own good action, shook the gorilla warmly by the hand. "My dear fellow," said he, "I cannot say how glad I am to see you out here among us. I am sure you have written a great novel in there; all the same, bars are very dangerous to literary men in the long run. You will find my little house altogether more propitious to your genius. Don't think that we are too desperately dull, however; everyone drops in on Sundays, and during the week we have a little dinner or two, at which you will meet the sort of people you should know. By the way, I hope you have not forgotten your manuscript."

"Fellow came snooping in just as I was making my get-away," said the gorilla. "So I had to dump it. See?" This was the most villainous lie in the world, for the unscrupulous ape had never written so much as a word.

"What a terrible pity!" cried the young man in dismay. "I suppose you feel you will have to return to it."

"Not me," said the gorilla, who had been watching some singularly handsome limousines pass the spot where they were standing, and had noticed the faultless complexions and attractive toilettes of the ladies whom these limousines were conveying from one party to another. "No," said he. "Never mind. I got the whole thing in my head. You put me up; I'll write it out all over again. So don't worry."

"Upon my word, I admire your spirit!" cried his deliverer enthusiastically. "There is something uncommerical about that, which appeals to me more than I can say. I am sure you are right; the work will be even more masterly for being written over again. A thousand little felicities, necessarily brushed aside in the first headlong torrent of creativeness, will now assert their claims. Your characters will appear, so to speak, more in the round than formerly. You will forget some little details, though of course you will invent others even more telling; very well, those that you forget will be the *real* shadows, which will impart this superior roundness to your characters. Oh, there is nothing like literature! You shall have a little study on the second floor, quiet, austere, but not uncomfortable, where you shall reconstruct your great work undisturbed. It will undoubtedly be the choice of the Book Society, and I really don't see why we should not hope for the Hawthornden as well."

By this time they were strolling along under the dozing trees, each of which was full-gorged with a large block of the day's heat, still undigested, and breathed spicily upon them as they passed below.

"We live quite near here," said the enthusiast. "My wife will be delighted to make your acquaintance. You two are going to be great friends. Here is the house. It is small, but luckily it is of just the right period, and, as you see, we have the finest wistaria in London." Saying this, he pushed open a little wooden gate, one of some half-dozen in a quiet cul-de-sac, which still preserved its Queen Anne serenity and charm. The gorilla, looking discontentedly at certain blocks of smart modern flats that towered up on either hand, said never a word.

The front garden was very small. It had flagstones, irises, and an amusing urn, overflowing with the smouldering red of geraniums, which burned in the velvet dark like the cigarette ends of the lesser gods.

"We have a larger patch behind," said the young man, "where there is a grass plot, nicotianas, and deck chairs in the shade of a fig tree. Come in, my dear fellow, come in! Joanna, where are you? Here is our new friend."

"I hope," said the gorilla in a low voice, "you ain't given her the low-down on *you know what*."

"No, no," whispered his host. "I have kept our little secret. A gentleman from Africa, I said—who has genius."

There was no time for more. Mrs. Grantly was descending the stairs. She was tall, with pale hair caught up in an unstudied knot behind, and a full-skirted gown which was artistic but not unfashionable.

"This is Ernest Simpson," said her husband. "My dear, Mr. Simpson has written a book which is going to create more than a passing stir. Unfortunately he has lost the manuscript, but (what do you think?) he has consented to stay with us while he rewrites it. He has it all in his head."

"How perfectly delightful!" cried Mrs. Grantly. "We live terribly simply here, I'm afraid, but at least you will be quiet. Will you wash your hands? There is a little supper waiting for us in the dining-room."

The gorilla, not accustomed to being treated with so much consideration, took refuge in an almost sullen silence. During the meal he spoke mostly in monosyllables, and devoured a prodigious number of bananas, and his hostess, with teeth and eyes respectively.

The young couple were as delighted by their visitor as children with a new toy. "He is unquestionably dynamic, original, and full of that true simplicity which is perhaps the clearest hall-mark of genius," said the young man when they were in bed together. "Did you notice him with the bananas?"

Mrs. Grantly folded her husband in her arms, which were delightfully long and round. "It will be wonderful," she said. "How I look forward to the day when both your books are published! He must meet the Booles and the Terrys. What discussions you will have! How delightful life is, to those who care for art!" They gave each other a score of kisses, talked of the days when first they had met, and fell happily asleep.

In the morning there was a fine breakfast, with fruit juice, cereals, bacon and mushrooms, and the morning papers. The gorilla was shown his little study; he tried the chairs and the sofa, and looked at himself in the glass.

"Do you think you will be happy here?" asked Mr. Grantly very anxiously. "Is the room conducive to the right mood, do you think? There are cigarettes in that box; there's a lavatory across the landing. If you'd care to try a pipe, I have a tobacco jar I'll send up here. What about the desk? Is there everything on it that you'll require?"

"I shall manage. I shall manage," said the gorilla, still looking at himself in the glass.

"If there's anything you want, don't hesitate to ring that bell," said his host. "I've told the maids that you are now one of the family. I'm in the front room on the floor below if you want me. Well, I suppose you are burning to get to work. Till lunchtime, then!" And with that he took his leave of the gorilla, who continued to stare at himself in the glass.

When he was tired of this, which was not for some time, he ate a few of the cigarettes, opened all the drawers, had a look up the chimney, estimated the value of the furniture, exposed his teeth very abominably, scratched, and finally flung himself on the sofa and began to make his plans.

He was of that nature which sets down every disinterested civility as a sign of weakness. Moreover, he regarded his host as a ham novelist as well as a milksop, for he had not heard a single word about percentages since he entered the house. "A washout! A highbrow!" he said. "A guy like that giving the handout to a guy like me, eh? We'll soon alter that. The question is, how?"

This gorilla wanted suits of a very light grey, pearl tie-pins, a noticeable automobile, blondes, and the society of *the boys*. Nevertheless, his vanity itself was greedy, and snatched at every crumb; he was unable to resist the young man's enthusiasm for his non-existent novel, and instead of seeking his fortune as a heavy-weight pug, he convinced himself in good earnest that he was a writer, unjustly hindered by the patronage and fussing of a blood-sucking so-called intellectual. He turned the pages of half the books in the book-case to see the sort of thing he should do, but found it rather hard to make a start. "This goddam place stifles me," he said.

"What's your plot like?" said he to the young man, one day soon afterwards, when they were sitting in the shade of the fig tree.

Grantly was good enough to recite the whole of his plot. "It sounds very trifling," he said, "but of course a lot depends on the style."

"Style? Style, the hell!" observed the gorilla with a toothy sneer.

"I thought you'd say that!" cried his entertainer. "No doubt you have all the vitality that I so consciously lack. I imagine your work as being very close to the mainsprings of life, the sultry passions, the crude lusts, the vital urges, the stark, the raw, the dynamic, the essentially fecund and primitive."

"That's it," said the gorilla.

"The sentence," continued the rhapsodist, "short to the point of curtness, attuned by a self-concealing art to the grunts, groans, and screams of women with great primeval paps, and men——"

"Sure," said the gorilla.

"They knock each other down," went on his admirer. "As they taste the salt blood flowing over their lips, or see the female form suddenly grow tender under the influence of innumerable upper-cuts, right hooks, straight lefts, they become aware of another emotion——"

"Yes!" cried the gorilla with enthusiasm.

"And with a cry that is half a sob——"

"Attaboy!" cried the gorilla.

"They leap, clutch, grapple, and in an ecstasy that is half sheer bursting, burning, grinding, soul-shattering pain——"

The gorilla, unable to contain himself any longer, bit through the best branch of Mr. Grantly's fig tree. "You said it! That's my book, sir!" said he, with a mouthful of splinters.

I hate to have to record it: this gorilla then rushed into the house and seized his hostess in a grip of iron. "I'm in a creative mood," he muttered thickly.

Mrs. Grantly was not altogether free from hero worship. She had taken her husband's word for it that the gorilla was a genius of the fiercest description. She admired both his complexion and his eyes, and she, too, observed that his grip was of iron.

At the same time, she was a young woman of exquisite refinement. "I can't help thinking of Dennis," said she. "I should hate to hurt him."

"Yeah?" cried the ill-bred anthropoid. "That poor fish? That ham writer? That bum artist? Don't you worry about him. I'll beat him up, baby! I'll——"

Mrs. Grantly interrupted him with some dignity. She was one of those truly noble women who would never dream of betraying their husbands, except at the bidding of a genuine passion, and with expressions of the most tender esteem.

"Let me go, Ernest," she said, with such an air as compelled the vain ape to obey her. This ape, like all vulgarians, was very sensitive to any hint that he appeared low. "You do not raise yourself in my opinion by disparaging Dennis," she continued. "It merely shows you are lacking in judgment, not only of men but of women."

"Aw, cut it out, Joanna," begged the humiliated gorilla. "See here: I only forgot myself. You know what we geniuses are!"

"If you were not a genius," said Joanna, "I should have you turned out of the house. As it is — you shall have another chance."

The gorilla had not the spirit to interpret these last words as liberally as some of us might. Perhaps it was because he had lived so long behind bars, but they fell upon his ear as upon that of some brutalized coward snuffling in the dock. The timid husky saw no invitation in Mrs. Grantly's smile, and he was panic-stricken at the thought of losing his snug quarters.

"Say, you won't split on me, sister?" he muttered.

"No, no," said Mrs. Grantly. "One takes the commonsense view of these trifles. But you must behave more nicely in future."

"Sure," said he, much relieved. "I'll start in working right now."

He went straightway up to his room, looked at himself in the glass, and thus, oddly enough, recovered his damaged self-esteem. "I'll show those po' whites how to treat a gentleman," said he. "What did that poor worm say? 'Leap — clutch — grapple ——' Oh, boy! Oh, boy! This book's goin' to sell like hot cakes."

He scribbled away like the very devil. His handwriting was atrocious, but what of that? His style was not the best in the world, but he was writing about life in the raw. A succession of iron grips, such as the one he had been forced to loosen, of violent consummations, interruptions, beatings-up, flowed from his pen, interspersed with some bitter attacks on effete civilization, and many eulogies of the primitive.

"This'll make 'em sit up," said he. "This'll go big."

When he went down to supper, he noticed some little chilliness in Mrs. Grantly's demeanour. This was no doubt due to his cowardly behaviour in the afternoon. He trusted no one, and now became damnably afraid she would report his conduct to her husband; consequently he was the more eager to get his book done, so that he should be independent and in a position to revenge himself. He went upstairs immediately after the meal, and toiled away till past midnight, writing like one who confesses to a Sunday newspaper.

Before many days had passed in this fashion, he was drawing near the end of his work, when the Grantlys announced to him, with all the appearance of repressed excitement, that the best selling of all novelists was coming to dine with them. The gorilla looked forward to the evening with equal eagerness; he looked forward to gleaning a tip or two.

The great man arrived; his limousine was sufficiently resplendent. The big ape eyed him with the very greatest respect all through the meal. Afterwards they sat about and took coffee, just as ordinary people do. "I hear," said the Best-Seller to Grantly, "that you are just finishing a novel."

"Oh, a poor thing!" said the good-natured fellow. "Simpson, here, is the man who's going to set the Thames on fire. I fear my stuff is altogether too niggling. It is a sort of social satire, I touch a little on the Church, War, Peace, Fascism,

Communism — one or two things of that sort, but hardly in a full-blooded fashion. I wish I could write something more primitive — fecund women, the urge of lust, blood hatred, all that, you know."

"Good heavens, my dear Grantly!" cried the great man. "This comes of living so far out of the world. You really must move to some place more central. Public taste is on the change. I can assure you, that before your book can be printed, Mr. P——" (he mentioned the critic who makes or breaks) "will no longer be engaged, but married, and to a young woman of Junoesque proportions. What chance do you think the urge of lust will have with poor P——, after a month of his marriage to this magnificently proportioned young woman? No, no, my boy, stick to social satire. Put a little in about feminism, if you can find room for it. Guy the cult of the he-man, and its effect on deluded women, and you're safe for a record review. You'll be made."

"I've got something of that sort in it," said Grantly with much gratification, for authors are like beds; even the most artistic requires to be made.

"Who's doing the book for you?" continued his benevolent mentor. "You must let me give you a letter to my publisher. Nothing is more disheartening than hawking a book round the market, and having it returned unread. But Sykes is good enough to set some weight on my judgment; in fact, I think I may say, without boasting, you can look on the matter as settled."

"Say, you might give me a letter, too!" cried the gorilla, who had been listening in consternation to the great man's discourse.

"I should be delighted, Mr. Simpson," returned that worthy with great suavity. "But you know what these publishers are. Pig-headed isn't the word for them. Well, Grantly, I must be getting along. A delightful evening! Mrs. Grantly," said he, slapping his host on the shoulder, "this is the man who is going to make us old fossils sit up. Take care of him. Give him some more of that delicious zabaglione. Good night! Good night!"

The gorilla was tremendously impressed by the great man's manner, his confidence, his pronouncements, his spectacles, his limousine, and above all by the snub he had given him, for such creatures are always impressed by that sort of thing. "That guy knows the works," he murmured in dismay. "Say, I been barking up the wrong tree! I oughta gone in for *style*."

The Grantlys returned from the hall, where they had accompanied their visitor, and it was obvious from their faces that they, too, placed great reliance on what they had heard. I am not sure that Mr. Grantly did not rub his hands.

"Upon my word!" he said. "It certainly sounds likely enough. Have you seen poor P——'s fiancée? His views will certainly change. Ha! Ha! Supposing, my dear, I became a best-seller?"

"It's terribly exciting!" cried Joanna. "Will it change your idea of going on a cruise when first the book comes out?"

"No, no," said he. "I think an author should detach himself from that side, however gratifyingly it may develop. I want to know nothing of the book from the moment it appears till it is forgotten."

"What? You going to spend a coupla days at Brighton?" struck in the gorilla bitterly.

"Ha! Ha! What a satirist you would make!" cried Grantly with the greatest good nature. "No. We thought of going for a trip round the world. I agree a shorter absence would outlast whatever stir the book may make; however, we want to see the sights."

The gorilla wrote never a word that night. He was overcome with mortification. He could not bear to think of the Grantlys sailing around the world, while the book he had despised piled up enormous royalties at home. Still less could he bear the thought of staying behind, left without a patron, and with his own book piling up no royalties at all. He saw a species of insult in his host's "striking gold", as he termed it, and then turning his back on it in this fashion.

"That guy don't *deserve* the boodle!" he cried in anguish of spirit. In fact, he uttered this sentiment so very often during the night that in the end an idea was born of its mere repetition.

During the next few days he hastily and carelessly finished his own masterpiece, to have it ready against the *coup* he planned. In a word, this vile ape had resolved to change the manuscripts. He had alternative title pages, on which the names of the authors were transposed, typed in readiness. When at last the good Grantly announced that his work was complete, the gorilla announced the same; the two parcels were done up on the same evening, and the plotter was insistent in his offers to take them to the post.

Grantly was the more willing to permit this, as he and his wife were already busy with preparations for their departure. Shortly afterwards, they took their farewell of the gorilla, and, pressing into his hand a tidy sum to meet his immediate necessities, they wished his book every success, and advised that his next should be a satire.

The cunning ape bade them enjoy themselves, and took up his quarters in Bloomsbury, where he shortly had the pleasure of receiving a letter from the publishers to say that they were accepting the satirical novel which he had sent them.

He now gave himself airs as a writer, and got all the publicity he could. On one occasion, however, he was at a party, where he beheld a woman of Junoesque proportions in the company of a bilious weakling. The party was a wild one, and he had no scruples about seizing her in a grip of iron, regardless of the fury of her companion. This incident made little impression on his memory, for he attended a great many Bloomsbury parties.

All the same, nothing is entirely unimportant. It so happened that the bilious weakling was no other than P——, the greatest of critics, and the Junoesque lady was his promised spouse. The critic reviewed her behaviour very bitterly, the engagement was broken off, and you may be sure he noted the name of the author of his misfortunes.

Very well, the two books came out: Grantly's, which the gorilla had stolen, and the gorilla's own raw outpourings, which now appeared under the name of Dennis Grantly. By a coincidence, they appeared on the same day. The gorilla opened the most influential of the Sunday newspapers, and saw the stimulating headline. "Book of the Century."

"That's me!" said he, smacking his lips, and, fixing a hungry gaze on the letter-press, he discovered to his horror that it actually was. The critic, still a celibate, and by now an embittered one also, had selected the anthropoid's original tough stuff as being "raw, revealing, sometimes dangerously frank, at all times a masterpiece of insight and passion." Farther down, in fact at the very bottom of the column, the stolen satire was dismissed in two words only — "unreadably dull."

As if this misfortune was not sufficient, the next day, when the poor gorilla was leaving his lodgings, a young man in a black shirt tapped him on the shoulder and asked him if he was Mr. Simpson. The gorilla replying in the affirmative, the black shirt introduced him to a dozen or so friends of his, similarly attired and armed with black jacks and knuckle dusters. It appeared that these young gentlemen disapproved of certain references Grantly had made to their association, and had decided to give the wretched Simpson a beating-up by way of acknowledgment.

The gorilla fought like a demon, but was overpowered by numbers. In the end he was battered insensible and left lying in the mews where the ceremony had taken place. It was not until the next morning that he was able to drag himself home. When he arrived there, he found a bevy of lawyers' clerks and policemen inquiring for him. It appeared that Dennis, for all his delicacy and restraint, had been guilty of blasphemy, ordinary libel, obscene libel, criminal libel, sedition, and other things, in his references to the State, the Church, and so forth. "Who would have thought," the gorilla moaned bitterly, "that there was all that in a little bit of style?"

During the various trials, he sat in a sullen silence, caring only to look at the newspapers, which contained advertisements of the book he had substituted for Grantly's. When the sales passed a hundred thousand, he became violent, and insulted the judge. When they reached double that figure he made a despairing attempt at confession, but this was put down as a clumsy simulation of insanity. In the end his sentences amounted to a book in themselves, and were issued in serial form. He was carted off, and put behind the bars.

"All this," said he, "comes of wanting a suit of clothes for the public to see me in. I've got the clothes, but I don't like them, and the public aren't allowed in anyway." This gave him a positive hatred of literature, and one who hates literature, and is moreover in prison for an interminable period of years, is in a truly miserable condition.

As for Dennis Grantly: by the time he returned he was so much the fashionable author that he never found a moment in which to open a book again, and thus he remained happily ignorant of the fraud. His wife, when she reflected on the fame and riches won by her husband, and remembered that afternoon when she had been almost too favourably impressed by the iron grip of the primitive, frequently went up to him and gave him an uninvited hug and kiss, and these hugs and kisses afforded him a very delicious gratification.

GRAHAM GREENE

AWFUL WHEN YOU THINK OF IT

When the baby looked up at me from its wicker basket and winked — on the opposite seat somewhere between Reading and Slough — I became uneasy. It was as if he had discovered my secret interest.

It is awful how little we change. So often an old acquaintance, whom one has not seen for forty years when he occupied the neighbouring chopped and inky desk, detains one in the street with his unwelcome memory. Even as a baby we carry the future with us. Clothes cannot change us, the clothes are the uniform of our character, and our character changes as little as the shape of the nose and the expression of the eyes.

It has always been my hobby in railway trains to visualize in a baby's face the man he is to become — the barlounger, the gadabout, the frequenter of fashionable weddings; you need only supply the cloth cap, the grey topper, the uniform of the sad, smug or hilarious future. But I have always felt a certain contempt for the babies I have studied with such superior wisdom (they little know), and it was a shock last week when one of the brood not only detected me in the act of observation but returned that knowing signal, as if he shared my knowledge of what the years would make of him.

He had been momentarily left alone by his young mother on the seat opposite. She had smiled towards me with a tacit understanding that I would look after her baby for a few moments. What danger after all could happen to *it*? (Perhaps she was less certain of his sex than I was. She knew the shape under the nappies, of course, but shapes can deceive: parts alter, operations are performed.) She could not see what I had seen — the tilted bowler and the umbrella over the arm. (No arm was yet apparent under the coverlet printed with pink rabbits.)

When she was safely out of the carriage I bent towards the basket and asked him a question. I had never before carried my researches quite so far.

"What's yours?" I said.

He blew a thick white bubble, brown at the edges. There could be no doubt at all that he was saying, "A point of the best bitter."

"Haven't seen you lately — you know — in the old place," I said.

He gave a quick smile, passing it off, then he winked again. You couldn't doubt that he was saying, "The other half?"

I blew a bubble in my turn — we spoke the same language.

Very slightly he turned his head to one side. He didn't want anybody to hear what he was going to say now.

"You've got a tip?" I asked.

Don't mistake my meaning. It was not racing information I wanted. Of course I could not see his waist under all those pink-rabbit wrappings, but I knew perfectly well that he wore a double-breasted waistcoat and had nothing to do with the tracks. I said very rapidly because his mother might return at any moment, "My brokers are Druce, Davis and Burrows."

He looked up at me with bloodshot eyes and a little line of spittle began to form at the corner of his mouth. I said, "Oh, I know they're not all that good. But at the moment they are recommending Stores."

He gave a high wail of pain — you could have mistaken the cause for wind, but I knew better. In his club they didn't have to serve dill water. I said, "I don't agree, mind you," and he stopped crying and blew a bubble — a little tough white one which lingered on his lip.

I caught his meaning at once. "My round," I said. "Time for a short?"

He nodded.

"Scotch?" I know few people will believe me, but he raised his head an inch or two and gazed unmistakably at my watch.

"A bit early?" I said. "Pink gin?"

I didn't have to wait for his reply. "Make them large ones," I said to the imaginary barman.

He spat at me, so I added, "Throw away the pink."

"Well," I said, "here's to you. Happy future," and we smiled at each other, well content.

"I don't know what you would advise," I said, "but surely Tobaccos are about as low as they will go. When you think Imps were a cool 80/— in the early Thirties and now you can pick them up for under 60/—... This cancer scare can't go on. People have got to have their fun."

At the word fun he winked again, looked secretively around, and I realized that perhaps I had been on the wrong track. It was not after all the state of the markets he had been so ready to talk about.

"I heard a damn good one yesterday," I said. "A man got into a tube train, and there was a pretty girl with one stocking coming down..."

He yawned and closed his eyes.

"Sorry," I said, "I thought it was new. You tell me one."

And do you know that damned baby was quite ready to oblige? But he belonged to the school who find their own jokes funny and when he tried to speak, he could only laugh. He couldn't get his story out for laughter. He laughed and winked and laughed again — what a good story it must have been. I could have dined out for weeks on the strength of it. His limbs twitched in the basket; he even tried to get his hands free from the pink rabbits, and then the laughter died. I could almost hear him saying, "Tell you later, old man."

His mother opened the door of the compartment. She said, "You've been amusing baby. How kind of you. Are you fond of babies?" And she gave me such a look — the love-wrinkles forming round the mouth and eyes — that I was tempted to reply with the warmth and hypocrisy required, but then I met the baby's hard relentless gaze.

"Well, as a matter of fact," I said, "I'm not. Not really," I drooled on, losing all my chances before that blue and pebbly stare. "You know how it is ... never had one of my own... I'm fond of fishes though..."

I suppose in a way I got my reward. The baby blew a whole succession of bubbles. He was satisfied; after all a chap shouldn't make passes at another chap's mother, especially if he belongs to the same club — for suddenly I knew inevitably to what club he would belong in twenty-five years' time. "On me," he was obviously saying now. "Doubles all round." I could only hope that I would not live so long.

THE ROOT OF ALL EVIL

This story was told me by my father who heard it directly from his father, the brother of one of the participants; otherwise I doubt whether I would have credited it. But my father was a man of absolute rectitude, and I have no reason to believe that this virtue did not then run in the family.

The events happened in 189-, as they say in old Russian novels, in the small market town of B —. My father was German, and when he settled in England he was the first of the family to go further than a few kilometres from the home commune, province, canton or whatever it was called in those parts. He was a Protestant who believed in his faith, and no one has a greater ability to believe, without doubt or scruple, than a Protestant of that type. He would not even allow my mother to read us fairy-stories, and he walked three miles to church rather than go to one with pews. "We've nothing to hide," he said. "If I sleep I sleep, and let the world know the weakness of my flesh. Why," he added, and the thought touched my imagination strongly and perhaps had some influence on my future, "they could play cards in those pews and no one the wiser."

That phrase is linked in my mind with the fashion in which he would begin this story. "Original sin gave man a tilt towards secrecy," he would say. "An open sin is only half a sin, and a secret innocence is only half innocent. When you have secrets, there, sooner or later, you'll have sin. I wouldn't let a Freemason cross my threshold. Where I come from secret societies were illegal, and the government had reason. Innocent though they might be at the start, like that club of Schmidt's."

It appears that among the old people of the town where my father lived were a couple whom I shall continue to call Schmidt, being a little uncertain of the nature of the laws of libel and how limitations and the like affect the dead. Herr Schmidt was a big man and a heavy drinker, but most of his drinking he preferred to do at his own board to the discomfort of his wife, who never touched a drop of alcohol herself. Not that she wished to interfere with her husband's potations; she had a proper idea of a wife's duty, but she had reached an age (she was over sixty and he well past seventy) when she had a great yearning to sit quietly with another woman knitting something or other for her grandchildren and talking about their latest maladies. You can't do that at ease with a man continually on the go to the cellar for another litre. There is a man's atmosphere and a woman's atmosphere, and they don't mix except in the proper place, under the sheets. Many a time Frau Schmidt in her gentle way had tried to persuade him to go out of an evening to the inn. "What and pay more for every glass?" he would say. Then she tried to persuade him that he had need of men's company and men's conversation. "Not when I'm tasting a good wine," he said.

So last of all she took her trouble to Frau Muller who suffered in just the same manner as herself. Frau Muller was a stronger type of woman and she set out to build an organization. She found four other women starved of female company and female interests, and they arranged to forgather once a week with their sewing and take their evening coffee together. Between them they could summon up more than two dozen grandchildren, so you can imagine they were never short of subjects to talk about. When one child had finished with the chicken-pox, at least two would have started the measles. There were all the varying treatments to compare, and there was one school of thought which took the motto "starve a cold" to mean "if you starve a cold you will feed a fever" and another school which took the more traditional view. But their debates were never heated like those they had with their husbands, and they took it in turn to act hostess and make the cakes.

But what was happening all this time to the husbands? You might think they would be content to go on drinking alone, but not a bit of it. Drinking's like reading a "romance" (my father used the term with contempt, he had never turned the pages of a novel in his life); you don't need talk, but you need company, otherwise it begins to feel like work. Frau Muller had thought of that and she suggested to her husband — very gently, so that he hardly noticed — that, when the women were meeting elsewhere, he should ask the other husbands in with their own drinks (no need to spend extra money at the bar) and they could sit as silent as they wished with their glasses till bedtime. Not, of course, that they would be silent all the time. Now and then no doubt one of them would remark on the wet or the fine day, and another would mention the prospects for the harvest, and a third would say that they'd never had so warm a summer as the summer of 188—. Men's talk, which, in the absence of women, would never become heated.

But there was one snag in this arrangement and it was the one which caused the disaster. Frau Muller roped in a seventh woman, who had been widowed by something other than drink, by her husband's curiosity. Frau Puckler had a husband whom none of them could abide, and, before they could settle down to their friendly evenings, they had to decide what to do about him. He was a little vinegary man with a squint and a completely bald head who would empty any bar when he come into it. His eyes, coming together like that, had the effect of a gimlet, and he would stay in conversation with one man for ten minutes on end with his eyes fixed on the other's forehead until you expected sawdust to come out. Unfortunately Frau Puckler was highly respected. It was essential to keep from her any idea that her husband was unwelcome, so for some weeks they had to reject Frau Muller's proposal. They were quite happy, they said, sitting alone at home with a glass when what they really meant was that even loneliness was preferable to the company of Herr Puckler. But they got so miserable all this time that often, when their wives returned home, they would find their husbands tucked up in bed and asleep.

It was then Herr Schmidt broke his customary silence. He called round at Herr Muller's door, one evening when the wives were away, with a four-litre jug of wine, and he hadn't got through more than two litres when he broke silence. This lonely drinking, he said, must come to an end — he had had more sleep the last few weeks than he had had in six months and it was sapping his strength. "The grave yawns for us," he said, yawning himself from habit.

"But Puckler?" Herr Muller objected. "He's worse than the grave."

"We shall have to meet in secret," Herr Schmidt said. "Braun has a fine big cellar," and that was how the secret began; and from secrecy, my father would moralize, you can grow every sin in the calendar. I pictured secrecy like the dark mould in the cellar where we cultivated our mushrooms, but the mushrooms were good to eat, so that their secret growth ... I always found an ambivalence in my father's moral teaching.

It appears that for a time all went well. The men were happy drinking together — in the absence, of course, of Herr Puckler, and so were the women, even Frau Puckler, for she always found her husband in bed at night ready for domesticities. He was far too proud to tell her of his ramblings in search of company between the strokes of the town-clock. Every night he would try a different house and every night he found only the closed door and the darkened window. Once in Herr Braun's cellar the husbands heard the knocker hammering overhead. At the Gasthof too he would look regularly in — and sometimes irregularly, as though he hoped that he might catch them off their guard. The street-lamp shone on his bald head, and often some late drinker going home would be confronted by those gimlet-eyes which believed nothing you said. "Have you seen Herr Muller tonight?" or "Herr Schmidt, is he at home?" he would demand of another reveller. He sought them here, he sought them there — he had been content enough aforetime drinking in his own home and sending his wife down to the cellar for a refill, but he knew only too well, now he was alone, that there was no pleasure possible for a solitary drinker. If Herr Schmidt and Herr Muller were not at home, where were they? And the other four with whom he had never been well acquainted, where were they? Frau Puckler was the very reverse of her husband, she had no curiosity, and Frau Muller and Frau Schmidt had mouths which clinked shut like the clasp of a well-made handbag.

Inevitably after a certain time Herr Puckler went to the police. He refused to speak to anyone lower than the Superintendent. His gimlet-eyes bored like a migraine into the Superintendent's forehead. While the eyes rested on the one spot, his words wandered ambiguously. There had been an anarchist outrage at Schloss — I can't remember the name; there were rumours of an attempt on a Grand Duke. The Superintendent shifted a little this way and a little that way on his seat, for these were big affairs which did not concern him, while the squinting eyes bored continuously at the sensitive spot above his nose where his migraine always began. Then the Superintendent blew loudly and said, "The times are evil," a phrase which he had remembered from the service on Sunday.

"You know the law about secret societies," Herr Puckler said.

"Naturally."

"And yet here, under the nose of the police," and the squint-eyes bored deeper, "there exists just such a society."

"If you would be a little more explicit..."

So Herr Puckler gave him the whole row of names, beginning with Herr Schmidt. "They meet in secret," he said. "None of them stays at home."

"They are not the kind of men I would suspect of plotting."

"All the more dangerous for that."

"Perhaps they are just friends."

"Then why don't they meet in public?"

"I'll put a policeman on the case," the Superintendent said half-heartedly, so now at night there were two men looking around to find where the six had their meeting-place. The policeman was a simple man who began by asking direct questions, but he had been seen several times in the company of Puckler, so the six assumed quickly enough that he was trying to track them down on Puckler's behalf and they became more careful than ever to avoid discovery. They stocked up Herr Braun's cellar with wine, and they took elaborate precautions not to be seen entering — each one sacrificed a night's drinking in order to lead Herr Puckler and the policeman astray. Nor could they confide in their wives for fear that it might come to the ears of Frau Puckler, so they pretended the scheme had not worked and it was every man for himself again now in drinking. That meant they had to tell a lot of lies if they failed to be the first home — and so, my father said, sin began to enter in.

One night too, Herr Schmidt, who happened to be the decoy, led Herr Puckler a long walk into the suburbs, and then seeing an open door and a light burning in the window with a comforting red glow and being by that time very dry in the mouth, he mistook the house in his distress for a quiet inn and walked inside. He was warmly welcomed by a stout lady and shown into a parlour, where he expected to be served with wine. Three young ladies sat on a sofa in various stages of undress and greeted Herr Schmidt with giggles and warm words. Herr Schmidt was afraid to leave the house at once, in case Puckler was lurking outside, and while he hesitated the stout lady entered with a bottle of champagne on ice and a number of glasses. So for the sake of the drink (though champagne was not his preference — he would have liked the local wine) he stayed, and thus out of secrecy, my father said, came the second sin. But it didn't end there with lies and fornication.

When the time came to go, if he were not to overstay his welcome, Herr Schmidt took a look out of the window, and there, in place of Puckler, was the policeman walking up and down the pavement. He must have followed Puckler at a distance, and then taken on his watch while Puckler went rabbiting after the others. What to do? It was growing late; soon the wives would be drinking their last cup and closing the file on the last grandchild. Herr Schmidt appealed to the kind stout lady; he asked her whether she hadn't a back-door so that he might avoid the man he knew in the street outside. She had no back-door, but she was a woman of great resource, and in no time she had decked Herr Schmidt out in a great cartwheel of a skirt, like peasant-woman in those days wore at market, a pair of white stockings, a blouse ample enough and a floppy hat. The girls hadn't enjoyed themselves so much for a long time, and they amused themselves decking his face with rouge, eye-shadow and lipstick. When he came out of the door, the policeman was so astonished by the sight that he stood rooted to the spot long enough for Herr Schmidt to billow round the corner, take to his heels down a side-street and arrive safely home in time to scour his face before his wife came in.

If it had stopped there all might have been well, but the policeman had not been deceived, and now he reported to the Superintendent that members of the secret society dressed themselves as women and in that guise frequented the gay houses of the town. "But why dress as women to do that?" the Superintendent asked, and Puckler hinted at orgies which went beyond the natural order of things. "Anarchy," he said, "is out to upset everything, even the proper relationship of man and woman."

"Can't you be more explicit?" the Superintendent asked him for the second time; it was a phrase of which he was pathetically fond, but Puckler left the details shrouded in mystery.

It was then that Puckler's fanaticism took a morbid turn; he suspected every large woman he saw in the street at night of being a man in disguise. Once he actually pulled off the wig of a certain Frau Hackenfurth (no one till that day, not even her husband, knew that she wore a wig), and presently he sallied out into the streets himself dressed as a woman with the belief that one transvestite would recognize another and that sooner or later he would find himself enlisted in the secret orgies. He was a small man and he played the part better than Herr Schmidt had done — only his gimlet-eyes would have betrayed him to an acquaintance in daylight.

The men had been meeting happily enough now for two weeks in Herr Braun's cellar, the policeman had tired of his search, the Superintendent was in hopes that all had blown over, when a disastrous decision was taken. Frau Schmidt and Frau Muller in the old days had the habit of cooking pasties for their husbands to go with the wine, and the two men began to miss this treat which they described to their fellow drinkers, their mouths wet with the relish of the memory. Herr Braun suggested that they should bring in a woman to cook for them — it would mean only a small contribution from each, for no one would charge very much for a few hours' work at the end of the evening. Her duty would be to bring in fresh warm pasties every half an hour or so as long as their wine-session lasted. He advertised the position openly enough in the local paper, and Puckler, taking a long chance — the advertisement had referred to a men's club — applied, dressed up in his wife's best Sunday blacks. He was accepted by Herr Braun, who was the only one who did not know Herr Puckler except by repute, and so Puckler found himself installed at the very heart of the mystery, with a grand opportunity to hear all their talk. The only trouble was that he had little skill at cooking and often with his ears to the cellar-door he allowed the pasties to burn. On the second evening Herr Braun told him that, unless the pasties improved, he would find another woman.

However Puckler was not worried by that because he had all the information he required for the Superintendent, and it was a real pleasure to make his report in the presence of the policeman, who contributed nothing at all to the inquiry.

Puckler had written down the dialogue as he had heard it, leaving out only the long pauses, the gurgle of the wine-jugs, and the occasional rude tribute that wind makes to the virtue of young wine. His report read as follows:

Inquiry into the Secret Meetings held in the Cellar of Herr Braun's House at 27 — strasse. The following dialogue was overheard by the investigator.

Muller: If the rain keeps off another month, the wine harvest will be better than last year.
Unidentified voice: Ugh.
Schmidt: They say the postman nearly broke his ankle last week. Slipped on a step.
Braun: I remember sixty-one vintages.
Dobel: Time for a pasty.
Unidentified voice: Ugh.
Muller: Call in that cow.
The investigator was summoned and left a tray of pasties.
Braun: Careful. They are hot.
Schmidt: This one's burnt to a cinder.
Dobel: Uneatable.
Kastner: Better sack her before worse happens.

Braun: She's paid till the end of the week. We'll give her till then.

Muller: It was fourteen degrees at midday.

Dobel: The town-hall clock's fast.

Schmidt: Do you remember that dog the mayor had with black spots?

Unidentified voice: Ugh.

Kastner: No, why?

Schmidt: I can't remember.

Muller: When I was a boy we had plum-duff they never make now.

Dobel: It was the summer of '87.

Unidentified voice: What was?

Muller: The year Mayor Kalnitz died.

Schmidt: '88.

Muller: There was a hard frost.

Dobel: Not as hard as '86.

Braun: That was a shocking year for wine.

So it went on for twelve pages. "What's it all about?" the Superintendent asked.

"If we knew that, we'd know all."

"It sounds harmless."

"Then why do they meet in secret?"

The policeman said "Ugh" like the unidentified voice.

"My feeling is," Puckler said, "a pattern will emerge. Look at all those dates. They need to be checked."

"There was a bomb thrown in '86," the Superintendent said doubtfully. "It killed the Grand Duke's best grey."

"A shocking year for wine," Puckler said. "They missed. No wine. No royal blood."

"The attempt was mistimed," the Superintendent remembered.

"The town-hall clock's fast," Puckler quoted.

"I can't believe it all the same."

"A code. To break a code we have need of more material."

The Superintendent agreed with some reluctance that the report should continue, but then there was the difficulty of the pasties. "We need a good assistant-cook for the pasties,"

Puckler said, "and then I can listen without interruption. They won't object if I tell them that it will cost no more."

The Superintendent said to the policeman, "Those were good pasties I had in your house."

"I cooked them myself," the policeman said gloomily.

"Then that's no help."

"Why no help?" Puckler demanded. "If I can dress up as a woman, so can he."

"His moustache?"

"A good blade and a good lather will see to that."

"It's an unusual thing to demand of a man."

"In the service of the law."

So it was decided, though the policeman was not at all happy about the affair. Puckler, being a small man, was able to dress in his wife's clothes, but the policeman had no wife. In the end Puckler was forced to agree to buy the clothes himself; he did it late in the evening, when the assistants were in a hurry to leave and were unlikely to recognize his gimlet-eyes as they judged the size of the skirt, blouse, knickers. There had been lies, fornication: I don't know in what further category my father placed the strange shopping expedition, which didn't, as it happened, go entirely unnoticed. Scandal — perhaps that was the third offence which secrecy produced, for a late customer coming into the shop did in fact recognize Puckler, just as he was holding up the bloomers to see if the seat seemed large enough. You can imagine how quickly that story got around, to every woman except Frau Puckler, and she felt at the next sewing-party an odd — well, it might have been deference or it might have been compassion. Everyone stopped to listen when she spoke; no one contradicted or argued with her, and she was not allowed to carry a tray or pour a cup. She began to feel so like an invalid that she developed a headache and decided to go home early. She could see them all nodding at each other as though they knew what was the matter better than she did, and Frau Muller volunteered to see her home.

Of course she hurried straight back to tell them about it. "When we arrived," she said, "Herr Puckler was not at home. Of course the poor woman pretended not to know where he could be. She got in quite a state about it. She said he was always there to welcome her when she came in. She had half a mind to go round to the police-station and report him missing, but I dissuaded her. I almost began to believe that she didn't know what he was up to. She muttered about the strange goings-on in town, anarchists and the like, and would you believe it, she said that Herr Puckler told her a policeman had seen Herr Schmidt dressed up in women's clothes."

"The little swine," Frau Schmidt said, naturally referring to Puckler, for Herr Schmidt had the figure of one of his own wine-barrels. "Can you imagine such a thing?"

"Distracting attention," Frau Muller said, "from his own vices. For look what happened next. We come to the bedroom, and Frau Puckler finds her wardrobe door wide open, and she looks inside, and what does she find — her black Sunday dress missing. 'There's truth in the story after all,' she said, 'and I'm going to look for Herr Schmidt,' but I pointed out to her that it would have to be a very small man indeed to wear her dress."

"Did she blush?"

"I really believe she knows nothing about it."

"Poor, poor woman," Frau Dobel said. "And what do you think he does when he's all dressed up?" and they began to speculate. So thus it was, my father would say, that foul talk was added to the other sins of lies, fornication, scandal. Yet there still remained the most serious sin of all.

That night Puckler and the policeman turned up at Herr Braun's door, but little did they know that the story of Puckler had already reached the ears of the drinkers, for Frau Muller had reported the strange events to Herr Muller, and at once he remembered the gimlet-eyes of the cook Anna peering at him out of the shadows. When the men met, Herr Braun reported that the cook was to bring an assistant to help her with the pasties and as she had asked for no extra money he had consented. You can imagine the babble of voices that broke out from these silent men when Herr Muller told his story. What was Puckler's motive? It was a bad one or it would not have been Puckler. One theory was that he was planning with the help of an assistant to poison them with the pasties in revenge for being excluded. "It's not beyond Puckler," Herr Dobel said. They had good reason to be suspicious, so my father, who was a just man, did not include unworthy suspicion among the sins of which the secret society was the cause. They began to prepare a reception for Puckler.

Puckler knocked on the door and the policeman stood just behind him, enormous in his great black skirt with his white stockings crinkling over his boots because Puckler had forgotten to buy him suspenders. After the second knock the bombardment began from the upper windows. Puckler and the policeman were drenched with unmentionable liquids, they were struck with logs of wood. Their eyes were endangered from falling forks. The policeman was the first to take to his heels, and it was a strange sight to see so huge a woman go beating down the street. The blouse had come out of the waistband and flapped like a sail as its owner tacked to avoid the flying objects — which now included a toilet-roll, a broken teapot and a portrait of the Grand Duke.

Puckler, who had been hit on the shoulder with a rolling-pin, did not at first run away. He had his moment of courage or bewilderment. But when the frying-pan he had used for pasties struck him, he turned too late to follow the policeman. It was then that he was struck on the head with a chamber-pot and lay in the street with the pot fitting over his head like a vizor. They had to break it with a hammer to get it off, and by that time he was dead, whether from the blow on the head or the fall or from fear or from being stifled by the chamber-pot nobody knew, though suffocation was the general opinion. Of course there was an inquiry which went on for many months into the existence of an anarchist plot, and before the end of it the Superintendent had become secretly affianced to Frau Puckler, for which nobody blamed her, for she was a popular woman — except my father who resented the secrecy of it all. (He suspected that the Superintendent's love for Frau Puckler had extended the inquiry, since he pretended to believe her husband's accusations.)

Technically, of course, it was murder — death arising from an illegal assault — but the courts after about six months absolved the six men. "But there's a greater court," my father would always end his story, "and in that court the sin of murder never goes unrequited. You begin with a secret," and he would look at me as though he knew my pockets were stuffed with them, as indeed they were, including the note I intended to pass the next day at school to the yellow-haired girl in the second row, "and you end with every sin in the calendar." He began to recount them over again for my benefit. "Lies, drunkenness, fornication, scandal-bearing, murder, the subornation of authority."

"Subornation of authority?"

"Yes," he said and fixed me with his glittering eye. I think he had Frau Puckler and the Superintendent in mind. He rose towards his climax. "Men in women's clothes — the terrible sin of Sodom."

"And what's that?" I asked with excited expectation.

"At your age," my father said, "some things must remain secret."

HERBERT ERNEST BATES

FINGER WET, FINGER DRY

My Uncle Silas was a man who could eat anything. He could eat stewed nails. He had lived on them, once, for nearly a week. He told me so.

I was a boy then. At that time we used to drive over to see him, in summer, about one Sunday a month arriving in time for dinner, tethering the white horse about noon in the shade of the big Pearmain overhanging the lane outside. It was always what were we going to eat and what were we going to wet with? At dinner, once, we had pheasant, which was something very special, and I asked him if he had shot it. "No," he said, "it just fell down the chimney." Another time we had a goose and I asked him if that fell down the chimney. "No," he said, "it was sittin' on eighteen eggs in the winter oats and I cut its two legs off wi' the scythe. Cut 'em off and never broke an egg. Ain't that right, George?"

"Yes, that's right," my grandfather said.

"Well, it ain't, then," Silas said, cocking his bloodshot eye at him. "Don't you go tellin' the kid such blamed lies. Cut the goose's legs off wi' the scythe!... tck! tck! tck! tck! Don't you believe it, boy. It's just his tale. He's just stuffin' you. The goose went to sleep in the wellbucket and I went to draw some water one night and let it down unbeknownst and it got drowned."

197

"Couldn't it swim?" I said.

"Oh! it was asleep. Never woke. It just went a belly-flopper and was done for."

Another time we had venison. I knew what that was. "A deer," I said. "Did that fall down the well?"

"No," he said. "I shot it. With a bow and arrow."

"With what?" I said, "How?"

"Bow and arrow. One o' these days I'll show you." And he did. I badgered and bothered him until, one summer Sunday afternoon, he made an ash-bow standing as high as himself and cut arrows out of flower-canes. "You don't believe me. Do you?" he said. "Well, I'll show you." He tipped the arrows with old shoe-awls and bits of filed wire and anything handy. "Course they ain't no venisons about," he said. "But I'll show you." Then we went into the field beyond the house and Silas stalked an old cow. Finally he stood about ten yards away from her and shot her in the backside. The cow leapt up about ten feet in the air and tore about the field as though she were heatcrazy. "That's how I done the venison," Silas said. "Only it was a bigger bow and a bigger arrow and I hit it a bit harder."

"Now you know when Silas tells y' anything it's right, don't you?"

"Yes," I said.

"You know Silas don't tell lies, don't you?" he said. "You know Silas don't stuff you with any old tale?"

"Yes," I said. "I know now."

It must have been some time after this that he told me the story of the nails, the stewed nails, because it was at some time when I had extra faith in him. I forget how it came up. Perhaps it was duck eggs; it may have been the sow. I know he said: "You kids... blimey, hair and teeth!... you don't know what it is to go without grub. Look at me. I can eat anything. Had to. Look at that time I live on stewed nails for a week."

I just stared.

"That's one for you, ain't it? That makes your eyes pop, don't it? Stewed nails. For a week. And glad to."

"Didn't they ... didn't they ... weren't you bad?" I said.

"Oh! they was just old nails. I had pepper and salt on 'em, too."

198

I asked him how it happened, and when. I remember having no fear at all that he would tell me. We were alone, sprawling under the elders beyond the bean-rows, in the shade. He could tell me anything if we were alone. It was only in the presence of others that, sometimes, he was not so sure.

"Oh, about fifty years ago. I was only a kid. About thirty." He stopped, eyed me seriously, squinted. "You ain't goin' tell nobody about this if I tell you?"

"No. Oh, no!"

"Thass right. There's a policeman at the bottom o' this. I don't want to git into trouble. You cork it in."

"I will."

"Sure? You promise?"

"Finger wet, finger dry," I said.

"Thass right. And cut *my* throat if I tell a lie. This what I'm telling y' *is* true."

He took a quick look round, spoke lower, dropped an eyelid at me, and said: "I'd gone up to Sam Tilley's to take the old sow to the boar. Sam was a policeman. His wife was a young gal about twenty. She was fiery an' all. Nice gal. I knew her. Sometimes Sam was on nights and sometimes he was on days. That time he was on days. Well, it was a hot day and after the boar had finished she said: 'If you're tired, come in and sit down a bit.' So I went in and she said she was tired too. So I made no more to do. 'Don't wear a chair out,' I said. 'Sit on my knee.' So she did. She was as light as a chicken, lovely." He paused, recollecting, licking his loose red lips, going off into a momentary trance. "Oh! and then ... dall it, what happened then? Where was I?"

"She was tired ... she was resting on your knee," I said.

"Ah! Thass it. And then... oh! I know. We started playing with her duck eggs."

"What duck eggs?"

"Oh! She kept ducks. Didn't I say that? She had some lovely ducks. And she used to let me have eggs sometimes. I forgot how it was, but we started fooling about with her duck eggs. She kept hiding 'em and I had to find 'em ... you know. Just fooling about."

"I know," I said. "Like hide the thimble."

"Thass it. Like hide the thimble. Like that. Only these was duck eggs."

"Where'd she hide 'em?" I said.

"Oh! In ... where what? Oh! all over the show. Upstairs, downstairs. Everywhere. In the oven. In bed. Oh, she was a Tartar. She was hot."

"With running about so much?"

"Ah, thass it! Running about so much. And then..." He looked hard at me, without a twinkle. "You goin' to cork this in? Keep it a secret all right?"

I promised faithfully to cork it in, and he went on:

"Well, then *he* turned up. Sam. All of a sudden she looks out of the window and there he is coming up the garden path. By God, that give me a turn."

He made motions of a man in a variety of agonies, sweat, thirst, fright, more thirst. I could see he must have been a good deal upset.

"What did you do?" I said.

"Oh! I never done anything. I couldn't. I was scared stiff. It was her who done it. 'Here, quick,' she says, 'in the cellar.' And there I was. And there I stopped."

"How long for?" I said.

"For a week!"

"A week! Why didn't she let you out?"

"She forgot! Forgot all about me. Didn't I tell you how forgetful she was? Oh, she was shocking! Sometimes I'd go up for a dozen duck eggs and she'd bring the boar out and then I'd go for apples and she'd bring me duck eggs. You see?"

"Yes," I said. "I see. But why did she lock you in at all? You were all right. You weren't doing anything."

"Here," he said. "You go up to the house and in the corner cupboard you'll see a bottle marked liniment. You bring it. I want to rub my back. It gives me what 'ho! every time I stir."

So I went to fetch the bottle and after that, for some reason, perhaps because he kept drinking the liniment instead of rubbing his back with it, the tale warmed up. He began to tell me how he lay in the cellar night and day, in complete darkness, not daring to shout out and wondering what would happen to him. But what I wanted to know most was how he had lived — what he had had to eat.

"Eat!" he said. "Eat? I never had a mossel. Not a mossel. All I'd got was a mite o' pepper and salt screwed up in a mite o' paper in my westcit pocket."

"You must have got down to skin and bone," I said.

"Skin and bone ... you're right," he said. "Thass about all I was. And shouldn't have been that if it hadn't been for the nails."

He went on to tell me, then, how after the third or fourth day, after he had searched every inch of the cellar, floor and ceiling, on his hands and knees, he got so desperate that he began to prize out the nails of the floor boards and how after that there was nothing for it but to eat them and how he made a fire of his pocket linings and splinters of floor board and anything handy and lit it with the only match he had and how he collected water off the damp walls in a tobacco tin and how at last he put the nails in and stewed them.

"Stewed 'em," he said. "All one night and all one day. And then ate 'em. I had to. It was either that or snuff it."

"By golly!" I said. "What did they taste like?"

"Course it's been a long time ago," he said. "They tasted like ... oh, I don't know. I had plenty o' pepper and salt on 'em. That took the taste out a bit."

I sat silent, thinking it over.

"Course it's the iron what done it," he said. "Iron's good for you. Ain't it? It was only the iron what done it."

I still sat silent. It was a fine story, but somehow it seemed, as I sat there in the hot shade of the elders, with their thick, sourish smell rank in the sun, almost too good. I couldn't swallow it. I believed all about the duck eggs and the woman and the cellar and everything — all except the nails. Stewed nails! I kept turning it over in my mind and wondering.

And he must have seen my unbelief. Because suddenly he said:

"You don' believe me now," he said. "Do you? You think I'm stuffin' you?"

He looked at me long and hard, with a gaze from which the habitual devilry had been driven out by a marvellous innocence.

"Look at that then."

He seemed suddenly to have had an inspiration. He opened

his mouth, baring his teeth. They were old and broken and stained by the yellow and brown of decay.

"See 'em," he said. "That's rust. Nail rust. It got into my teeth." He spoke with impressive reverence. "It got into my teeth eating them nails and I never been able to get it out again."

He gave a sigh, as though burdened with the telling of too much truth.

"That's where women land you," he said.

PETER FLEMING

ADVICE TO THE READER

C'est une étrange entreprise que celle de faire rire les honnêtes gens — MOLIÈRE

The process known as Going Downhill has always had for me a powerful, though of course a purely theoretical, fascination. In the kind of fiction I like best there is always a character who Goes Downhill. The stages of his descent are never very closely followed (he is a subsidiary character), but in the last chapter, or in the epilogue if there is one, we get a glimpse of him at the bottom....

Old Etonian braces gleam through a match-seller's rags. An Authentics blazer shows for a moment in the noisome portals of an opium den. A beachcomber quotes Horace between hiccoughs.

"Don't look, my dear," says the hero, thrusting his new-won bride into a taxi, or a rickshaw, or a dhow.

"Why not?" she asks (girl-like) as they get under way.

"That was Carruthers," replies the hero, in a husky voice. "I didn't want him to know we saw.[1] Carruthers... My God! To have sunk as low as this.... He was Captain of the XI," explains the hero, "my first term."

---

[1] Or "to see we knew."

It is most affecting. The degradation of Carruthers never fails to move me. To start as Captain of the XI, and to end as a match-seller, or an opium-pedlar, or a beachcomber — what a falling off is there! Could any one — I mean, of course, any one who has been to a public school — sink from such heights so low?

I used to think that they could not. I used to think that opium-peddling and the rest of it marked the ultimate dark bottom of the abyss — that one could go no further downhill. But now I know that this is not so. There are worse fates, greater depths of humiliation. Or, to be quite accurate, there is one. Carruthers might have become a Humorous Writer.

If he had, revulsion would have strangled the pity which we felt for him before, for what is viler or more despicable than a man whose life-work consists in Trying to be Funny? And yet, poor fellow, his claim on our compassion would be stronger than ever. Carruthers' case was pitiful enough already, no doubt: a man who habitually bowled to three slips can hardly have enjoyed selling matches. But as a Humorous Writer his lot would be ten times worse.

As a match-seller, he had at least a niche in the impressive and complicated structure of World Trade; as an opium-pedlar, he satisfied a constant and even (they tell me) an acute demand; while for the existence of a beachcomber there is justification in the thought that, after all, somebody has got[1] to be a beachcomber. But no one can make out any sort of an excuse for the Humorous Writer.

The Humorous Writer is a superfluous monster, an unhappy freak. There is enough humour about the place already without adding to the world's stock by making black marks on a bit of paper. Life is a funny business. The road winds uphill all the way, but it is covered, as Nietzsche pointed out, with banana skins. To publish humour in a literary form is indeed to do mankind a disservice; for it breeds in them a neglect for the raw humour of life, and they keep their laughter for *Punch* as they keep their piety for church. The Humorous Writer is an anti-social pest.

---

[1] For proof of this necessity, see Professor R. W. V. Farbetter's monograph on "Occupational Misfits on Polynesia," and also Miss Stamina Tells' more sympathetic "Leisure at the Helm."

His genesis was accidental. Humorous writing started in England in the ninth century A. D., and it started by mistake. What happened, if my memory serves me right, was this:

The King of Wessex, Hrogswith the Ineffectual (not to be confused with his son, Hrogswith the Good, or his uncle, Hrogswith the Filthy-Minded: not to be confused with any one, in fact — it's not fair on him) — well, the King of Wessex wanted an ode composed in honour of his wife, the beautiful Stoppa of Northamptonshire. A young poet called Hacklefroth (or, as we should say today, Hacklefroth) got the job, and turned out 504 verses of very decent stuff indeed. Professor Wind, of Cincinnati University, says that verse 2 is much the best, but I can't help feeling that is because he didn't get any further than verse 2; all the verses look good to me.

They all looked good to Hrogswith, too. The thing was a best-seller for those days. The King ordered no less than eight copies to be made, and the Queen said she really must learn to read one of these days, if only she could find the time.

Then a most unfortunate thing happened. Two of the monks (their names were Hodda and Staotun) who were at work on one of the copies made a misprint. They were frivolous young fellows, who ought never to have gone into the Church at all, and instead of getting another sheepskin and starting their copy again they deliberately let the misprint stand. It was a particularly unfortunate one; in verse 89, line 3, Hodda had written down *byngorlichthan* (which means a wissel-throde) as *byngorlochthan* (which means a sney, or flinge). The passage, you will scarcely need to be reminded, is one in which the poet is comparing the Queen's nose to a number of beautiful things, among them the dainty wissel-throde; the misprint — which made it appear as if the analogy drawn was with a sney, or flinge — rendered the whole verse not only nonsensical but slightly obscene. One would have thought that only to people with very depraved minds, or to foreigners, could the consequences of this distortion appear laughable; but Hodda and Staotun were so tickled by the humorous possibilities of their initial blunder that they began to misprint words deliberately. That is why one of the three extant copies of Hacklefroth's ode amounts to nothing better than a lampoon, which, as *lèse majesté*, reaches its culminating point in verse 492, where Stoppa is likened, not to the moon sailing in the sky, but to a young badger gorging itself on worts.

The discovery of their elaborate and disgraceful joke provided one of the court scandals of the day, and Hodda and Staotun fled to East Anglia. They knew that it was unlikely that they would ever be asked to copy anything out again; but the new vice had fast hold of them, and it was not long before they realized that it was in their power to satisfy, unaided, their insatiate craving for what a later age was to describe us literary compositions of a humorous nature. Soon they were hard at it, turning out Light Verse and Occasional Essays whenever they could get hold of a sheepskin. A new influence had been born in English literature; and you can judge what sort of an influence it was from the fact that Professor Wind calls Hodda "an East Anglian Elia" and Staotun "the Milne of the Middle Ages." Humorous writing had started.

Since then it has raged practically unchecked: an unnatural practice, superfluous, degrading, in every way to be deplored. Those who can do anything, however small, to stamp it out are public benefactors; and I therefore appeal to the reader of these words to buy up all the available copies of this book and burn them. If the publisher brings out another edition, buy that up, too. Go on till he stops. It's practically a duty, when you come to think of it.

IMMORTAL LONGINGS

I suppose it isn't really funny, but the brochure which accompanied a letter from New York inviting me to join the Authors Guild of America, and which explains the aims and aspirations of the Guild, is entitled "You Too Can Own a Fur-Collared Overcoat."

ON GOING TO THE MOON

Space! The challenge of the wheeling and unconquered planets, the awful immensities of the ionosphere, the ultraviolet light stabbed unpredictably by cosmic rays, the tight-lipped men in scientific hats crouched over instrument panels in hurtling cockpits, the sheer grandeur of the interplanetary conception — the whole business leaves me, for some discreditable reason, absolutely cold. When I read of the launching of satellites into the upper atmosphere, I am not even ashamed of my inability to understand anything at all about any of the factors involved. I am not conscious of vistas opening, of horizons expanding. My attitude is one of flaccid and reprehensible indifference.

The news about the satellites did, however, remind me that a lady I knew had booked a passage to the moon two or three years ago, and I rang her up to find out how matters stood in this context. She confirmed that she had answered an advertisement in a respectable newspaper offering accommodations for a limited number of passengers on the first rocket to the moon. It was, she vaguely remembered, to an address in America that she had sent her application for a seat (or whatever it is you take your ease on in a rocket), and she had never had a reply. As far as she could remember, the advertisement had implied that the rocket's ETD, or estimated time of departure, was several years ahead, but she had more or less given up hoping to be aboard it.

She had, nevertheless, done her best; she had jumped at a chance of getting to the moon, and I think this showed a good spirit, contrasting markedly with my own spineless, *un-Elizabethan attitude* to the remoter regions of the Universe. How many of us would take passage to the moon if we were given the opportunity of doing so? Supposing, my gentle readers and fellow-planetmen, you saw this week the following advertisement: "The Moon. Commodious Spaceship leaving December for above destination. Safe arrival guaranteed. Return passages available, if desired, at six-monthly intervals. References." What thoughts would pass through your minds while you decided whether or not to answer the advertisement?

I can answer only for myself. I am the sort of person who finds it difficult to dismiss improbable projects out of hand, and I should certainly not have written this one off on sight. When weighing up the pros and cons I should have numbered among the former the fact that I have actually seen the moon with my own eyes on a large number of occasions. Its existence is not in doubt, as was the existence of the American continent until comparatively recent times. There is no question of traipsing off to some obscure and practically invisible planet which nobody has ever heard of.

(The saddest of all stories about voyages of discovery is the old story about the Turkish squadron which, in the latter days of the *Ottoman Empire*, set out from Constantinople to pay a good will visit to Malta. Weeks passed. At length the iron-clads made their overdue return. The admiral in command looked more haggard and weather-beaten than might have been expected after a mainly social expedition. "Well," they asked him, "how did you get on at Malta?" The admiral's features registered exhaustion and disgust. "Malta yok!" he said. "There is no such place as Malta.")

I know that I should be less interested in the rocket's flight plan than in her passenger list. Who else would be going? I have a horror of organized travel, and something tells me that a fairly high degree of organization would be thought desirable on the first trip between the earth and the moon. Who would do this organizing? I feel instinctively that I should submit with an ill grace to being ordered about by a brassy-voiced man in a space-suit. It is all too probable that I should sulk.

It would undeniably be a stimulating experience to step out of the rocket on to the surface of the moon. If, however, the moon in any way resembles our own planet, a good deal would depend upon which portion of its surface one landed on. A party of moonmen who arrived in the middle of the *Gobi* would form a very different impression of the earth's amenities from that formed by a similar party which descended near Slough. I cannot help feeling that, in the present state of our knowledge about the moon, sheer luck might play a disproportionate part in the final, and very important, phase of the flight plan.

Then what about these moonmen? We do not, I think I am right in saying, know for certain whether they exist or not. If they do not, what are we pioneers going to do all the time? We can go, if conditions permit, for some good long walks; we can collect specimens of whatever there is to collect specimens of; we can make a little map; we can organize discussion groups about the affairs that were current when we took off. But something tells me that, when the excitement of actually finding ourselves on the moon wears off, time is going to hang heavy on our hands.

It will be better if the moon is inhabited, provided of course that the inhabitants are decent sort of people who do not knock us on the head or put us in the zoo. I am quick at picking up languages, and I rather see myself coming into my own during the early stages of the pour-parlers. "Glung zook", I shall say. "Earthmen tot rum muck eigg, uist ni kafka?" The moonmen will giggle and cry, "Ho chok! He chok!" or words to that effect.

"What are you telling them?" the man in the space-suit will ask suspiciously. I shall silence him with an impatient gesture. It will be at about this stage that the balance of power within the expedition will begin to shift decisively.

People are saying it is a bad thing that the West is behind the Communist world with its plans for the conquest of space. I rather doubt whether this is true as far as the moonmen are concerned. They are bound, as I see it, to question the first arrivals closely about what conditions are like on earth, and from a Russian expedition they will get the sort of simple, consistent, unanimous answers which will enable them to form a clear, coherent, black-and-white picture of our planet.

It will be quite otherwise if earth's first envoys to the moon are British. From the irreconcilable convictions, the disparate opinions, the varied backgrounds and the diverse tastes to be found in any rocket-load of my compatriots, how the deuce are the poor moonmen going to make head or tail of the nature of the society to which their visitors belong? It will be far kinder to let them learn the facts of life from good, solid, Party men; it may even deter them from coming down here and falling into the clutches of the *British Council*; and it will give me a valid excuse for not being on the first rocket to the moon.

PISTOLS WEAKEN

"Have you," said the note from a friend, "a spare revolver I could take with me to Kenya?" Obscurely gratified by the assumption underlying this request, which was that I am the sort of chap who (a) owns several revolvers and (b) needs at least one of them in the conduct of his day-to-day life, I fell to pondering on pistols and on how they have come down in the world. They are still carried by criminals and by army officers, and they are sometimes fired by the former; but they have, I think, ceased to be a gentleman's weapon. It is probable that more people owned a case of dueling pistols than ever used either of the side arms in it; but nobody ever owns one now. In the personal luggage of *Anthony Hope's* heroes a pistol was almost as prerequisite as a razor, and as recently as the twenties *Bulldog Drummond*, when ordering his man-servant to pack for a weekend in Surrey, often told him to include a revolver in the contents of the suitcase. On the films pistols are still discharged by cowboys with an abandon partly attributable to the fact that they never have to reload (at least I have never seen one doing this), and in literature they are handled with slick bravado by *the Callaghans and the Cautions*. But I cannot help feeling that they are on their way out, that Queen's Messengers will less and less frequently stop dead in their tracks at the sight of the tiny jeweled revolver which the Countess has drawn from her muff. Already among the lower age-groups I notice a growing predilection for a weapon called the Space-Gun. This is meant for shooting Martians and, luckily for the purchasers, is not normally jeweled.

JAMES B. BOOTHROYD

X = O

"It's from the life insurance," said Mr. Corfe, tucking the good-quality letter under the marmalade. "They're declaring a forty-pound bonus. I can take it in cash."

"It couldn't have come at a better time," said Mrs. Corfe. "I was wondering where we were going to find this forty pounds for the people who did the woodworm." She passed him the bill.

On the Wednesday Mr. Corfe couldn't start the car, and after he'd gone to the station by bus the garage men came and took it away. Mrs. Corfe was on the telephone when he got back from the office. "You want a new battery, fourteen pounds ten," she told him, covering the mouthpiece as he stood in the hall unzipping his briefcase.

"That's lucky," said Mr. Corfe, taking out a cheque for fourteen pounds ten. "I got my expenses today for the conference at Harrowgate."

"It's just right then," she said, hanging up.

At the week-end she told him about the estimate for filling up the holes in the front path. Twenty-nine pounds. They had to be done before the postman broke a leg.

"What a coincidence," said Mr. Corfe. "Robinson has offered me twenty-nine pounds for the ciné-camera, which we do not need as we shall not be taking a holiday this year."

"Providential," said his wife.

It had been rather funny over the holiday. The ninety pounds saved up for it in their No. 2 account had been the exact sum needed for the unexpected road charges. It reminded them at the time of when Mr. Corfe got a hundred and six pounds for a back-dated pay rise on the very day he heard the income tax had undercharged him a hundred and six pounds for the years before.

Some days later Mrs. Corfe woke to find him standing beside her with the morning tea and something behind his back. He said, "The post was early and what do you think? We have won twenty-five pounds on an Ernie."

"A wonderful surprise," said Mrs. Corfe. "I meant to tell you that the demand for the Rates came, twenty-four pounds five. Oh, and fifteen shillings for the glass in the larder window."

"Good old Ernie," said her husband. "Things really work out very pat."

It was on the Friday that he came home to find her fanning out twelve soiled pound notes on the kitchen table. He said, "You didn't even tell me you were in the Housewives Guild pools syndicate on Australian football. But never mind, because I have just met our jobbing gardener and he would like twelve pounds for the turf he put over the little end rosebed." The back door bell rang. "Here he is," said Mr. Corfe, picking up the money.

All month things went well. There was the eight guineas for Alice Dow's wedding-present and fifty-two and sixpence for the wreath for old Mrs. Wauchope. "It's almost as if they knew," said Mr. Corfe, when the BBC sent him a pink cheque for a repeat of one of the small talks he sometimes sent to a gardening programme. Eleven pounds and sixpence exactly.

"How very fortunate," said Mrs. Corfe when he showed it to her. "It is nearly the end of the month. Have they paid your salary yet, and what does it come to, with, of course deductions?"

"Yes," said Mr. Corfe, taking a strip of electronic accounting from his waistcoat pocket. "One hundred and sixteen pounds nine." She looked up from some papers and lightly clapped her hands. "That is the total of the household accounts to the very shilling."

"How excellent," said Mr. Corfe. "We are so lucky to be free of financial worry at the end of each month."

"It is the advantage of living in an affluent society," said Mrs. Corfe.

She was in half a mind to mention that the telephone had been cut off, the front window-sills were cracking, and she suspected the tube was going in the TV. She decided to wait. Tomorrow there would be a legacy, perhaps, or they would dig up some old gold coins in the garden.

DISPOSING OF THE WEAPON

"Here," she said. "This one. Why didn't you stop?"

I drove on. Wives are often hazy about braking distances. Besides, it was too big. I wanted a rustic police station, where the constable touched his forelock and there was no danger of getting sent down to forensic, or something. I finally chose a small Victorian one in a biggish village somewhere near Tonbridge, or possibly Tunbridge Wells, attracted by the drive-in courtyard. There's a rich satisfaction for the law-abiding, driving into the heart of blue-lamp territory and knowing they can't touch you.

The revolver was in the glove compartment. I took it out and weighed its chunky compactness for the last time. Actually I'd only weighed its chunky compactness about once before, and that was twenty-five years ago. My Home Guard detachment at that time were planning to hurl back Hitler's hordes with wooden replicas of rifles issued for drill purposes. This was all right. A belt over the head with a wooden rifle

214

could have been discouraging. I just happened to fancy a bit of more advanced personal weaponry and, out of my own pocket—for war makes the best of us reckless—I bought the .38 Belgian police pistol and twenty-five rounds of suitable ammo. I only fired it once, to make sure that the ammo was suitable. I took it out into the Hampshire woodlands and fired pointblank at a big tree, missing it. But the repost was deafening. All the birds left the forest, and a passing aircraft swerved off course. The noise alone would send the Wehrmacht bolting for home. Then, the very next day, with the sort of contrariness which has always pursued me, our Lee-Enfields arrived. My armament was obsolete already.

"You're pointing it at me again," she said. "Go on, take it in. We shall be late for the Wilberforces."

"You take it in," I said. "It was your idea."

It had been her idea for over twenty years, as a matter of fact. "We must hand in your gun," she said, every time they declared an amnesty. I'd never been eager. The idea of a gun in the house—not that I could have found it—stiffened my manhood. Supposing I got involved in a puma-hunt, or a roof-top skirmish with an armed maniac? But last night, when the television announced yet another three months of free pardons, she had got up and fetched it, and the ammunition, from secret and separated dumps. We would turn them in on the way to the Wilberforces, at the first station we saw, while the amnesty was still new and shining.

"We'll both take it in," she said. "And don't try and be funny with them. Just hand it over and leave."

The constable approached the counter with schooled deliberation, moved the lost property register from one side to the other and glanced at the clock, which timed an incident at eleven minutes to four.

"Yes, sir?"

I drew a bead on his belt buckle. "This is a stick-up," I said. "Release all the prisoners."

He reached over and disarmed me, which was plainly more than I'd done for him. He was one of those lucky men with no sense of fun. Not for him the aching ribs, the stinging tears of mirth; nor, on the other side of the picture, the eternal casting around in the mind for some way to raise a laugh.

"I see," he said.

"My husband wants——"

"This is your husband, madam?"

"It is," she said, with overtones. "He wants to hand his gun in. Is that all right?"

I could have told her that policemen never answer questions. This one searched the revolver for bullets, found none, and put it down well out of my reach.

"You are the owner of this weapon, sir?"

"Yes. I want to hand it——"

"Name?"

He wrote down my name, address and telephone number, with rounded legibility and unsparing punctuation. "You're a long way from home, sir?" They were all questions. But it was his first approach to sociability and I was prepared to meet him. "If you call forty miles a long way," I said.

"We're going to Hawkhurst." My wife confessed afterwards that she didn't know why she said this. It caused him to step back half a pace and read something in practical black print on the noticeboard. It was all right. Hawkhurst seemed to be in the clear. I made a note to tell the Wilberforces the heat was off.

"Something wrong with your local station, sir?"

"It hasn't got a drive-in courtyard."

"Shut up," my wife said, driving her stiletto lightly into my instep. "He means we don't pass it, coming this way."

"Much off your route, sir, is it?"

"All of half-a-mile."

He gave me a look that Barlow would have been proud of. Then he gave the clock one. Message timed at sixteen-o-one.

"You have a permit for this firearm?"

"He's lost it. He loses things. He——"

"The television said——"

"Are you in possession of a valid certificate for this firearm?"

"Look here," I said. I'd given him every chance to make the occasion a jolly one. The time had come to stand on my rights as an innocent man. "Last night on the television——"

"It's quite a simple question, sir."

"There's some ammunition," said my moll, inspired to

a distraction. She poured it out of her handbag. "Twenty-five rounds."

"Twenty-four. Remember I shot a tree."

He collected the bullets and arranged them in four ranks of six, glancing as he did so at some murals, three portraits of wanted train-robbers.

"You are not in possession of a valid firearms certificate," he said, and made a note. "I must warn you——" But the telephone rang and a lady fully reported a lost dog, whose particulars the constable courteously took down to the last ear-bite.

"He's going to caution us," I said. "It's the beginning of the end. Do you realise that this classifies us as people assisting the police in their inquiries? Let's run for it. He's all alone."

"George," said the constable, in mid-dog. A colleague, who had been treacherously lurking behind frosted glass, came out and stood watching us.

My wife said it was all my fault for trying to be funny. She felt like something hauled off the streets under the vice-laws. She recommended me to take a firm attitude, give the reference of a titled friend, and go.

"Now, sir," said the constable, waving George back into hiding. The words were loaded. The interrogation proper was only just beginning. Where had I acquired the weapon? When? For what purpose? Why had I shot a tree? How did I account...? I threw his mind back to the time when we stood alone, when the bombs rained down, and the invasion barges massed nightly, when Churchill rallied the people, and the Hampshire Home Guard, including me, crouched bravely in the prickly gorse waiting to hit the Nazi tyrant over the head with wooden guns. I spoke of Dunkirk, the banana shortage, barrage balloons, Woolton Pie and Anderson shelters. He seemed to know nothing of these things.

"So you acquired this weapon"——he began——and I suddenly thought of a question.

"How old were you in 1940?"

Its unexpectedness caught him off guard. He answered it. "One," he said.

"Constable," I said. "I acquired this weapon for you."

He went into a back room shortly after that and came back with a little tiny receipt. Fortunately for me, he said, it appeared that what is known as an amnesty had come into force as from midnight, British Summer Time. It was therefore possible to take the lighter view. But it was his duty to warn me for the future, that it was an offence under the Act——.

The phone rang. "Not yet, madam," he said into it. "In the event of the animal's whereabouts coming to our notice..."

But we were outside. The getaway vehicle was waiting. It was great to be free.

KNOWING A THING OR TWO

I suppose it's safe to say that you can divide the inhabitants of the Englishman's home into two distinct categories: Things and People. I don't know that I need go into a lot of detail at this stage. The Things include pot-plants, banisters, salad-shakers and those old curtain-poles that don't fit anywhere, but we just keep so that they can fall out of cupboards when we go to look for fuse-wire... And of course the People are chiefly wives, meter-readers, church workers who happen to call just at tea-time, and so on.

I realise that this doesn't allow for dogs, but they're a bit of a problem when it comes to classification, because in some homes they count as people, and in others as things. You can tell the difference as soon as you step inside. In a house where the dog is a person, it's got its paws on your chest, rubbing noses, before you've got your hat off — have you noticed that dogs are getting bigger? We seem to be turning into a nation of retrievers — but in a house where the dog is a thing, you never know it's there, except that you hear the man inside saying, "Ge-et out of the way, can't you!" as he comes to open the door, and the sound of him trying to score a hit on a moving target. I didn't mean to go on about dogs particularly, but it does occur to me that in houses where the dogs are people, oddly enough there are lots more Things too — some sort of law of compensation, I suppose. The other evening I was at a friend's house and there happened to be a fifteen-minute television programme I wanted to see. They didn't want to, so they shut me up with the TV and the dog — distinctly a person; stood about two foot nine in its socks. And it had two leads, three old tennis balls, a boy's boxing-glove, a red rubber bone flavoured with chocolate and a pair of small brass firetongs; and it was determined to interest me in one or more of these objects, mainly by trying to stuff them into my side-pockets while I tried to squint round it at the screen. Actually, it never got any of them in — so much for all the talk about dogs' intelligence. After about five minutes of this I went into the other room, and they said, "Oh, we thought you were going to be a quarter of an hour," and I said, "No, I'm afraid the reception wasn't too good." Of course, I didn't say whose. But the incident was nothing, really, in terms of the dog-persoality cult. I once dined with a lady of title, and *her* dog took the seat at the head of the table... with my host on his right.

By the way, you notice I began by specifying the Englishman's home. In some countries the simple two-category business doesn't work. In Yugoslavia you're apt to get goats, of course — but I don't know whether they come up and try to shove fire-tongs into the guests' pockets.

However, it's the Things I really want to talk about just at the moment. For one thing, there are more of them than there are People — I mean, unless you've got a cocktail party on. And for another — although you'd have an awful job to convince a psychiatrist — they need to be much more diplomatically handled... and the sooner the newly-married man makes up his mind to this, the better. I know when I was first married, I came home one evening and found a pair of flannel trousers on the piano — I don't mean neatly folded, but astride, as you might say. Naturally, I wanted to know what they were doing there, so I asked, and I was told that that was where I'd left them, that's all. And I realised that years and years in bachelor lodgings, with indulgent landladies, had spoiled me. I'd been leaving trousers on the piano for years — not to mention ukuleles on the hall-table and cricket bats in the sink — but I never realised it because some invisible agency always tidied them away. This doesn't happen after matrimony has been committed, except in very rare cases. You have to make one of those agonizing reappraisals we're always hearing about, and mind where you put your feet. Take Wellington boots, talking of that. These are usually kept in the downstairs... well, I don't know where *you* keep them. The point is that if you put them on in a hurry, without proper care, you'll find that one's got an old scrubbing brush in it and the other's being used as an umbrella-stand for a quart bottle of turpentine. One of the certain ways to tell a man who's really come to terms with the Things in his house is to watch him putting his Wellingtons on; quite automatically he upends them and shakes them first; and anything that falls out he puts in his wife's Wellingtons.

Take wardrobe doors. Wardrobe doors are designed, as you know, of course, to adopt the open position. This is an age-old tradition of British cabinet-making, and it means that when you get a vest out and shut the door, it immediately opens again, so when you go back a moment later because you've forgotten the pants, you walk into it and get a black eye. Now cabinet-makers, after centuries of complaints about this, began fitting wardrobes with locks. But they're special locks. The key will only turn one way — and to make up for this, you can go on turning it as long as you like without in any way affecting the latch inside. They do say that a professional safe-breaker, a combination man used to listening for delicate mechanisms, can actually tell if about the twenty-fifth turn of the key has done the trick, but the ordinary man stands no chance at all. Sometimes, in his early struggles with wardrobe doors, he tries kicking. This isn't much good, usually, unless he actually splinters a panel and coaxes his vest and pants out through the crack, and in any case, when you do get the door open after a kicking session you only find that the vibration's shaken all your suits off the hangers, and they're lying like a heap of derelict concertinas among the old hair-oil bottles and the evening shirt you wore on your last wedding anniversary but one.

If a personal tip is any use, perhaps you'd like to know that I've solved my wardrobe problem by taking the lock off altogether, and keeping the door shut by propping a small suitcase against it. You'd be surprised how soon you get used to stepping over this on the way to the chest of drawers, and it really works very well, unless I want to use the suitcase — and even then it's fine, because it means I'm away for the week-end and don't care anyway. The only snag is that whenever I want a stud out of my stud box I'm held up because the wardrobe lock and six little battered screws are in there, that I somehow can't bring myself to throw away.

And that brings me to an important aspect of Things in the home — how to get rid of them. Somehow they've got to be kept down — thrown out, lost, given away, sold, buried, jumbled — anything. I sometimes wonder, on long walks on winter afternoons, when philosophical problems of this kind present themselves for solution, what happens to all the things in the world that people keep making, and other people keep buying and taking home. After all, there's been a tremendous lot of stuff produced since the first early Briton set up a fling axe works. When you consider that British manufacturers turn out eight hundred thousand metal door-mats every month — well, I mean, I'm guessing... let's make it a million and a half... or take oil-stoves, or clothes-airers, or things for unstopping sinks, or those little glass sockets for standing the piano legs in... what do you suppose becomes of them? Will future archaeologists find curious stratifications when they prod around in our cities — a layer of spring mattresses, another of plastic washing-up bowls, and so on? So much of the stuff isn't what you might call disposable. How do you set about breaking up old treadle sewing machines for scrap, or Japanese soldiers' tin hats, or a medical encyclopaedia published in ten volumes during the Crimean War? Where does it all go to, I ask myself; and I've finally come to the conclusion that it doesn't go anywhere. People still have it. They say to themselves, "Oh, don't let's throw away this lovely old broken trouser-press, you never know when we might want it," and it's wonderful how you can absorb a thing like that into your life. You know very well that if you want to get a roll of draught-excluder out of the cupboard under the stairs you have to move the lovely old broken trouser-press first; it's just a natural law; you'd no sooner expect to get anything without moving the trouser-press than you'd expect to make tea without boiling a kettle...

...Perhaps I ought to mention that in the cupboard under *my* stairs, in a tea-chest full of old boots and left-handed gloves, I've got a bowler hat that I wore at an uncle's funeral in 1923. It didn't fit then. As a matter of fact — and I've never told anyone this before — it was his hat. So I'm really in no position to preach about miscellaneous hoarding. But, really, when you think how much of it goes on, it does explain why people photographed in the papers after their houses have burnt down always seem to be smiling so bravely.

Mind you, lots of these things we keep because we're going to mend them. Take electric torches, for instance. Most cupboards have enough electric torches at the back of them to floodlight the Palace of Westminster if they were in working order — and if anyone wanted to flood-light the Palace of Westminster. It's only a matter of a bulb or a battery or a bit of paper stuffed in to stop that rattling. But somehow it doesn't get done. One reason for this is that you can't mend an electric torch without two more electric torches: one to take to bits and use for testing the bust one, and another to shine on your work and keep rolling off the table. You start by taking the patient — torch number one — and switching it on and off a few times, hoping it will suddenly start working out of sheer good nature after spending the last three years in a dusty vegetable dish. It doesn't, because it hasn't got a bulb; and where the battery used to be is a sort of sago pudding, with bits of blue paper in it. So you clean all that out and put the bulb and battery in out of torch number two; it still doesn't go; so you put the bulb back into number two to test it, and it still doesn't, because you've forgotten to put the battery back as well; so you put that back, and try it. Not a sausage. So the only thing now is to try the bulb out of the torch you're working by, which has just rolled off the table; and you take the bulb out of that and work in the dim light of the television screen — the family's probably watching a Do-It-Yourself programme on how to move a chimney stack from one side of a house to the other — and after an hour or two the net result is that you started with one bust torch and two good ones and you're finishing with three bust ones. I can't explain this; I'm just telling you. However, I don't suppose anything *I* say will put you off if you really fancy yourself as an electrician. All I say is that you'll *end* by rushing the whole lot out in the garden and digging it well in... you might just as well do it to begin with.

Before I finish, I'd just like to go back to that business about expecting things to work out of sheer good nature. It's a mistake we all make in our early days as householders. The fact is that Things About the House hate a Man About the House to take them for granted. It pays to respect these feelings, and to develop a bit of humility. A common delusion with the inexperienced house-husband is that he has three hands. This is not so. The result is that he thinks he can simultaneously carry a loaded tea-tray, turn the gas out, straighten the kitchen linoleum, hang the dishcloth on the taps, switch off the light and shut the door. This isn't so, either. I know it sounds obvious, but you'd be surprised how many people try it. And what is so bad for a man's character is the language he uses when he finds himself walking in milk and sugar with hot tea streaming up his sleeve. But who's to blame, when you come right down to it? After all, if you were a teapot, and anyone was as off-hand with you as that, wouldn't *you* feel like getting your own back?

GEORGE MIKES

HOW TO BE AN ALIEN

"I have seen much to hate here, much to forgive. But in a world where England is finished and dead, I do not wish to live."

Alice Duer Miller: The White Cliffs.

PREFACE

I believe, without undue modesty, that I have certain qualifications to write on "how to be an alien." I am an alien myself. What is more, I have been an alien all my life. Only during the first twenty-six years of my life I was not aware of this plain fact. I was living in my own country, a country full of aliens, and I noticed nothing particular or irregular about myself; then I came to England, and you can imagine my painful surprise.

Like all great and important discoveries it was a matter of a few seconds. You probably all know from your school-days how Isaac Newton discovered the law of gravitation. An apple fell on his head. This incident set him thinking for a minute or two, then he exclaimed joyfully: "Of course! The gravitation constant is the acceleration per second that a mass of one gram causes at a distance of one centimetre." You were also taught that James Watt one day went into the kitchen where cabbage was cooking and saw the lid of the saucepan rise and fall. "Now let me think," he murmured — "let me think." Then he struck his forehead and the steam engine was discovered. It was the same with me, although circumstances were rather different.

It was like this. Some years ago I spent a lot of time with a young lady who was very proud and conscious of being English. Once she asked me — to my great surprise — whether I would marry her. "No," I replied, "I will not. My mother would never agree to my marrying a foreigner." She looked at me a little surprised and irritated, and retorted: "I, a foreigner? What a silly thing to say. I am English. You are the foreigner. And your mother, too." I did not give in. "In Budapest, too?" I asked her. "Everywhere," she declared with determination. "Truth does not depend on geography. What is true in England is also true in Hungary and in North Borneo and Venezuela and everywhere."

I saw that this theory was as irrefutable as it was simple. I was startled and upset. Mainly because of my mother whom I loved and respected. Now, I suddenly learned what she really was.

It was a shame and bad taste to be an alien, and it is no use pretending otherwise. There is no way out of it. A criminal may improve and become a decent member of society. A foreigner cannot improve. Once a foreigner, always a foreigner. There is no way out for him. He may become British; he can never become English.

So it is better to reconcile yourself to the sorrowful reality. There are some noble English people who might forgive you. There are some magnanimous souls who realise that it is not your fault, only your misfortune. They will treat you with condescension, understanding and sympathy. They will invite you to their homes. Just as they keep lap-dogs and other pets, they are quite prepared to keep a few foreigners.

The title of this book, *How to be an Alien*, consequently expresses more than it should. How to be an alien? One should not be an alien at all. There are certain rules, however, which

15—1151

have to be followed if you want to make yourself as acceptable and civilised as you possibly can.

Study these rules, and imitate the English. There can be only one result: if you don't succeed in imitating them you become ridiculous; if you do, you become even more ridiculous.

G. M.

I. HOW TO BE A GENERAL ALIEN

A WARNING TO BEGINNERS

In England * everything is the other way round.

On Sundays on the Continent even the poorest person puts on his best suit, tries to look respectable, and at the same time the life of the country becomes gay and cheerful; in England even the richest peer or motor-manufacturer dresses in some peculiar rags, does not shave, and the country becomes dull and dreary. On the Continent there is one topic which should be avoided — the weather; in England, if you do not repeat the phrase "Lovely day, isn't it?" at least two hundred times a day, you are considered a bit dull. On the Continent Sunday papers appear on Monday; in England — a country of exotic oddities — they appear on Sunday. On the Continent people use a fork as though a fork were a shovel; in England they turn it upside down and push everything — including peas — on top of it.

On a continental bus approaching a request-stop the conductor rings the bell if he wants his bus to go on without stopping; in England you ring the bell if you want the bus to stop. On the Continent stray cats are judged individually on their merit — some are loved, some are only respected; in England they are universally worshipped as in ancient Egypt. On the Continent people have good food; in England people have good table manners.

On the Continent public orators try to learn to speak

---

* When people say England, they sometimes mean Great Britain, sometimes the United Kingdom, sometimes the British Isles — but never England.

fluently and smoothly; in England they take a special course in Oxonian stuttering. On the Continent learned persons love to quote Aristotle, Horace, Montaigne and show off their knowledge; in England only uneducated people show off their knowledge, nobody quotes Latin and Greek authors in the course of a conversation, unless he has never read them.

On the Continent almost every nation whether little or great has openly declared at one time or another that it is superior to all other nations; the English fight heroic wars to combat these dangerous ideas without ever mentioning which is *really* the most superior race in the world. Continental people are sensitive and touchy; the English take everything with an exquisite sense of humour — they are only offended if you tell them that they have no sense of humour. On the Continent the population consists of a small percentage of criminals, a small percentage of honest people and the rest are a vague transition between the two; in England you find a small percentage of criminals and the rest are honest people. On the other hand, people on the Continent either tell you the truth or lie; in England they hardly ever lie, but they would not dream of telling you the truth.

Many continentals think life is a game; the English think cricket is a game.

INTRODUCTION

This is a chapter on how to introduce people to one another.

The aim of introduction is to conceal a person's indentity. It is very important that you should not pronounce anybody's name in a way that the other party may be able to catch it. Generally speaking, your pronunciation is a sound guarantee for that. On the other hand, if you are introduced to someone there are two important rules to follow.

1. If he stretches out his hand in order to shake yours, you must not accept it. Smile vaguely, and as soon as he gives up the hope of shaking you by the hand, you stretch out your own hand and try to catch *his* in vain. This game is repeated until the greater part of the afternoon or evening has elapsed. It is

exremely likely that this will be the most amusing part of the afternoon or evening, anyway.

2. Once the introduction has been made you have to inquire after the health of your new acquaintance.

Try the thing in your own language. Introduce the persons, let us say, in French and murmur their names. Should they shake hands and ask:

"Comment allez-vous?"

"Comment allez-vous?" — it will be a capital joke, remembered till their last days.

Do not forget, however, that your new friend who makes this touchingly kind inquiry after your state of health does not care in the least whether you are well and kicking or dying of delirium tremens. A dialogue like this:

HE: "How d'you do?"

YOU: "General state of health fairly satisfactory. Slight insomnia and a rather bad corn on left foot. Blood pressure low, digestion slow but normal."

— well, such a dialogue would be unforgivable.

In the next phase you must not say "Pleased to meet you." This is one of the very few lies you must never utter because, for some unknown reason, it is considered vulgar. You must not say "Pleased to meet you," even if you are definitely disgusted with the man.

A few general remarks:

1. Do not click your heels, do not bow, leave off gymnastic and choreographic exercises altogether for the moment.

2. Do not call foreign lawyers, teachers, dentists, commercial travellers and estate agents "Doctor." Everybody knows that the little word "doctor" only means that they are Central Europeans. This is painful enough in itself, you do not need to remind people of it all the time.

THE WEATHER

This is the most important topic in the land. Do not be misled by memories of your youth when, on the Continent, wanting to describe someone as exceptionally dull, you remarked:

"He is the type who would discuss the weather with you." In England this is an ever-interesting, even thrilling topic, and you must be good at discussing the weather.

EXAMPLES FOR CONVERSATION

For Good Weather

"Lovely day, isn't it?"
"Isn't it *beau*tiful?"
"The sun..."
"Isn't it gorgeous?"
"Wonderful, isn't it?"
"It's so nice and hot ..."
"Personally, I think it's so nice when it's hot — isn't it?"
"I adore it — don't you?"

For Bad Weather

"Nasty day, isn't it?"
"Isn't it dreadful?"
"The rain ... I hate rain..."
"I don't like it at all. Do you?"
"Fancy such a day in July. Rain in the morning, then a bit of sunshine, and then rain, rain, rain, all day long."
"I remember exactly the same July day in 1936."
"Yes, I remember too."
"Or was it in 1928?"
"Yes, it was."
"Or in 1939?"
"Yes, that's right."

Now observe the last few sentences of this conversation. A very important rule emerges from it. You must never contradict anybody when discussing the weather. Should it hail and snow, should hurricanes uproot the trees from the sides of the road, and should someone remark to you: "Nice day, isn't it?" — answer without hesitation: "Isn't it lovely?"

Learn the above conversation by heart. If you are a bit slow

229

in picking things up, learn at least one conversation, it would do wonderfully for any occasion.

If you do not say anything else for the rest of your life, just repeat this conversation, you still have a fair chance of passing as a remarkably witty man of sharp intellect, keen observation and extremely pleasant manners.

English society is a class society, strictly organised almost on corporative lines. If you doubt this, listen to the weather forecasts. There is always a different weather forecast for farmers. You often hear statements like this on the radio:

"To-morrow it will be cold, cloudy and foggy; long periods of rain will be interrupted by short periods of showers."

And then:

"Weather forecast for farmers. It will be fair and warm, many hours of sunshine."

You must not forget that the farmers do grand work of national importance and deserve better weather.

It happened on innumerable occasions that nice, warm weather had been forecast and rain and snow fell all day long, or *vice versa*. Some people jumped rashly to the conclusion that something must be wrong with the weather forecasts. They are mistaken and should be more careful with their allegations.

I have read an article in one of the Sunday papers and now I can tell you what the situation really is. All troubles are caused by anti-cyclones. (I don't quite know what anti-cyclones are, but this is not important; I hate cyclones and am very anti-cyclone myself.) The two naughtiest anti-cyclones are the Azores and the Polar anti-cyclones.

The British meteorologists forecast the *right* weather — as it really *should* be — and then these impertinent little anti-cyclones interfere and mess up everything.

That again proves that if the British kept to themselves and did not mix with foreign things like Polar and Azores anti-cyclones they would be much better off.

SOUL AND UNDERSTATEMENT

Foreigners have souls; the English haven't.

On the Continent you find any amount of people who sigh deeply for no conspicuous reason, yearn, suffer and look in the air extremely sadly. This is soul.

The worst kind of soul is the great Slav soul. People who suffer from it are usually very deep thinkers. They may say things like this: "Sometimes I am so merry and sometimes I am so sad. Can you explain why?" (You cannot, do not try.) Or they may say: "I am so mysterious....I sometimes wish I were somewhere else than where I am." (Do not say: "I wish you were.") Or "When I am alone in a forest at night-time and jump from one tree to another, I often think that life is so strange."

All this is very deep: and just soul, nothing else.

The English have no soul; they have the understatement instead.

If a continental youth wants to declare his love to a girl, he kneels down, tells her that she is the sweetest, the most charming and ravishing person in the world, that she has *something* in her, something peculiar and individual which only a few hundred thousand other women have and that he would be unable to live one more minute without her. Often, to give a little more emphasis to the statement, he shoots himself on the spot. This is a normal, week-day declaration of love in the more temperamental continental countries. In England the boy pats his adored one on the back and says softly: "I don't object to you, you know." If he is quite mad with passion, he may add: "I rather fancy you, in fact."

If he wants to marry a girl, he says:

"I say ... would you?..."

If he wants to make an indecent proposal:

"I say ... what about..."

Overstatement, too, plays a considerable part in English social life. This takes mostly the form of someone remarking: "I say..." and then keeping silent for three days on end.

TEA

The trouble with tea is that originally it was quite a good drink.

So a group of the most eminent British scientists put their heads together, and made complicated biological experiments to find a way of spoiling it.

To the eternal glory of British science their labour bore fruit. They suggested that if you do not drink it clear, or with lemon or rum and sugar, but pour a few drops of cold milk into it, and no sugar at all, the desired object is achieved. Once this refreshing, aromatic, oriental beverage was successfully transformed into colourless and tasteless gargling-water, it suddenly became the national drink of Great Britain and Ireland — still retaining, indeed usurping, the high-sounding title of tea.

There are some occasions when you must not refuse a cup of tea, otherwise you are judged an exotic and barbarous bird without any hope of ever being able to take your place in civilised society.

If you are invited to an English home, at five o'clock in the morning you get a cup of tea. It is either brought in by a heartily smiling hostess or an almost malevolently silent maid. When you are disturbed in your sweetest morning sleep you must not say: "Madame (or Mabel), I think you are a cruel, spiteful and malignant person who deserves to be shot." On the contrary, you have to declare with your best five o'clock smile: "Thank you so much. I do adore a cup of early morning tea, especially early in the morning." If they leave you alone with the liquid, you may pour it down the washbasin.

Then you have tea for breakfast; then you have tea at eleven o'clock in the morning; then after lunch; then you have tea for tea; then after supper; and again at eleven o'clock at night.

You must not refuse any additional cups of tea under the following circumstances: if it is hot; if it is cold; if you are tired; if anybody thinks that you might be tired; if you are nervous; if you are gay; before you go out; if you are out; if you have just returned home; if you feel like it; if you do not feel like it; if you have had no tea for some time; if you have just had a cup.

You definitely must not follow my example. I sleep at five o'clock in the morning; I have coffee for breakfast; I drink innumerable cups of black coffee during the day; I have the most unorthodox and exotic teas even at tea-time.

The other day, for instance — I just mention this as a terrifying example to show you how low some people can sink — I wanted a cup of coffee and a piece of cheese for tea. It was one of those exceptionally hot days and my wife (once a good Englishwoman, now completely and hopelessly led astray by my wicked foreign influence) made some cold coffee and put it in the refrigerator, where it froze and became one solid block. On the other hand, she left the cheese on the kitchen table, where it melted. So I had a piece of coffee and a glass of cheese.

SEX

Continental people have sex life; the English have hot-water bottles.

A WORD ON SOME PUBLISHERS

I heard of a distinguished, pure-minded English publisher who adapted John Steinbeck's novel, *The Grapes of Wrath*, so skilfully that it became a charming little family book on grapes and other fruits, with many illustrations.

On the other hand, a continental publisher in London had a French political book, *The Popular Front*, translated into English. It became an exciting, pornographic book, called *The Popular Behind*.

THE LANGUAGE

When I arrived in England I thought I knew English. After I'd been here an hour I realised that I did not understand one word. In the first week I picked up a tolerable working knowledge of the language and the next seven years convinced me gradually but thoroughly that I would never know it really well, let alone perfectly. This is sad. My only consolation being that nobody speaks English perfectly.

Remember that those five hundred words an average Englishman uses are far from being the whole vocabulary of the language. You may learn another five hundred and another five thousand and yet another fifty thousand and still you may come across a further fifty thousand you have never heard of before, and nobody else either.

If you live here long enough you will find out to your greatest amazement that the adjective *nice* is not the only adjective the language possesses, in spite of the fact that in the first three years you do not need to learn or use any other adjectives. You can say that the weather is nice, a restaurant is nice, Mr. Soandso is nice, Mrs. Soandso's clothes are nice, you had a nice time, and all this will be very nice.

Then you have to decide on your accent. You will have your foreign accent all right, but many people like to mix it with something else. I knew a Polish Jew who had a strong Yiddish-Irish accent. People found it fascinating though slightly exaggerated. The easiest way to give the impression of having a good accent or no foreign accent at all is to hold an unlit pipe in your mouth, to mutter between your teeth and finish all your sentences with the question: "isn't it?" People will not understand much, but they are accustomed to that and they will get a most excellent impression.

I have known quite a number of foreigners who tried hard to acquire an Oxford accent. The advantage of this is that you give the idea of being permanently in the company of Oxford dons and lecturers on medieval numismatics; the disadvantage is that the permanent singing is rather a strain on your throat and that it is a type of affection that even many English people find hard to keep up incessantly. You may fall out of it, speak naturally, and then where are you?

The Mayfair accent can be highly recommended, too. The advantages of Mayfair English are that it unites the affected air of the Oxford accent with the uncultured flavour of a half-educated professional hotel-dancer.

The most successful attempts, however, to put on a highly cultured air have been made on the polysyllabic lines. Many foreigners who have learnt Latin and Greek in school discover with amazement and satisfaction that the English language has absorbed a huge amount of ancient Latin and Greek expressions, and they realise that (a) it is much easier to learn these expressions than the much simpler English words; (b) that these words as a rule are interminably long and make a simply superb impression when talking to the greengrocer, the porter and the insurance agent.

Imagine, for instance, that the porter of the block of flats where you live remarks sharply that you must not put your dustbin out in front of your door before 7.30 A. M. Should you answer "Please don't bully me," a loud and tiresome argument may follow, and certainly the porter will be proved right, because you are sure to find a clause in your contract (small print, bottom of last page) that the porter is always right and you owe absolute allegiance and unconditional obedience to him. Should you answer, however, with these words: "I repudiate your petulant expostulations," the argument will be closed at once, the porter will be proud of having such a highly cultured man in the block, and from that day onwards you may, if you please, get up at four o'clock in the morning and hang your dustbin out of the window.

But even in Curzon Street society, if you say, for instance, that you are a *tough guy* they will consider you a vulgar, irritating and objectionable person. Should you declare, however, that you are *an inquisitorial and peremptory homo sapiens*, they will have no idea what you mean, but they will feel in their bones that you must be something wonderful.

When you know all the long words it is advisable to start learning some of the short ones, too.

You should be careful when using these endless words. An acquaintance of mine once was fortunate enough to discover the most impressive word *nostalgia* for back-ache. Mistakenly, however, he declared in a large company:

"I have such a nostalgia."

"Oh, you want to go home to Nizhne-Novgorod?" asked his most sympathetic hostess.

"Not at all," he answered. "I just cannot sit down."

Finally, there are two important points to remember:

1. Do not forget that it is much easier to write in English than to speak English, because you can *write* without a foreign accent.

2. In a bus and in other public places it is more advisable to speak softly in good German than to shout in abominable English.

Anyway, this whole language business is not at all easy. After spending eight years in this country, the other day I was told by a very kind lady: "But why do you complain? You really speak a most excellent accent without the slightest English."

HOW NOT TO BE CLEVER

"You foreigners are so clever," said a lady to me some years ago. First, thinking of the great amount of foreign idiots and half-wits I had had the honour of meeting, I considered this remark exaggerated but complimentary.

Since then I have learnt that it was far from it. These few words expressed the lady's contempt and slight disgust for foreigners.

If you look up the word *clever* in any English dictionary, you will find that the dictionaries are out of date and mislead you on this point. According to the Pocket Oxford Dictionary, for instance, the word means quick and neat in movement ... skilful, talented, ingenious. Nuttall's Dictionary gives these meanings: dexterous, skilful, ingenious, quick or ready-witted, intelligent. All nice adjectives, expressing valuable and estimable characteristics. A modern Englishman, however, uses the word *clever* in the sense: shrewd, sly, furtive, surreptitious, treacherous, sneaking, crafty, un-English, un-Scottish, un-Welsh.

In England it is bad manners to be clever, to assert something confidently. It may be your own personal view that two and two make four, but you must not state it in a self-assured way, because this is a democratic country and others may be of a different opinion.

A continental gentleman seeing a nice panorama may remark:

"This view rather reminds me of Utrecht, where the peace treaty concluding the War of Spanish Succession was signed on the 11th April, 1713. The river there, however, recalls the Guadalquivir, which rises in the Sierra de Cazorla and flows south-west to the Atlantic Ocean and is 650 kilometres long. Oh, rivers... What did Pascal say about them? 'Les rivières sont les chemins qui marchent...'"

This pompous, showing-off way of speaking is not permissible in England. The Englishman is modest and simple. He uses but few words and expresses so much — but so much — with them. An Englishman looking at the same view would remain silent for two or three hours and think about how to put his profound feelings into words. Then he would remark:

"It's pretty, isn't it?"

An English professor of mathematics would say to his maid checking up the shopping list:

"I'm no good at arithmetic, I'm afraid. Please correct me, Jane, if I am wrong, but I believe that the square root of 97344 is 312."

And about knowledge. An English girl, of course, would be able to learn just a little more about, let us say, geography. But it is just not "chic" to know whether Budapest is the capital of Roumania, Hungary or Bulgaria. And if she happens to know that Budapest *is* the capital of Roumania, she should at least be perplexed if Bucharest is mentioned suddenly.

It is so much nicer to ask, when someone speaks of Barbados, Banska Bystrica or Fiji:

"Oh those little islands... Are they British?"

(They usually are.)

HOW TO BE RUDE

It is easy to be rude on the Continent. You just shout and call people names of a zoological character.

On a slightly higher level you may invent a few stories against your opponents. In Budapest, for instance, when a rather unpleasant-looking actress joined a nudist club, her younger and prettier colleagues spread the story that she had been accepted only under the condition that she should wear a fig-leaf on her face. Or in the same city there was a painter of limited abilities who was a most successful card-player. A colleague of his remarked once: "What a spendthrift! All the money he makes on industrious gambling at night, he spends on his painting during the day."

In England rudeness has quite a different technique. If somebody tells you an obviously untrue story, on the Continent you would remark "You are a liar, Sir, and a rather dirty one at that." In England you just say "Oh, is that so?" Or "That's rather an unusual story, isn't it?"

When some years ago, knowing ten words of English and using them all wrong, I applied for a translator's job, my would-be employer (or would-not-be employer) softly remarked: "I am afraid your English is somewhat unorthodox." This translated into any continental language would mean: EMPLOYER (to the commissionaire): "Jean, kick this gentleman down the steps!"

In the last century, when a wicked and unworthy subject annoyed the Sultan of Turkey or the Czar of Russia, he had his head cut off without much ceremony; but when the same happened in England, the monarch declared: "We are not amused"; and the whole British nation even now, a century later, is immensely proud of how rude their Queen was.

Terribly rude expressions (if pronounced grimly) are: "I am afraid that...", "unless...", "nevertheless...", "How queer..." and "I am sorry, but..."

It is true that quite often you can hear remarks like: "You'd better see that you get out of here!" Or "Shut your big mouth!" Or "Dirty pig!" etc. These remarks are very un-

English and are the results of foreign influence. (Dating back, however, to the era of the Danish invasion.)

HOW TO COMPROMISE

Wise compromise is one of the basic principles and virtues of the British.

If a continental greengrocer asks 14 shillings (or crowns, or francs, or pengoes, or dinars or leis or δραχμαί or лева, or whatever you like) for a bunch of radishes, and his customer offers 2, and finally they strike a bargain agreeing on 6 shillings, francs, roubles, etc., this is just the low continental habit of bargaining; on the other hand, if the British dock-workers or any workers claim a rise of 4 shillings per day, and the employers first flatly refuse even a penny, but after a six weeks strike they agree to a rise of 2 shillings per day — that is yet another proof of the British genius for compromise. Bargaining is a repulsive habit; compromise is one of the highest human virtues — the difference between the two being that the first is practised on the Continent, the latter in Great Britain.

The genius for compromise has another aspect, too. It has a tendency to unite together everything which is bad. English club life, for instance, unites the liabilities of social life with the boredom of solitude. An average English house combines all the curses of civilisation with the vicissitudes of life in the open. It is all right to have windows, but you must not have double windows because double windows would indeed stop the wind from blowing right into the room, and after all, you must be fair and give the wind a chance. It is all right to have central heating in an English home, except the bath room, because that is the only place where you are naked *and* wet at the same time, and you must give British germs a fair chance. The open fire is an accepted, indeed a traditional, institution. You sit in front of it and your face is hot whilst your back is cold. It is a fair compromise between two extremes and settles the problem of how to burn and catch cold at the same time. The fact that you may have a drink at five past six P. M., but that it is a criminal offence to have it at five to six is an extremely wise compromise between two things (I do not quite know between what, certainly not between prohibition and licentiousness), achieving the great aim that nobody can get drunk between three o'clock and six o'clock in the afternoon unless he wants to and drinks at home.

English spelling is a compromise between documentary expressions and an elaborate code-system; spending three hours in a queue in front of a cinema is a compromise between entertainment and asceticism; the English weather is a fair compromise between rain and fog; to employ an English charwoman is a compromise between having a dirty house or cleaning it yourself; Yorkshire pudding is a compromise between a pudding and the county of Yorkshire.

The Labour Party is a fair compromise between Socialism and Bureaucracy; the Beveridge Plan is a fair compromise between being and not being a Socialist at the same time; the Liberal Party is a fair compromise between the Beveridge Plan and Toryism; the Independent Labour Party is a fair compromise between Independent Labour and a political party; the Tory-reformers are a fair compromise between revolutionary conservatism and retrograde progress; and the whole British political life is a huge and non-compromising fight between compromising Conservatives and compromising Socialists.

HOW TO BE A HYPOCRITE

If you want to be really and truly British, you must become a hypocrite.

Now: how to be a hypocrite?

As some people say that an example explains things better than the best theory, let me try this way.

I had a drink with an English friend of mine in a pub. We were sitting on the high chairs in front of the counter when a flying bomb exploded about a hundred yards away. I was truly and honestly frightened, and when a few seconds later I looked around, I could not see my friend anywhere. At last I noticed that he was lying on the floor, flat as a pancake. When he realised that nothing particular had happened in the pub he got up a little embarrassed, flicked the dust of his suit, and turned to me with a superior and sarcastic smile.

"Good Heavens! Were you so frightened that you couldn't move?"

ABOUT SIMPLE JOYS

It is important that you should learn to enjoy simple joys, because that is extremely English. All serious Englishmen play darts and cricket and many other games; a famous English statesman was reported to be catching butterflies in the interval between giving up two European states to the Germans; there was even some misunderstanding with the French because they considered the habit of English soldiers of singing and playing football and hide and seek and blind man's buff slightly childish.

Dull and pompous foreigners are unable to understand why ex-cabinet ministers get together and sing "Daisy, Daisy" in choir; why serious business men play with toy locomotives while their children learn trigonometry in the adjoining room; why High Court judges collect rare birds when rare birds are rare and they cannot collect many in any case; why it is the ambition of grown-up persons to push a little ball into a small hole; why a great politician who saved England and made history is called a "jolly good fellow."

They cannot grasp why people sing when alone and yet sit silent and dumb for hours on end in their clubs, not uttering a word for months in the most distinguished company, and pay twenty guineas a year for the privilege.

THE NATIONAL PASSION

Queueing is the national passion of an otherwise dispassionate race. The English are rather shy about it, and deny that they adore it.

On the Continent, if people are waiting at a bus-stop they

loiter around in a seemingly vague fashion. When the bus arrives they make a dash for it; most of them leave by the bus and a lucky minority is taken away by an elegant black ambulance car. An Englishman, even if he is alone, forms an orderly queue of one.

The biggest and most attractive advertisements in front of cinemas tell people: Queue here for 4s 6d; Queue here for 9s 3d; Queue here for 16s 8d (inclusive of tax). Those cinemas which do not put out these queueing signs do not do good business at all.

At week-ends an Englishman queues up at the bus-stop, travels out to Richmond, queues up for a boat, then queues up for tea, then queues up for ice cream, then joins a few more odd queues just for the sake of the fun of it, then queues up at the bus-stop and has the time of his life.

Many English families spend lovely evenings at home just by queueing up for a few hours, and the parents are very sad when the children leave them and queue up for going to bed.

THREE SMALL POINTS

If you go for a walk with a friend, don't say a word for hours; if you go out for a walk with your dog, keep chatting to him.

There is a three-chamber legislation in England. A bill to become law has to be passed by the House of Commons and the House of Lords and finally approved by the Brains Trust.

A fishmonger is the man who mongs fish; the ironmonger and the warmonger do the same with iron and war. They just mong them.

A BLOOMSBURY INTELLECTUAL

They all hate uniforms so much that they all wear a special uniform of their own: brown velvet trousers, canary yellow pullover, green jacket with sky-blue checks.

The suit of clothes has to be chosen with the utmost care and is intended to prove that its wearer does not care for suits and other petty, worldly things.

A walking-stick, too, is often carried by the slightly dandyfied right-wing of the clan.

A golden chain around the ankle, purple velvet shoes and a half-wild angora cat on the shoulders are strongly recommended as they much increase the appearance of arresting casualness.

It is extremely important that the B. I. should *always* wear a three-days beard, as shaving is considered a contemptible bourgeois habit. (The extremist left-wing holds the same view concerning washing, too.) First one will find it a little trying to shave one's four-day beard in such a way that, after shaving, a three days old beard ration should be left on the cheeks, but practise and devoted care will bring their fruits.

A certain amount of rudeness is quite indispensable, because you have to prove day and night that the silly little commonplace rules and customs of society are not meant for *you*. If you find it too difficult to give up these little habits — to say "Hullo" and "How d'you do?" and "Thank you," etc.— because owing to Auntie Betty's or Tante Bertha's strict upbringing they have become second nature, then join a Bloomsbury school for bad manners, and after a fortnight you will feel no pang of conscience when stepping deliberately on the corn of the venerable literary editor of a quarterly magazine in the bus.

Literary opinions must be most carefully selected. Statements like this are most impressive. "There have been altogether two real poets in England: Sir Thomas Wyatt and John Ford. The works of the rest are rubbish." Of course, you should include, as the third really great, colossal and epoch-making talent your own friend, T. B. Williams, whose neo-expressionist poetry is so terribly deep that the over-whelming majority of editors do not understand it and refuse to publish it. T. B. Williams, you may proudly claim, has never used a comma or a full stop, and what is more, he has improved Apollinaire's and Aragon's primitive technique by the fact that he *does* use question marks. (The generous and extravagant praise of T. B. Williams is absolutely essential, otherwise who will praise *you*?)

As to your own literary activities, your poems, dramas and great novels may lie at the bottom of your drawer in manu-script form. But it is important that you should publish a few literary reviews, scolding and disparaging everything and eve-rybody on earth from a very superior and high-brow point of view, quoting Sir Thomas Wyatt and anything in French and letting the reader feel what *you* would be able to do if you could only find a publisher.

(Some practical advice. It is not difficult to have a few lit-erary reviews published. Many weeklies and monthlies would publish anything in their so-called literary columns, if it costs nothing. You must not call your action unfair competition with qualified reviewers; call it devotion to the "cause." Al-most every paper has a cause—if yours has not, invent one, it is quite easy. And it really does not matter what you write. I remember one B. I. writing of a significant philosophical work and admitting in the opening sentence that he did not understand it; still, I suppose, the review passed as buoyant and alarmingly sincere.)

Politically you must belong to the extreme left. You must, however, bear a few things in mind:

1. You must not care a damn about the welfare of the peo-ple in this country or abroad, because that would be " practi-cal politics" — and you should only be interested in the ideo-logical side of matters.

2. Do not belong to any party, because that would be "regi-mentation." Whatever different parties achieve, it is much more interesting to criticise everyone than to belong to the herd.

3. Do not hesitate to scorn Soviet Russia as reactionary and imperialistic, the British Labour Party as a conglomeration of elderly Trade Union Blimps, the French Socialists as "con-

fused people," the other Western Socialist parties as meek, bourgeois clubs, the American labour movements as being in the pay of big business; and call all republicans, communists, anarchists and nihilists "backward, reactionary crypto-fascists."

You should also invent a few truly original, constructive theories too, such as:

Only Brahmanism can save the world.

Spiritualism is a factor, growing immensely in importance, and a practical, working coalition between ghosts and Trotskyites would be highly desirable.

The abolition of all taxation would enrich the population so enormously that everybody would be able to pay much more taxes than before.

Finally, remember the main point. *Always* be original! It is not as difficult as it sounds: you just have to copy the habits and sayings of a few thousand other B. I. s.

MAYFAIR PLAYBOY

Fix the little word *de* in front of your name. It has a remarkable attraction. I knew a certain Leo Rosenberg from Graz who called himself Lionel de Rosenberg and was a huge success in Deanery Mews as a Tryolean nobleman.

Believe that the aim of life is to have a nice time, go to nice places and meet nice people. (Now: to have a nice time means to have two more drinks daily than you can carry; nice places are the halls of great hotels, intimate little clubs, night clubs and private houses with large radiograms and no bookshelves; nice people are those who say silly things in good English — nasty people are those who drop clever remarks as well as their aitches.)

In the old days the man who had no money was not considered a gentleman. In the era of an enlightened Mayfair this attitude has changed. A gentleman may have money or may sponge on his friends; the criterion of a gentleman is that however poor he may be he still refuses to do useful work.

You have to develop your charm with the greatest care. Always laugh at everybody's jokes — but be careful to tell a joke from a serious and profound observation. Be polite in a teasing, nonchalant manner. Sneer at everything you are not intelligent enough to understand. You may flirt with anybody's wife, but respect the ties of illegitimate friendships — unless you have a really good opportunity which it would be such a pity to miss. Don't forget that well-pressed trousers, carefully knotted ties and silk shirts are the greatest of all human values. Never be sober after 6.30 P. M.

HOW TO BE A FILM PRODUCER

A little foreign blood is very advantageous, almost essential, to become a really great British film producer.

The first aim of a British film producer should be to teach Hollywood a lesson. Do not be misled, however, by the examples of *Henry V* or *Pygmalion*, which tend to prove that excellent films can be made of great plays without changing the out-of-date words of Shakespeare and the un-film-like dialogues of Shaw by ten "experts" who really know better.

Forget these misleading examples because it is obvious that Shakespeare could not possibly have had any film technique, and recent research has proved that he did not even have an eight-seater saloon car with his own uniformed chauffeur.

You must not touch any typically American subject. For instance: a young man of Carthage (Kentucky) who can whistle beautifully goes to town, and after many disappointments forms his own swing-band and becomes the leading conductor of New York's night life — which, if you can take the implication of Hollywood films seriously, is one of the highest honours which can be conferred on anyone in that country. At the same time he falls in love with the cloakroom attendant of a drug-store * round the corner, a platinum-blonde, ravishingly beautiful, who sings a little better than Galli Curci and Deanna Durbin rolled into one and, in secret, has the greatest histrionic talent of the century. After a last-minute scandal

---

* Please note my extensive knowledge of the American language.

with the world-famous prima donna she saves the first night of her lover's show in the presence of an audience of six million people by singing Gounod's slightly adapted song. ("If you would be *my* tootsie-bootsie, I would be *your* tootsie-bootsie.") The young and mighty successful band-leader marries the girl and employs Toscanini to clean his mouthorgan.

Or — to mention just one more example of the serious and "deep" type of American films — there is a gay, buoyant, happy and miserably poor young man in New Golders Green (Alabama), who becomes tremendously rich just by selling thousands of tractors and jet-propelled aeroplanes to other poor fellows. The richer he becomes, the unhappier he is — which is a subtle point to prove that money does not mean happiness, consequently one had better be content to remain a poor labourer, possibly unemployed. He buys seven huge motor cars and three private planes and is bitter and pained; he builds a magnificent and ostentatious palace and gets gloomier and gloomier; and when the woman he has loved without hope for fifteen years at last falls in love with him, he breaks down completely and groans and moans desperately for three days. To increase the "deep" meaning of the film they photograph the heroes from the most surprising angles: the cameraman crawls under people's feet, swings on the chandelier, and hides himself in a bowl of soup. Everybody is delighted with the new technique and admires the director's richness of thought.

English film directors follow a different and quite original line. They have discovered somehow that the majority of the public does not consist, after all, of idiots, and that an intelligent film is not necessarily foredoomed to failure. It was a tremendous risk to make experiments based on this assumption, but it has proved worth while.

There are certain rules you must bear in mind if you want to make a really and truly British film.

1. The "cockney heart" has definitely been discovered, *i.e.* the fact that even people who drop their aitches have a heart. The discovery was originally made by Mr. Noel Coward, who is reported to have met a man who knew someone who had actually seen a cockney from quite near. Ever since it has been

essential that a cockney should figure in every British film and display his heart throughout the performance.

2. It has also been discovered that ordinary men occasionally use unparliamentary expressions in the course of their every-day conversation. It has been decided that the more often the adjective referring to the sanguinary character of certain things or persons is used and the exclamation "Damn!" is uttered, the more realistic and more convincing the film becomes, as able seamen and flight-sergeants sometimes go so far as to say "Damn!" when they are carried away by passion. All bodies and associations formed to preserve the purity of the English soul should note that I do not agree with this habit — I simply record it. But as it is a habit, the author readily agrees to supply by correspondence a further list of the most expressive military terms which would make any new film surprisingly realistic.

3. Nothing should be good enough for a British film producer. I have heard of a gentleman (I don't know whether the story is true, or only characteristic) who made a film about Egypt and had a sphinx built in the studio. When he and his company sailed to Egypt to make some exterior shots, he took his own sphinx with him to the desert. He was quite right, because first of all the original sphinx is very old and film people should not use second-hand stuff; secondly, the old sphinx might have been good enough for Egyptians (who are all foreigners, after all) but not for a British film company.

4. As I have seen political events successfully filmed as detective-stories, and historical personages appear as "great lovers" (and nothing else), I have come to the conclusion that this slight change in the character of a person is highly recommendable, and I advise the filming of *Peter Pan* as a thriller, and the *Concise Oxford Dictionary* as a comic opera.

DRIVING CARS

It is about the same to drive a car in England as anywhere else. To change a punctured tyre in the wind and rain gives about the same pleasure outside London as outside Rio de

Janeiro; it is not more fun to try to start up a cold motor with the handle in Moscow than in Manchester; the roughly 50-50 proportion between *driving* an average car and *pushing* it is the same in Sydney and Edinburgh.

There are, however, a few characteristics which distinguish the English motorist from the continental, and some points which the English motorist has to remember.

1. In English towns there is a thirty miles an hour speed-limit and the police keep a watchful eye on law-breakers. The fight against reckless driving is directed extremely skilfully and carefully according to the very best English detective-traditions. It is practically impossible to find out whether you are being followed by a police car or not. There are, however, a few indications which may help people of extraordinary intelligence and with very keen powers of observation:

(*a*) The police always use a 13 h. p., blue Wolseley car;

(*b*) three uniformed policemen sit in it; and

(*c*) on these cars you can read the word POLICE written in large letters in front and rear, all in capitals — lit up during the hours of darkness.

2. I think England is the only country in the world where you have to leave your lights on even if you park in a brilliantly lit-up street. The advantage being that your battery gets exhausted, you cannot start up again and consequently the number of road accidents are greatly reduced. Safety first!

3. Only motorists can answer this puzzling question: What are taxis for? A simple pedestrian knows that they are certainly not there to carry passengers.

Taxis, in fact, are a Christian institution. They are here to teach drivers modesty and humility. They teach us never to be over confident; they remind us that we never can tell what the next moment will bring for us, whether we shall be able to drive on or a taxi will bump into us from the back or the side. "...and thou shalt fear day and night, and shalt have none assurance of thy life" (Deut., chapter 28, verse 66).

4. There is a huge ideological warfare going on behind the scenes of the motorist world.

Whenever you stop your car in the City, the West End or many other places, two or three policemen rush at you and tell you that you must not park *there*. Where may you park? They shrug their shoulders. There are a couple of spots on the South Coast and in a village called Minchinhampton. Three cars may park there for half an hour every other Sunday morning between 7 and 8 A. M.

The police are perfectly right. After all, cars have been built to run, and run fast, so they should not stop.

This healthy philosophy of the police has been seriously challenged by a certain group of motorists who maintain that cars have been built to park and not to move. These people drive out to Hampstead Heath or Richmond on beautiful, sunny days, pull up all their windows and go to sleep. They do not get a spot of air; they are miserably uncomfortable; they have nightmares, and the whole procedure is called "spending a lovely afternoon in the open."

THREE GAMES FOR BUS DRIVERS

If you become a bus driver there are three lovely and very popular games you must learn to play.

1. *Blind man's buff.* When you turn right just signal by showing two millimetres of your finger-tips. It is great fun when motorists do not notice your signal and run into your huge bus with their tiny cars.

2. *Hide and seek.* Whenever you approach a request stop hide behind a large lorry or another bus and when you have almost reached the stop shoot off at a terrific speed. It is very amusing to see people shake their fists at you. It is ten to one they miss some important business appointment.

3. *Hospital game.* If you have to stop for one reason or another, never wait until the conductor rings the bell. If you start moving quickly and unexpectedly, and if you are lucky — and in slippery weather you have a very good chance — people will fall on top of one another. This looks extremely

funny from the driver's seat. (Sometimes the people them-selves, who fall into a muddy pool and break their legs, make a fuss, but, alas! every society has its bores who have no sense of humour and cannot enjoy a joke at their own expense.)

HOW TO PLAN A TOWN

Britain, far from being a "decadent democracy," is a Spar-tan country. This is mainly due to the British way of building towns, which dispenses with the reasonable comfort enjoyed by all the other weak and effeminate peoples of the world.

Medieval warriors wore steel breast-plates and leggings not only for defence but also to keep up their fighting spirit; priests of the Middle Ages tortured their bodies with hair-shirts; In-dian yogis take their daily nap lying on a carpet of nails to re-main fit. The English plan their towns in such a way that these replace the discomfort of steel breast-plates, hair-shirts and nail-carpets.

On the Continent doctors, lawyers, booksellers — just to mention a few examples — are sprinkled all over the city, so you can call on a good or at least expensive doctor in any dis-trict. In England the idea is that it is the address that makes the man. Doctors in London are crowded in Harley Street, solici-tors in Lincoln's Inn Fields, second-hand-book-shops in Char-ing Cross Road, newsparer offices in Fleet Street, tailors in Sa-vile Row, car-merchants in Great Portland Street, theatres around Piccadilly Circus, cinemas in Leicester Square, etc. If you have a chance of replanning London you can greatly im-prove on this idea. All greengrocers should be placed in Horn-sey Lane (N. 6), all butchers in Mile End (E. 1), and all gentle-men's conveniences in Bloomsbury (W. C.).

Now I should like to give you a little practical advice on how to build an English town.

You must understand that an English town is a vast con-spiracy to mislead foreigners. You have to use century-old little practices and tricks.

1. First of all, never build a street straight. The English love privacy and do not want to see one end of the street from the

other end. Make sudden curves in the streets and build them S-shaped too; the letters L, T, V, Y, W and O are also becoming increasingly popular. It would be a fine tribute to the Greeks to build a few φ and θ-shaped streets; it would be an ingenious compliment to the Russians to favour the shape of Я, and I am sure the Chinese would be more than flattered to see some 中文 shaped thoroughfares.

2. Never build the houses of the same street in a straight line. The British have always been a freedom-loving race and the "freedom to build a muddle" is one of their most ancient civic rights.

3. Now there are further camouflage possibilities in the numbering of houses. Primitive continental races put even numbers on one side, odd numbers on the other, and you always know that small numbers start from the north or west. In England you have this system, too; but you may start numbering your houses at one end, go up to a certain number on the same side, then continue on the other side, going back in the opposite direction.

You may leave out some numbers if you are superstitious; and you may continue the numbering in a side street; you may also give the same number to two or three houses.

But this is far from the end. Many people refuse to have numbers altogether, and they choose names. It is very pleasant, for instance, to find a street with three hundred and fifty totally similar bungalows and look for "The Bungalow." Or to arrive in a street where all the houses have a charming view of a hill and try to find "Hill View." Or search for "Seven Oaks" and find a house with three apple-trees.

4. Give a different name to the street whenever it bends; but if the curve is so sharp that it really makes two different streets, you may keep the same name. On the other hand, if, owing to neglect, a street has been built in a straight line it must be called by many different names (High Holborn, New Oxford Street, Oxford Street, Bayswater Road, Notting Hill Gate, Holland Park, and so on).

5. As some cute foreigners would be able to learn their way about even under such circumstances, some further precautions are necessary. Call streets by various names: street, road, place, mews, crescent, avenue, rise, lane, way, grove, park, gar-

dens, alley, arch, path, walk, broadway, promenade, gate, terrace, vale, view, hill, etc.*

Now two further possibilities arise:

(*a*) Gather all sorts of streets and squares of the same name in one neighbourhood: Belsize Park, Belsize Street, Belsize Road, Belsize Gardens, Belsize Green, Belsize Circus, Belsize Yard, Belsize Viaduct, Belsize Arcade, Belsize Heath, etc.

(*b*) Place a number of streets of *exactly* the same name in different districts. If you have about twenty Princes Squares and Warwick Avenues in the town, the muddle — you may claim without immodesty — will be complete.

6. Street names should be painted clearly and distinctly on large boards. Then hide these boards carefully. Place them too high or too low, in shadow and darkness, upside down and inside out, or, even better, lock them up in a safe in your bank, otherwise they may give people some indication about the names of the streets.

7. In order to break down the foreigner's last vestige of resistance and shatter his morale, one further trick is advisable: Introduce the system of squares — real squares, I mean — which run into four streets like this:

---

* While this book was at the printers' a correspondence in *The Times* showed that the English have almost sixty synonyms for "street". If you add to these the street names which stand alone (Piccadilly, Strand, etc.) and the accepted and frequently used double names ("Garden Terrace," "Church Street," "Park Road," etc.) the number of street names reaches or exceeds a hundred. It has been suggested by one correspondent that this clearly proves what wonderful imagination the English have. I believe it proves the contrary. A West End street in London is not called "Haymarket" because the playful fancy of Londoners populates the district with romantically clad medieval food dealers, but simply because they have not noticed as yet that the hay trade has considerably declined between Piccadilly and Pall Mall in the last three hundred years.

With this simple device it is possible to build a street of which the two sides have different names.

P. S.—I have been told that my above-described theory is all wrong and is only due to my Central European conceit, because the English do not care for the opinion of foreigners. In every other country, it has been explained, people just build streets and towns following their own common sense. England is the only country of the world where there is a Ministry of Town and Country Planning. That is the real reason for the muddle.

CIVIL SERVANT

There is a world of difference between the English Civil Servant and the continental.

On the Continent (not speaking now of the Scandinavian countries), Civil Servants assume a certain military air. They consider themselves little generals; they use delaying tactics; they cannot withdraw armies, so they withdraw permissions; they thunder like cannons and their speech is like machine-gun fire; they cannot lose battles, they lose documents instead. They consider that the sole aim of human society is to give jobs to Civil Servants. A few wicked individuals, however (contemptible little groups of people who are not Civil Servants), conspire against them, come to them with various requests, complaints, problems, etc., with the sole purpose of making a nuisance of themselves. These people get the reception they deserve. They are kept waiting in cold and dirty antechambers (some of them clean these rooms occasionally, but there are hired commissionaires whose duty it is to re-dirty these rooms every morning); they have to stand, often at attention, whilst they are spoken to; they are always shouted at in a rude manner and their requests are turned down with malicious pleasure. Sometimes — this is a popular cat and mouse game — they are sent to another office on the fifth floor, from there they are directed to a third office in the basement, where they are told that they should not have come there at all and sent back to the original office. In that office they are thoroughly told off in acrimonious language and dispatched to the fifth floor once again, from there to the basement and the procedure goes on endlessly until the poor fellows either get tired of the whole business and give up in despair or become raving lunatics and go to an asylum asking for admittance. If the latter case occurs they are told in the reception office that they have come to the wrong place, they should go to another office on the fifth floor, from which they are sent down to the basement, etc., etc., until they give up being lunatics.

(If you want to catch me out and ask me who are then the people who fill the continental lunatic asylums, I can give you the explanation: they are all Civil Servants who know the ways and means of dealing with officials and succeed in getting in somehow.)

If a former continental Civil Servant thought that this martial behaviour would be accepted by the British public he would be badly mistaken. The English Civil Servant considers himself no soldier but a glorified businessman. He is smooth and courteous; he smiles in a superior way; he is agreeable and obliging.

If so — you may ask — how can he achieve the supreme object of his vast and noble organisation, namely, not to transact any business and be left in peace to read a good murder story undisturbed?

There are various, centuries-old, true British traditions to secure this aim.

1. All orders and directives to the public are worded in such a way that they should have no meaning whatever.

2. All official letters are written in such a language that the oracles of Delphi sound as examples of clear, outspoken, straightforward statements compared with them.

3. Civil Servants never make decisions, they only promise to "consider," — "consider favourably" — or — and this the utmost — "reconsider" certain questions.

4. In principle the British Civil Servant stands always at the disposal of the public. In practice he is either in "conference" or out for lunch, or in but having his tea, or just out. Some develop an admirable technique of going out for tea before coming back from lunch.

The British Civil Servant, unlike the rough bully we often find on the Continent, is the Obedient Servant of the public. Before the war, an alien in this country was ordered to leave. He asked for extension of his staying permit, but was refused. He stayed on all the same, and after a while he received the following letter (I quote from memory):

"Dear Sir,
The Under-Secretary of State presents his compliments and regrets that he is unable to reconsider your case, and begs to inform you that unless you kindly leave this country within 24 hours you will be forcibly expelled."

Your Obedient Servant,
***

On the Continent rich and influential people, or those who have friends, cousins, brothers-in-law, tenants, business associates, etc., in an office may have their requests fulfilled. In England there is no such corruption and your obedient servant just will not do a thing whoever you may be. And this is the real beauty of democracy.

JOURNALISM, OR THE FREEDOM OF THE PRESS

The Fact

There was some trouble with the Buburuk tribe in the Pacific Island, Charamak. A party of ten English and two American soldiers, under the command of Capt. R. L. A. T. W. Tilbury, raided the island and took 217 revolutionary, native troublemakers prisoner and wrecked two large oil-dumps. The party remained ashore an hour-and-a-half and returned to their base without loss to themselves.

How to report this event? It depends which newspaper you work for.

THE TIMES

...It would be exceedingly perilous to overestimate the significance of the raid, but it can be fairly proclaimed that it would be even more dangerous to underestimate it. The success of the raid clearly proves that the native defences are not invulnerable; it would be fallacious and deceptive, however, to conclude that these defences are vulnerable. The number of revolutionaries captured cannot be safely stated, but it seems likely that the number is well over 216 but well under 218.

IN THE HOUSE

You may become an M. P. (Nothing is impossible — this would not be even unprecedented.) You may hear then the following statement by a member of Her Majesty's Government:

"Concerning the two wrecked oil-dumps I can give this information to the House. In the first half of this year the amount of native oil destroyed by the Army, Navy and the R. A. F.—excluding however, the Fleet Air Arm—is one-half as much as three times the amount destroyed during the corresponding months of the previous year, seven and a half times as much as the two-fifths destroyed two years ago and three-quarters as much again as twelve times one-sixth destroyed three years ago. (Loud cheers from the Government benches.)

You jump to your feet and ask this question:

YOU: Is the Right Hon. Gentleman aware that people in this country are puzzled and worried by the fact that Charamak was raided and not Ragamak?

THE RIGHT HON. MEMBER: I have nothing to add to my statement given on the 2nd August, 1892.

17—1151

The most interesting feature of the Charamak raid is the fact that Reggie Tilbury is the fifth son of the Earl of Bayswater. He was an Oxford Blue, a first-class cricketer and quite good at polo. When I talked to his wife (Lady Clarisse, the daughter of Lord Elasson) at Claridges today she wore a black suit and a tiny black hat with a yellow feather in it. She said: "Reggie was always very much interested in warfare." Later she remarked: "It was clever of him, wasn't it?"

You may write a letter to the Editor of *The Times*:

"Sir,— In connection with the Charamak raid I should like to mention as a matter of considerable interest that it was in that little Pacific Island that the distinguished English poet, John Flat, wrote his famous poem 'The Cod' in 1693. Yours, etc...."

You may read this answer on the following day:

"Sir,— I am very grateful to Mr...for calling attention to John Flat's poem 'The Cod.' May I be allowed to use this opportunity, however, to correct a widespread and in my view very unfortunate error which the great masses of the British people seem to share with your correspondent. 'The Cod,' although John Flat started writing it in 1693, was only finished in the early days of January, 1694.

Yours, etc. ..."

If you are the London correspondent of the American paper

THE OKLAHOMA SUN

simply cable this:

"Yanks Conquer Pacific Ocean."

IF NATURALISED

The verb *to naturalise* clearly proves what the British think of you. Before you are admitted to British citizenship you are not even considered a natural human being. I looked up the word natural (na'tural) in the Pocket Oxford Dictionary (p. 251); it says: *Of or according to or provided by nature, physically existing, innate, instinctive, normal, not miraculous or spiritual or artificial or conventional....* Note that before you obtain British citizenship, they simply doubt that you are provided by nature.

According to the Pocket Oxford Dictionary the word "natural" has a second meaning, too: *Half-witted person.* This second meaning, however, is irrelevant from the point of view of our present argument.

If you are tired of not being provided by nature, not being physically existing and being miraculous and conventional at the same time, apply for British citizenship. Roughly speaking, there are two possibilities: it will be granted to you, or not.

In the first case you must recognise and revise your attitude to life. You must pretend that you are everything you are not and you must look down upon everything you are.

Copy the attitude of an English acquaintance of mine — let us call him Gregory Baker. He, an English solicitor, feels particularly deep contempt for following classes of people: foreigners, Americans, Frenchmen, Irishmen, Scotsmen and Welshmen, Jews, workers, clerks, poor people, non-professional men, business men, actors, journalists and literary men, women, solicitors who do not practise in his immediate neighbourhood, solicitors who are hard up and solicitors who are too rich, Socialists, Liberals, Tory-reformers (Communists are not worthy even of his contempt); he looks down upon his mother, because she has a business mind, his wife, because she comes from a non-professional county family, his brother, because although he is a professional officer he does not serve with the Guards, Hussars, or at least with a county regiment. He adores and admires his seven-years old son, because the shape of his nose resembles his own.

If naturalised, remember these rules:

1. You must start eating porridge for breakfast and allege that you like it.

2. Speak English with your former compatriots. Deny that you know any foreign language (including your mother tongue). The knowledge of foreign languages is very un-English. A little French is permissible, but only with an atrocious accent.

3. Revise your library. Get rid of all foreign writers whether in the original or translated into English. The works of Dostoevsky should be replaced by a volume on English Birds; the collected works of Proust by a book called "Interior Decoration in the Regency Period"; and Pascal's *Pensées* by the "Life and Thoughts of a Scottish Salmon."

4. Speaking of your new compatriots, always use the first person plural.

In this aspect, though, a certain caution is advisable. I know a na'turalised Britisher who, talking to a young man, repeatedly used the phrase "We Englishmen." The young man looked at him, took his pipe out of his mouth and remarked softly: "Sorry, Sir, I'm a Welshman," turned his back on him and walked away.

The same gentleman was listening to a conversation. It was mentioned that the Japanese had claimed to have shot down 22 planes.

"What — ours?" he asked indignantly.

His English hostess answered icily:

"No — *ours*."

ROALD DAHL

THE GREAT AUTOMATIC
GRAMMATISATOR

"Well Knipe, my boy. Now that it's all finished, I just called
you in to tell you I think you've done a fine job."

Adolph Knipe stood still in front of Mr. Bohlen's desk.
There seemed to be no enthusiasm in him at all.

"Aren't you pleased?"

"Oh yes, Mr. Bohlen."

"Did you see what the papers said this morning?"

"No sir, I didn't."

The man behind the desk pulled a folded newspaper toward
him, and began to read: "The building of the great automatic
computing engine, ordered by the government some time ago,
is now complete. It is probably the fastest electronic calculat-
ing machine in the world today. Its function is to satisfy the
ever-increasing need of science, industry, and administration
for rapid mathematical calculation which, in the past, by traditional methods, would have been physically impossible, or
would have required more time than the problems justified.
The speed with which the new engine works, said Mr. John
Bohlen, head of the firm of electrical engineers mainly responsible for its construction, may be grasped by the fact that it can
provide the correct answer in five seconds to a problem that
would occupy a mathematician for a month. In three minutes,

261

it can produce a calculation that by hand (if it were possible) would fill half a million sheets of foolscap paper. The automatic computing engine uses pulses of electricity, generated at the rate of a million a second, to solve all calculations that resolve themselves into addition, subtraction, multiplication, and division. For practical purposes there is no limit to what it can do..."

Mr. Bohlen glanced up at the long, melancholy face of the younger man. "Aren't you proud, Knipe? Aren't you pleased?"

"Of course, Mr. Bohlen."

"I don't think I have to remind you that your own contribution, especially to the original plans, was an important one. In fact, I might go so far as to say that without you and some of your ideas, this project might still be on the drawing-boards today."

Adolph Knipe moved his feet on the carpet, and he watched the two small white hands of his chief, the nervous fingers playing with a paper-clip, unbending it, straightening out the hairpin curves. He didn't like the man's hands. He didn't like his face either, with the tiny mouth and the narrow purple-coloured lips. It was unpleasant the way only the lower lip moved when he talked.

"Is anything bothering you, Knipe? Anything on your mind?"

"Oh no, Mr. Bohlen. No."

"How would you like to take a week's holiday? Do you good. You've earned it."

"Oh, I don't know, sir."

The older man waited, watching this tall, thin person who stood so sloppily before him. He was a difficult boy. Why couldn't he stand up straight? Always drooping and untidy, with spots on his jacket, and hair falling all over his face.

"I'd like you to take a holiday, Knipe. You need it."

"All right, sir. If you wish."

"Take a week. Two weeks if you like. Go somewhere warm. Get some sunshine. Swim. Relax. Sleep. Then come back, and we'll have another talk about the future."

Adolph Knipe went home by bus to his two-room apartment. He threw his coat on the sofa, poured himself a drink of whiskey, and sat down in front of the typewriter that was on the table. Mr. Bohlen was right. Of course he was right. Except that he didn't know the half of it. He probably thought it was a woman. Whenever a young man gets depressed, everybody thinks it's a woman.

He leaned forward and began to read through the half-finished sheet of typing still in the machine. It was headed "A Narrow Escape," and it began "*The night was dark and stormy, the wind whistled in the trees, the rain poured down like cats and dogs...*"

Adolph Knipe took a sip of whiskey, tasting the malty-bitter flavour, feeling the trickle of cold liquid as it travelled down his throat and settled in the top of his stomach, cool at first, then spreading and becoming warm, making a little area of warmness in the gut. To hell with Mr. John Bohlen anyway. And to hell with the great electrical computing machine. To hell with...

At exactly that moment, his eyes and mouth began slowly to open, in a sort of wonder, and slowly he raised his head and became still, absolutely motionless, gazing at the wall opposite with this look that was more perhaps of astonishment than of wonder, but quite fixed now, unmoving, and remaining thus for forty, fifty, sixty seconds. Then gradually (the head still motionless), a subtle change spreading over the face, astonishment becoming pleasure, very slight at first, only around the corners of the mouth, increasing gradually, spreading out until at last the whole face was open wide and shining with extreme delight. It was the first time Adolph Knipe had smiled in many, many months.

"Of course," he said, speaking aloud, "it's completely ridiculous." Again he smiled, raising his upper lip and baring his teeth in a queerly sensual manner.

"It's a delicious idea, but so impracticable it doesn't really bear thinking about at all."

From then on, Adolph Knipe began to think about nothing else. The idea fascinated him enormously, at first because it gave him a promise — however remote — of revenging himself in a most devilish manner upon his greatest enemies. From this angle alone, he toyed idly with it for perhaps ten or fifteen minutes; then all at once he found himself examining it quite

263

seriously as a practical possibility. He took paper and made some preliminary notes. But he didn't get far. He found himself, almost immediately, up against the old truth that a machine, however ingenious, is incapable of original thought. It can handle no problems except those that resolve themselves into mathematical terms — problems that contain one, and only one, correct answer.

This was a stumper. There didn't seem any way around it. A machine cannot have a brain. On the other hand, it *can* have a memory, can it not? Their own electronic calculator had a marvellous memory. Simply by converting electric pulses, through a column of mercury, into supersonic waves, it could store away at least a thousand numbers at a time, extracting any one of them at the precise moment it was needed. Would it not be possible, therefore, on this principle, to build a memory section of almost unlimited size?

Now what about that?

Then suddenly, he was struck by a powerful but simple little truth, and it was this: *That English grammar is governed by rules that are almost mathematical in their strictness!* Given the words, and given the sense of what is to be said, then there is only one correct order in which those words can be arranged.

No, he thought, that isn't quite accurate. In many sentences there are several alternative positions for words and phrases, all of which may be grammatically correct. But what the hell. The theory itself is basically true. Therefore, it stands to reason that an engine built along the lines of the electric computer could be adjusted to arrange words (instead of numbers) in their right order according to the rules of grammar. Give it the verbs, the nouns, the adjectives, the pronouns, store them in the memory section as a vocabulary, and arrange for them to be extracted as required. Then feed it with plots and leave it to write the sentences.

There was no stopping Knipe now. He went to work immediately, and there followed during the next few days a period of intense labour. The living-room became littered with sheets of paper: formulae and calculations; lists of words, thousands and thousands of words; the plots of stories, curiously broken up and subdivided; huge extracts from *Roget's Thesaurus*; pages filled with the first names of men and women; hundreds of surnames taken from the telephone directory; intricate drawings of wires and circuits and switches and thermionic valves; drawings of machines that could punch holes of different shapes in little cards, and of a strange electrical typewriter that could type ten thousand words a minute. Also, a kind of control panel with a series of small push-buttons, each one labelled with the name of a famous American magazine.

He was working in a mood of exultation, prowling around the room amidst this littering of paper, rubbing his hands together, talking out loud to himself; and sometimes, with a sly curl of the nose, he would mutter a series of murderous imprecations in which the word "editor" seemed always to be present. On the fifteenth day of continuous work, he collected the papers into two large folders which he carried — almost at a run — to the offices of John Bohlen Inc., electrical engineers.

Mr. Bohlen was pleased to see him back.

"Well Knipe, good gracious me, you look a hundred per cent better. You have a good holiday? Where'd you go?"

He's just as ugly and untidy as ever, Mr. Bohlen thought. Why doesn't he stand up straight? He looks like a bent stick. "You look a hundred per cent better, my boy." I wonder what he's grinning about. Every time I see him, his ears seem to have got larger.

Adolph Knipe placed the folders on the desk. "Look, Mr. Bohlen!" he cried. "Look at these!"

Then he poured out his story. He opened the folders and pushed the plans in front of the astonished little man. He talked for over an hour, explaining everything, and when he had finished, he stepped back, breathless, flushed, waiting for the verdict.

"You know what I think, Knipe? I think you're nuts." Careful now, Mr. Bohlen told himself. Treat him carefully. He's valuable, this one is. If only he didn't look so awful, with that long horse face and the big teeth. The fellow had ears as big as rhubarb leaves.

"But Mr. Bohlen! It'll work! I've proved to you it'll work! You can't deny that!"

"Take it easy now, Knipe. Take it easy, and listen to me."

Adolph Knipe watched his man, disliking him more every second.

"This idea," Mr. Bohlen's lower lip was saying, "is very ingenious — I might almost say brilliant — and it only goes to confirm my high opinion of your abilities, Knipe. But don't take it too seriously. After all, my boy, what possible use can it be to us? Who on earth wants a machine for writing stories? And where's the money in it, anyway? Just tell me that."

"May I sit down, sir?"

"Sure, take a seat."

Adolph Knipe seated himself on the edge of a chair. The older man watched him with alert brown eyes, wondering what was coming now.

"I would like to explain something, Mr. Bohlen, if I may, about how I came to do all this."

"Go right ahead, Knipe." He would have to be humoured a little now, Mr. Bohlen told himself. The boy was really valuable — a sort of genius, almost — worth his weight in gold to the firm. Just look at these papers here. Darnedest thing you ever saw. Astonishing piece of work. Quite useless, of course. No commercial value. But it proved again the boy's ability.

"It's a sort of confession, I suppose, Mr. Bohlen. I think it explains why I've always been so ... so kind of worried."

"You tell me anything you want, Knipe. I'm here to help you — you know that."

The young man clasped his hands together tight on his lap, hugging himself with his elbows. It seemed as though suddenly he was feeling very cold.

"You see, Mr. Bohlen, to tell the honest truth, I don't really care much for my work here. I know I'm good at it and all that sort of thing, but my heart's not in it. It's not what I want to do most."

Up went Mr. Bohlen's eyebrows, quick like a spring. His whole body became very still.

"You see, sir, all my life I've wanted to be a writer."

"A writer!"

"Yes, Mr. Bohlen. You may not believe it, but every bit of spare time I've had, I've spent writing stories. In the last ten years I've written hundreds, literally hundreds of short stories.

Five hundred and sixty-six, to be precise. Approximately one a week."

"Good heavens, man! What on earth did you do that for?"

"All I know, sir, is I have the urge."

"What sort of urge?"

"The creative urge, Mr. Bohlen." Every time he looked up he saw Mr. Bohlen's lips. They were growing thinner and thinner, more and more purple.

"And may I ask you what you do with these stories, Knipe?"

"Well sir, that's the trouble. No one will buy them. Each time I finish one, I send it out on the rounds. It goes to one magazine after another. That's all that happens, Mr. Bohlen, and they simply send them back. It's very depressing."

Mr. Bohlen relaxed. "I can see quite well how you feel, my boy." His voice was dripping with sympathy. "We all go through it one time or another in our lives. But now — now that you've had proof — positive proof — from the experts themselves, from the editors, that your stories are — what shall I say — rather unsuccessful, it's time to leave off. Forget it, my boy. Just forget all about it."

"No, Mr. Bohlen! No! That's not true! I *know* my stories are good. My heavens, when you compare them with the stuff some of those magazines print — oh my word, Mr. Bohlen! — the sloppy, boring stuff that you see in the magazines week after week — why, it drives me mad!"

"Now wait a minute, my boy..."

"Do you ever read the magazines, Mr. Bohlen?"

"You'll pardon me, Knipe, but what's all this got to do with your machine?"

"Everything, Mr. Bohlen, absolutely everything! What I want to tell you is, I've made a study of the magazines, and it seems that each one tends to have its own particular type of story. The writers — the successful ones — know this, and they write accordingly."

"Just a minute, my boy. Calm yourself down, will you. I don't think all this is getting us anywhere."

"*Please*, Mr. Bohlen, hear me through. It's all terribly important." He paused to catch his breath. He was properly worked up now, throwing his hands around as he talked. The

267

long, toothy face, with the big ears on either side, simply shone with enthusiasm, and there was an excess of saliva in his mouth which caused him to speak his words wet. "So you see, on my machine, by having an adjustable co-ordinator between the 'plot-memory' section and the 'word-memory' section, I am able to produce any type of story I desire simply by pressing the required button."

"Yes, I know, Knipe, I know. This is all very interesting, but what's the point of it?"

"Just this, Mr. Bohlen. The market is limited. We've got to be able to produce the right stuff, at the right time, whenever we want it. It's matter of business, that's all. I'm looking at it from *your* point of view now — as a commercial proposition."

"My dear boy, it can't possibly be a commercial proposition — ever. You know as well as I do what it costs to build one of these machines."

"Yes sir, I do. But with due respect, I don't believe you know what the magazines pay writers for stories."

"What do they pay?"

"Anything up to twenty-five hundred dollars. It probably averages around a thousand."

Mr. Bohlen jumped.

"Yes *sir*, it's true."

"Absolutely impossible, Knipe! Ridiculous!"

"No sir, it's true."

"You mean to sit there and tell me that these magazines pay out money like that to a man for ... just for scribbling off a story! Good heavens, Knipe! Whatever next! Writers must all be millionaires!"

"That's exactly it, Mr. Bohlen! That's where the machine comes in. Listen a minute, sir, while I tell you some more. I've got it all worked out. The big magazines are carrying approximately three fiction stories in each issue. Now, take the fifteen most important magazines — the ones paying the most money. A few of them are monthlies, but most of them come out every week. All right. That makes, let us say, around forty big money stories being bought each week. That's forty thousand dollars. So with our machine — when we get it working properly — we can collar nearly the whole of this market!"

"My dear boy, you're mad!"

"No sir, honestly, it's true what I say. Don't you see that with volume alone we'll completely overwhelm them! This machine can produce a five-thousand word story, all typed and ready for dispatch, in thirty seconds. How can the writers compete with that? I ask you, Mr. Bohlen, *how*?"

At that point, Adolph Knipe noticed a slight change in the man's expression, an extra brightness in the eyes, the nostrils distending, the whole face becoming still, almost rigid. Quickly, he continued. "Nowadays, Mr. Bohlen, the hand-made article hasn't a hope. It can't possibly compete with mass-production, especially in this country — you know that. Carpets ... chairs ... shoes ... bricks ... crockery ... anything you like to mention — they're all made by machinery now. The quality may be inferior, but that doesn't matter. It's the cost of production that counts. And stories — well — they're just another product, like carpets or chairs, and no one cares how you produce them so long as you deliver the goods. We'll sell them wholesale, Mr. Bohlen! We'll undercut every writer in the country! We'll corner the market!"

Mr. Bohlen edged up straighter in his chair. He was leaning forward now, both elbows on the desk, the face alert, the small brown eyes resting on the speaker.

"I still think it's impracticable, Knipe."

"Forty thousand a week!" cried Adolph Knipe. "And if we halve the price, making it twenty thousand a week, that's still a million a year!" And softly he added, "You didn't get any million a year for building the old electronic calculator, did you, Mr. Bohlen?"

"But seriously now, Knipe. D'you really think they'd buy them?"

"Listen, Mr. Bohlen. Who on earth is going to want custom-made stories when they can get the other kind at half the price? It stands to reason, doesn't it?"

"And how will you sell them? Who will you say has written them?"

"We'll set up our own literary agency, and we'll distribute them through that. And we'll invent all the names we want for the writers."

"I don't like it, Knipe. To me, that smacks of trickery, does it not?"

"And another thing, Mr. Bohlen. There's all manner of valuable by-products once you've got started. Take advertising, for example. Beer manufacturers and people like that are willing to pay good money these days if famous writers will lend their names to their products. Why, my heavens, Mr. Bohlen! This isn't any children's play-thing we're talking about. It's big business."

"Don't get too ambitious, my boy."

"And another thing. There isn't any reason why we shouldn't put *your* name, Mr. Bohlen, on some of the better stories, if you wished it."

"My goodness, Knipe. What should I want that for?"

"I don't know, sir, except that some writers get to be very much respected — like Mr. Erle Gardner or Kathleen Norris, for example. We've got to have names, and I was certainly thinking of using my own on one or two stories, just to help out."

"A writer, eh?" Mr. Bohlen said, musing. "Well, it would surely surprise them over at the club when they saw my name in the magazines — the good magazines."

"That's right, Mr. Bohlen."

For a moment, a dreamy, faraway look came into Mr. Bohlen's eyes, and he smiled. Then he stirred himself and began leafing through the plans that lay before him.

"One thing I don't quite understand, Knipe. Where do the plots come from? The machine can't possibly invent plots."

"We feed those in, sir. That's no problem at all. Everyone has plots. There's three or four hundred of them written down in that folder there on your left. Feed them straight into the 'plot-memory' section of the machine."

"Go on."

"There are many other little refinements too, Mr. Bohlen. You'll see them all when you study the plans carefully. For example, there's a trick that nearly every writer uses, of inserting at least one long, obscure word into each story. This makes the reader think that the man is very wise and clever. So I have the machine do the same thing. There'll be a whole stack of long words stored away just for this purpose."

"Where?"

"In the 'word-memory' section," he said, epexegetically.

Through most of that day the two men discussed the possibilities of the new engine. In the end, Mr. Bohlen said he would have to think about it some more. The next morning, he was quietly enthusiastic. Within a week, he was completely sold on the idea.

"What we'll have to do, Knipe, is to say that we're merely building another mathematical calculater, but of a new type. That'll keep the secret."

"Exactly, Mr. Bohlen."

And in six months the machine was completed. It was housed in a separate brick building at the back of the premises, and now that it was ready for action, no one was allowed near it excepting Mr. Bohlen and Adolph Knipe.

It was an exciting moment when the two men — the one, short, plump, breviped — the other tall, thin and toothy — stood in the corridor before the control panel and got ready to run off the first story. All around them were walls dividing up into many small corridors, and the walls were covered with wiring and plugs and switches and huge glass valves. They were both nervous, Mr. Bohlen hopping from one foot to the other, quite unable to keep still.

"Which button?" Adolph Knipe asked, eyeing a row of small white discs that resembled the keys of a typewriter. "You choose, Mr. Bohlen. Lots of magazines to pick from — *Saturday Evening Post, Collier's, Ladies' Home Journal* — any one you like."

"Goodness me, boy! How do I know." He was jumping up and down like a man with hives.

"Mr. Bohlen," Adolph Knipe said gravely, "do you realize that at this moment, with your little finger alone, you have it in your power to become the most versatile writer on this continent?"

"Listen Knipe, just get on with it, will you please — and cut out the preliminaries."

"Okay, Mr. Bohlen. Then we'll make it ... let me see — this one. How's that?" He extended one finger and pressed down a button with the name *TODAY'S WOMAN* printed across it in diminutive black type. There was a sharp click, and when he took his finger away, the button remained down, below the level of the others.

"So much for the selection," he said. "Now — here we go!" He reached up and pulled a switch on the panel. Immediately, the room was filled with a loud humming noise, and a crackling of electric sparks, and the jingle of many, tiny, quickly-moving levers; and almost in the same instant, sheets of quarto paper began sliding out from a slot to the right of the control panel and dropping into a basket below. They came out quick, one sheet a second, and in less than half a minute it was all over. The sheets stopped coming.

"That's it!" Adolph Knipe cried. "There's your story!"

They grabbed the sheets and began to read. The first one they picked up started as follows: "Aifkjmbsaoegwcztppln-voqudskigt&, fuhpekanvbertyuiolkjghfdsazxcvbnm, peruit-rehdjkgmvnb, wmsuy..." They looked at the others. The style was roughly similar in all of them. Mr. Bohlen began to shout. The younger man tried to calm him down.

"It's all right, sir. Really it is. It only needs a little adjustment. We've got a connection wrong somewhere, that's all. You must remember, Mr. Bohlen, there's over a million feet of wiring in this room. You can't expect everything to be right first time."

"It'll never work," Mr. Bohlen said.

"Be patient, sir. Be patient."

Adolph Knipe set out to discover the fault, and in four days time he announced that all was ready for the next try.

"It'll never work," Mr. Bohlen said. "I know it'll never work."

Knipe smiled and pressed the selector button marked *Reader's Digest*. Then he pulled the switch, and again the strange, exciting, humming sound filled the room. One page of typescript flew out of the slot into the basket.

"Where's the rest?" Mr. Bohlen cried. "It's stopped! It's gone wrong!"

"No sir, it hasn't. It's exactly right. It's for the *Digest*, don't you see?"

This time, it began: "Fewpeopleyetknowthatarevolutiona-rynewcurehasbeendiscoveredwhichmaywellbringpermanentre-lieftosufferersofthemostdreadeddiseaseofourtime..." And so on.

"It's gibberish!" Mr. Bohlen shouted.

"No sir, it's fine. Can't you see? It's simply that she's not breaking up the words. That's an easy adjustment. But the story's there. Look, Mr. Bohlen, look! It's all there except that the words are joined together."

And indeed it was.

On the next try a few days later, everything was perfect, even the punctuation. The first story they ran off, for a famous women's magazine, was a solid, plotty story of a boy who wanted to better himself with his rich employer. This boy arranged, so the story went, for a friend to hold up the rich man's daughter on a dark night when she was driving home. Then the boy himself, happening by, knocked the gun out of his friend's hand and rescued the girl. The girl was grateful. But the father was suspicious. He questioned the boy sharply. The boy broke down and confessed. Then the father, instead of kicking him out of the house, said that he admired the boy's resourcefulness. The girl admired his honesty — and his looks. The father promised him to be head of the Accounts Department. The girl married him.

"It's tremendous, Mr. Bohlen! It's exactly right!"

"Seems a bit sloppy to me, my boy."

"No sir, it's a seller, a real seller!"

In his excitement, Adolph Knipe promptly ran off six more stories in as many minutes. All of them — except one, which for some reason came out a trifle lewd — seemed entirely satisfactory.

Mr. Bohlen was now mollified. He agreed to set up a literary agency in an office downtown, and to put Knipe in charge. In a couple of weeks, this was accomplished. Then Knipe mailed out the first dozen stories. He put his own name to four of them, Mr. Bohlen's one, and for the others he simply invented names.

Five of these stories were promptly accepted. The one with Mr. Bohlen's name on it was turned down with a letter from the fiction editor saying, "This is a skilful job, but in our opinion it doesn't quite come off. We would like to see more of this writer's work..." Adolph Knipe took a cab out to the factory and ran off another story for the same magazine. He again put Mr. Bohlen's name to it, and mailed it out immediately. That one they bought.

273

The money started pouring in. Knipe slowly and carefully stepped up the output, and in six months' time he was delivering thirty stories a week, and selling about half.

He began to make a name for himself in literary circles as a prolific and successful writer. So did Mr. Bohlen; but not quite such a good name, although he didn't know it. At the same time, Knipe was building up a dozen or more fictitious persons as promising young authors. Everything was going fine.

At this point it was decided to adapt the machine for writing novels as well as stories. Mr. Bohlen, thirsting now for greater honours in the literary world, insisted that Knipe go to work at once on this prodigious task.

"I want to do a novel," he kept saying. "I want to do a novel."

"And so you will, sir. And so you will. But please be patient. This is a very complicated adjustment I have to make."

"Everyone tells me I ought to do a novel," Mr. Bohlen cried. "All sorts of publishers are chasing after me day and night begging me to stop fooling around with stories and do something really important instead. A novel's the only thing that counts — that's what they say."

"We're all going to do novels," Knipe told him. "Just as many as we want. But please be patient."

"Now listen to me, Knipe. What I'm going to do is a *serious* novel, something that'll make 'em sit up and take notice. I've been getting rather tired of the sort of stories you've been putting my name to lately. As a matter of fact, I'm none too sure you haven't been trying to make a monkey out of me."

"A monkey, Mr. Bohlen?"

"Keeping all the best ones for yourself, that's what you've been doing."

"Oh no, Mr. Bohlen! No!"

"So this time I'm going to make damn sure I write a high class intelligent book. You understand that."

"Look, Mr. Bohlen. With the sort of switchboard I'm rigging up, you'll be able to write any sort of book you want."

And this was true, for within another couple of months, the genius of Adolph Knipe had not only adapted the machine for novel writing, but had constructed a marvellous new control system which enabled the author to pre-select literally any type of plot and any style of writing he desired. There were so many dials and levers on the thing, it looked like the instrument panel of some enormous airplane.

First, by pressing one of a series of master buttons, the writer made his primary decision: historical, satirical, philosophical, political, romantic, erotic, humorous, or straight. Then, from the second row (the basic buttons), he chose his theme: army life, pioneer days, civil war, world war, racial problem, wild west, country life, childhood memories, seafaring, the sea bottom, and many, many more. The third row of buttons gave a choice of literary style: classical, whimsical, racy, Hemingway, Faulkner, Joyce, feminine, etc. The fourth row was for characters, the fifth for wordage — and so on and so on — ten long rows of pre-selector buttons.

But that wasn't all. Control had also to be exercised during the actual writing process (which took about fifteen minutes per novel), and to do this the author had to sit, as it were, in the driver's seat, and pull (or push) a battery of labelled stops, as on an organ. By so doing, he was able continually to modulate or merge fifty different and variable qualities such as tension, surprise, humour, pathos, and mystery. Numerous dials and gauges on the dashboard itself told him throughout exactly how far along he was with his work.

Finally, there was the question of "passion." From a careful study of the books at the top of the best-seller lists for the past year, Adolph Knipe had decided that this was the most important ingredient of all — a magical catalyst that somehow or other could transform the dullest novel into a howling success — at any rate financially. But Knipe also knew that passion was powerful, heady stuff, and must be prudently dispensed — the right proportions at the right moments; and to ensure this, he had devised an independent control consisting of two sensitive sliding adjustors operated by footpedals, similar to the throttle and brake in a car. One pedal governed the percentage of passion to be injected, the other regulated its intensity. There was no doubt, of course — and this was the only drawback — that the writing of a novel by the Knipe method was going to be rather like flying a plane and driving a car and playing an organ all at the same time, but this did not trouble the inventor. When all was ready, he proudly escorted Mr. Bohlen into the machine house and began to explain the operating procedure for the new wonder.

"Good God, Knipe! I'll never be able to do all that! Dammit, man, it'd be easier to write the thing by hand!"

"You'll soon get used to it. Mr. Bohlen, I promise you. In a week or two, you'll be doing it without hardly thinking. It's just like learning to drive."

Well, it wasn't quite as easy as that, but after many hours of practice, Mr. Bohlen began to get the hang of it, and finally, late one evening, he told Knipe to make ready for running off the first novel. It was a tense moment, with the fat little man crouching nervously in the driver's seat, and the tall toothy Knipe fussing excitedly around him.

"I intend to write an important novel, Knipe."

"I'm sure you will, sir. I'm sure you will."

With one finger, Mr. Bohlen carefully pressed the necessary pre-selector buttons:

Master button — *satirical*

Subject — *racial problem*

Style — *classical*

Characters — *six men, four women, one infant*

Length — *fifteen chapters.*

At the same time he had his eye particularly upon three organ stops marked *power*, *mystery*, *profundity*.

"Are you ready, sir?"

"Yes, yes, I'm ready."

Knipe pulled the switch. The great engine hummed. There was a deep whirring sound from the oiled movement of fifty thousand cogs and rods and levers; then came the drumming of the rapid electrical typewriter, setting up a shrill, almost intolerable clatter. Out into the basket flew the typewritten pages — one every two seconds. But what with the noise and the excitement, and having to play upon the stops, and watch the chapter-counter and the pace-indicator and the passion-gauge, Mr. Bohlen began to panic. He reacted in precisely the way a learner driver does in a car — by pressing both feet hard down on the pedals and keeping them there until the thing stopped.

"Congratulations on your first novel," Knipe said, picking up the great bundle of typed pages from the basket.

Little pearls of sweat were oozing out all over Mr. Bohlen's face. "It sure was hard work, my boy."

"But you got it done, sir. You got it done."

"Let me see it, Knipe. How does it read?"

He started to go through the first chapter, passing each finished page to the younger man.

"Good heavens, Knipe! What's this!" Mr. Bohlen's thin purple fish-lip was moving slightly as it mouthed the words, his cheeks were beginning slowly to inflate.

"But look here, Knipe! This is outrageous!"

"I must say it's a bit fruity, sir."

"*Fruity!* It's perfectly revolting! I can't possibly put my name to this!"

"Quite right, sir. Quite right."

"Knipe! Is this some nasty trick you've been playing on me?"

"Oh no, sir! No!"

"It certainly looks like it."

"You don't think, Mr. Bohlen, that you mightn't have been pressing a little hard on the passion-control pedals, do you?"

"My dear boy, how should *I* know."

"Why don't you try another?"

So Mr. Bohlen ran off a second novel, and this time it went according to plan.

Within a week, the manuscript had been read and accepted by an enthusiastic publisher. Knipe followed with one in his own name, then made a dozen more for good measure. In no time at all, Adolph Knipe's Literary Agency had become famous for its large stable of promising young novelists. And once again the money started rolling in.

It was at this stage that young Knipe began to display a real talent for big business.

"See here, Mr. Bohlen," he said. "We still got too much competition. Why don't we just absorb all the other writers in the country?"

Mr. Bohlen, who now sported a bottle-green velvet jacket and allowed his hair to cover two-thirds of his ears, was quite content with things the way they were. "Don't know what you mean, my boy. You can't just absorb writers."

"Of course you can, sir. Exactly like Rockefeller did with his oil companies. Simply buy 'em out, and if they won't sell, squeeze 'em out. It's easy!"

"Careful now, Knipe. Be careful."

"I've got a list here, sir, of fifty of the most successful writers in the country, and what I intend to do is offer each one of them a lifetime contract with pay. All *they* have to do is undertake never to write another word; and, of course, to let us use their names on our own stuff. How about that?"

"They'll never agree."

"You don't know writers, Mr. Bohlen, You watch and see."

"What about that creative urge, Knipe?"

"It's bunk! All they're really interested in is the money — just like everybody else."

In the end, Mr. Bohlen reluctantly agreed to give it a try, and Knipe, with his list of writers in his pocket, went off in a large chauffeur-driven Cadillac to make his calls.

He journeyed first to the man at the top of the list, a very great and wonderful writer, and he had no trouble getting into the house. He told his story and produced a suitcase full of sample novels, and a contract for the man to sign which guaranteed him so much a year for life. The man listened politely, decided he was dealing with a lunatic, gave him a drink, then firmly showed him to the door.

The second writer on the list, when he saw Knipe was serious, actually attacked him with a large metal paperweight, and the inventor had to flee down the garden followed by such a torrent of abuse and obscenity as he had never heard before.

But it took more than this to discourage Adolph Knipe. He was disappointed but not dismayed, and off he went in his big car to seek his next client. This one was a female, famous and popular, whose fat romantic books sold by the million across the country. She received Knipe graciously, gave him tea, and listened attentively to his story.

"It all sounds very fascinating," she said. "But of course I find it a little hard to believe."

"Madam," Knipe answered. "Come with me and see it with your own eyes. My car awaits you."

So off they went, and in due course, the astonished lady was ushered into the machine house where the wonder kept. Eagerly, Knipe explained its workings, and after a while he even permitted her to sit in the driver's seat and practice with the buttons.

"All right," he said suddenly, "You want to do a book now?"

"Oh yes?" she cried. "Please!"

She was very competent and seemed to know exactly what she wanted. She made her own pre-selections, then ran off a long, romantic, passion-filled novel. She read through the first chapter and became so enthusiastic that she signed up on the spot.

"That's one of them out of the way." Knipe said to Mr. Bohlen afterwards. "A pretty big one too."

"Nice work, my boy."

"And you know *why* she signed?"

"Why?"

"It wasn't the money. She's got plenty of that."

"Then why?"

Knipe grinned, lifting his lip and baring a long pale upper gum. "Simply because she saw the machine-made stuff was better than her own."

Thereafter, Knipe wisely decided to concentrate only upon mediocrity. Anything better than that — and there were so few it didn't matter much — was apparently not quite so easy to seduce.

In the end, after several months of work, he had persuaded something like seventy per cent of the writers on his list to sign the contract. He found that the older ones, those who were running out of ideas and had taken to drink, were the easiest to handle. The younger people were more troublesome. They were apt to become abusive, sometimes violent when he approached them; and more than once Knipe was slightly injured on his rounds.

But on the whole, it was a satisfactory beginning. This last year — the first full year of the machine's operation — it was estimated that at least one half of all the novels and stories published in the English language were produced by Adolph Knipe upon the Great Automatic Grammatisator.

Does this surprise you?

I doubt it.

And worse is yet to come. Today, as the secret spreads, many more are hurrying to tie up with Mr. Knipe. And all the time the screw turns tighter for those who hesitate to sign their names.

This very moment, as I sit here listening to the howling of my nine starving children in the other room, I can feel my own hand creeping closer and closer to that golden contract that lies over on the other side of the desk.

Give us strength, oh Lord, to let our children starve.

NORMAN FREDERICK SIMPSON

ONE BLAST AND HAVE DONE

Characters:
Freda
Ivy

FREDA: Ivy!
IVY: Hallo, Freda.
FREDA: Come in. Sit down and have a cup of tea.
IVY: No, thank you, Freda. I mustn't stop. I'm on the cadge really. You wouldn't have such a thing as a flute? We've had a flautist call.
FREDA: A flute. Goodness.
IVY: No warning or anything.
FREDA: I'm just trying to think, Ivy. I know we did have one.
IVY: We haven't got a thing in the house except percussion.
FREDA: I suppose a bassoon wouldn't do? If I can find one.
IVY: Anything at all, Freda.
FREDA: I'll see what there is in the cupboard.
IVY: As long as it's something he can blow down.
FREDA: He wants to be able to blow across it, really, if he's a flautist but ... no, there's only this. Would that do,

281

	do you think? It's one of mum's old bassoons. She never used it.
IVY:	That would do fine, Freda.
FREDA:	I think it works all right. As long as he doesn't mind a bit of coal dust in it.
IVY:	If you're sure you can spare it.
FREDA:	Let me put a duster over it for you. Get some of the worst off.
IVY:	Don't bother, Freda.
FREDA:	It won't take a minute.
IVY:	He could have made do with it as it was.
FREDA:	I wish I knew where to put my hands on a flute for you. There's one somewhere I'm almost certain. We had an old harmonium with a flute in it at one time but I don't know till Tom gets in what he's done with it.
IVY:	It doesn't matter, Freda. This is fine.
FREDA:	Tell him to mind the coal dust inside when he starts to blow.
IVY:	It gets into everything, doesn't it?
FREDA:	We had *coal* once.
IVY:	No!
FREDA:	We did. In the American organ. Great lumps the size of cricket balls.
IVY:	How on earth did that happen?
FREDA:	We made the mistake of lending it to some people we knew down the road. And that's how it come back.
IVY:	With coal in it.
FREDA:	And all stuck in any old how, of course. At the back and underneath.
IVY:	It's not right, is it?
FREDA:	No attempt at putting all the big lumps together, or separating out the slack, or anything like that.
IVY:	Too much trouble.
FREDA:	Under the bellows and everywhere. I said to Tom — you'll never play it while it's in that state.
IVY:	It's not the place for it.
FREDA:	He had a rousing tune he could have played if it hadn't been for that. Nearly a hundredweight of it altogether there must have been when we cleared it out.
IVY:	Fancy.
FREDA:	What's that noise?
IVY:	I didn't hear anything.

FREDA: I thought I heard knocking.

(*Knocks are heard on wall.*)

IVY: You're right. He's getting impatient for his flute.

FREDA: Who is it? If it's not a rude question.

IVY: I've never set eyes on him before, Freda, in my life. Just came in, out of the blue, about half an hour ago.

FREDA: You haven't left him in there by himself?

IVY: Yes — I'd better go back. Before he starts getting up to anything. This is the second one we've had this week.

FREDA: Go on?

IVY: We had one in on Monday. They seem to be making a bee-line for us for some reason.

FREDA: And what did *he* want?

IVY: Could he come in for a minute and beat hell out of our timpani, if you please!

FREDA: No!

IVY: No credentials or anything, of course.

FREDA: Isn't it the limit?

IVY: Tried to tell me he was over here on a day trip from Vladivostock.

FREDA: *That* speaks volumes.

IVY: Looking for his brother.

FREDA: Just as well it was a Monday.

IVY: In any case, even if he was genuine, you don't want complete strangers walking in whenever they feel like it and going for all they're worth at your timpani.

FREDA: Of course you don't. (*Knocking repeated.*) There he is again. He's getting impatient.

IVY: (*shouts*). I'm just coming. (*To Freda.*) If it had been anything but timpani I should very likely have fallen for it, but it so happened I was saving the timpani for Fred and Doris when they came in, so they could have a bit of percussion before they went to bed. Otherwise I might have let him in.

(*Knocking repeated.*)

FREDA: You'll have him singing in there, Ivy. All over the furniture.

IVY: (*going*) Goodness — don't say that. I don't want that happening. I've had enough singing to last *me* for

283

	a little while. I didn't tell you about Wednesday, did I?
FREDA:	Not Mrs. Bargold again?
IVY:	(*returning*) You know what a nice afternoon it was, Wednesday — after it brightened up. So I thought I'll just have half an hour with a book out in the garden while I can...
FREDA:	And Mrs. Bargold started up.
IVY:	Started up! I've never heard anything like it. Right through the trellis-work.
FREDA:	It isn't as if she's exactly a Peach Melba, either.
IVY:	I stuck it for as long as I could, but....
FREDA:	She must have a sixth sense.
IVY:	Every time I sit down out there. In the end I called over to her. I couldn't stand it any longer. I said I don't mind you singing, Mrs. Bargold — but not through my trellis-work if you don't mind.
FREDA:	It's not as if it's just once or twice, is it?
IVY:	*Rock of Ages.* Full blast at the top of her voice.
FREDA:	*Rock of Ages?* That's a change, isn't it?
IVY:	Right through the trellis-work. I couldn't read or do anything.
FREDA:	I don't think I've heard Mrs. Bargold sing *Rock of Ages* since Mr. Stepupper called her in to sing down the overflow pipe while the stopcock was being seen to.
IVY:	I told her — I didn't have trellis-work put up for her to sing *Rock of Ages* through whenever it happened to suit her convenience.
FREDA:	Of course not.
IVY:	It's not cheap, either. Ten-and-six a yard it was, all told, to put up. With the labour.
FREDA:	I can imagine.
IVY:	I complained about the nails too. Thick green mould all over them where she's been corroding them month in month out.
FREDA:	It's no joke getting it off, either. Especially on her side of the fence.
IVY:	I have to stand on a step-ladder and lean right over. I wouldn't mind so much if it was ordinary rust. You'd get that with anything. You'd get it with the National Anthem. But this isn't

rust — it's green mould. She must be able to see it forming in front of her eyes, but she makes no attempt to stop.

FREDA: The same as what Mrs. Bates had, I expect. On her front door. It took her nearly a week to get it off. Somebody singing *Shenandoah* through her letter-box when she was out.

IVY: And do you know what she had the cheek to say to me? She said I was the first one who'd complained! (*Mimicking.*) "No one else has ever complained."

FREDA. Only because they knew it wouldn't make any difference.

IVY: I told her — I wouldn't have minded so much if they'd been stainless steel.

FREDA: Or plastic.

IVY: "No one else had complained!" I said to her — no one else has had *Rock of Ages* sung through their trellis-work week after week for months on end. (*A single, prolonged, loud note from a trombone is heard.*) What was that?

FREDA: It sounded like a trombone, Ivy.

IVY: (*going off*) What's he getting up to in there?

FREDA: (*loudly, after her*) He couldn't wait, I expect. He's blown down the nearest thing. (*Pause. Then in an undertone, sardonically.*) "Nothing in the house except percussion!"

Curtain

OH

Characters:

Humphrey Savernake
Laura Savernake

HUMPHREY: No, Laura, I don't think it's the kind of thing we could expect Graham to show much interest in.

LAURA: Oh?

HUMPHREY: He's very orthodox in many ways. As far as his painting is concerned.

LAURA: I must say he doesn't show much preference for orthodox methods in anything else.

HUMPHREY: All the same, Laura, I think that to fix the brush in a vice and move the canvas about on the end of it would create more problems than it would solve.

LAURA: I should have thought it would have been the very thing for Graham.

HUMPHREY: I'll suggest it to him, of course — but you mustn't be surprised if he turns it down. Don't forget he's got all this fuss on his mind still about Colonel Padlock's portrait — that must be taking up practically every spare minute of his time.

LAURA: What fuss about Colonel Padlock's portrait? He's finished it. He *must* have.

HUMPHREY: He's had a great deal to do, Laura.

LAURA.   You don't mean to say poor Colonel Padlock is still sitting there? Waiting?

HUMPHREY: It isn't just a matter of setting an easel up, Laura, and a canvas, and beginning to paint. Just like that.

LAURA: I think that's absolutely disgraceful! What for heaven's sake has he been doing?

HUMPHREY: He hasn't been wasting his time, my dear.

LAURA: Six weeks it must be since all this started. At least. I can't think what he can have been doing all that time.

HUMPHREY: So far as I know, Colonel Padlock hasn't complained.

LAURA: Why on earth doesn't he get people to help him?

HUMPHREY: You won't persuade Graham to delegate responsibility, my dear.

LAURA: Doing every single thing himself from scratch.

HUMPHREY: Yes, well, there it is. If he prefers to work that way....

LAURA: I'd say nothing if it were simply a question of constructing his own easels. With home-made glue.

HUMPHREY: After all....

LAURA: Or even weaving his canvases himself. But growing his own hemp or whatever it is to do it with! That's carrying it too far.

HUMPHREY: Yes, well—I'm afraid I side with Graham over this, Laura.

LAURA: Felling the timber himself for his brush handles and planing it down till it's small enough.

HUMPHREY: What other way is there, Laura, if you're determined to keep control over the finished picture? And that's the whole crux of it as far as Graham is concerned. As you know.

LAURA: And in the meantime, Colonel Padlock has to sit there.

HUMPHREY: As far as that goes, I should think Colonel Padlock would be the last person to want to see Graham com-

287

LAURA:	promise his professional integrity on his account. So he just has to sit waiting. While Graham goes off all over the world looking for natural pigments and one thing and another.
HUMPHREY:	My dear Laura, what else can he possibly do but collect the pigments? He can't paint without them. Be sensible.
LAURA:	No. (*Quietly and unemphatically after a brief pause*). But there's an artist's colourman not three doors away.
HUMPHREY:	You don't seem to understand, Laura.
LAURA:	And I can't see how it could possibly hurt his professional integrity to at least buy his brushes ready-made.
HUMPHREY:	Perhaps not, but....
LAURA:	A whole Sunday morning spent going over one camel for the sake of three or four miserable hairs! It's utterly ridiculous!
HUMPHREY:	In any case, that part of it's more or less finished. It's this wretched problem now of where to sit Colonel Padlock. How far back from the easel.
LAURA:	(*After a shocked pause*). That was decided.
HUMPHREY:	Not finally, my dear.
LAURA:	It really is too bad!
HUMPHREY:	Yes, well....
LAURA:	How many months is it since we all sat round listening to Graham explaining about "giving the background a chance" and "not letting the sitter choke the canvas" and all the rest of it?
HUMPHREY:	It's one thing to have worked something out in principle, Laura. It's a different matter putting it into practice.
LAURA:	All he has to do surely is to sit Colonel Padlock far enough back from the easel. That shouldn't take him eight weeks.
HUMPHREY:	Don't forget Colonel Padlock is travelling backwards. It's bound to slow him down a little bit.
LAURA:	*Travelling backwards?*
HUMPHREY:	You know Graham as well as I do, my dear. He doesn't often do things by halves.

(*Pause.*)

LAURA: That, I suppose, accounts for his sending home for field-glasses.

HUMPHREY: It's gone well beyond field-glasses, Laura.

LAURA: Oh? What is it now, then? Descriptions once a week by transatlantic telephone?

HUMPHREY: Every half hour, actually. By ticker tape.

LAURA: (*weakly*). I see.

HUMPHREY: Or that was the position at any rate last week. He was in Yokohama then.

LAURA: Who was in Yokohama?

HUMPHREY: Colonel Padlock.

(*Pause.*)

He's in all probability more than half-way round the globe by now.

LAURA: Oh.

(*Pause.*)

What happens when he's circled it?

HUMPHREY: They're expecting to end up back to back.

LAURA: Back to *what*?

HUMPHREY: That's if Graham's calculations are as reliable as he thinks they are.

(*Pause.*)

LAURA: I see.

HUMPHREY: And by that time he hopes to have the television cameras ready.

(*Pause.*)

Rigged up behind him.

(*Pause.*)

And if he puts the screen where he can get a clear view of it while he's painting, he can go right ahead the moment Colonel Padlock comes in range of the cameras.

(*Pause.*)

289

I think it rather appeals to Graham — the idea of painting direct from a television screen.

(*Pause.*)

It would, of course.

(*Long pause.*)

LAURA: I suppose as soon as he gets back we ought to send him a greetings telegram.

HUMPHREY: Who?

LAURA: Colonel Padlock. If he ever does.

(*Pause.*)

HUMPHREY: I suppose we ought.

Curtain

REQUEST STOP

A queue at a Request Bus Stop. A WOMAN *at the head, with a* SMALL MAN *in a raincoat next to her, two other* WOMEN *and a* MAN.

WOMAN [*to* SMALL MAN]: I beg your pardon, what did you say?

Pause.

All I asked you was if I could get a bus from here to Shepherds Bush.

Pause.

Nobody asked you to start making insinuations.

Pause.

Who do you think you are?

Pause.

Huh. I know your sort, I know your type. Don't worry, I know all about people like you.

Pause.

We can all tell where you come from. They're putting your sort inside every day of the week.

Pause.

291

All I've got to do, is report you, and you'd be standing in the dock in next to no time. One of my best friends is a plain clothes detective.

Pause.

I know all about it. Standing there as if butter wouldn't melt in your mouth. Meet you in a dark alley it'd be... another story. [*To the others, who stare into space.*] You heard what this man said to me. All I asked him was if I could get a bus from here to Shepherds Bush. [*To him.*] I've not witnesses, don't you worry about that.

Pause.

Impertinence.

Pause.

Ask a man a civil question he treats you like a threepenny bit. [*To him.*] I've got better things to do, my lad, I can assure you. I'm not going to stand here and be insulted on a public highway. Anyone can tell you're a foreigner. I was born just around the corner. Anyone can tell you're just up from the country for a bit of a lark. I know your sort.

Pause.

She goes to a LADY.

Excuse me, lady. I'm thinking of taking this man up to the magistrate's court, you heard him make that crack, would you like to be a witness?

The LADY *steps into the road.*

LADY   Taxi...

She disappears.

WOMAN. We know what sort she is. [*Back to position.*] I was the first in this queue.

Pause.

Born just round the corner. Born and bred. These people from the country haven't the faintest idea of how to behave. Peruvians. You're bloody lucky I don't put you on a charge. You ask a straightforward question — *The others suddenly thrust out their arms at a passing bus. They run off left after it. The* WOMAN, *alone, clicks her teeth and mutters. A* MAN *walks from the right to the stop, and waits. She looks at him out of the corner of her eye. At length she speaks shyly, hesitantly, with a slight smile.*

Excuse me. Do you know if I can get a bus from here... to Marble Arch?

APPLICANT

An office. LAMB, *a young man, eager, cheerful, enthusiastic, is striding nervously, alone. The door opens.* MISS PIFFS *comes in. She is the essence of efficiency.*

PIFFS: Ah, good morning.
LAMB: Oh, good morning, miss.
PIFFS: Are you Mr. Lamb?
LAMB: That's right.

PIFFS: [*studying a sheet of paper*]: Yes. You're applying for
          this vacant post, aren't you?
AMБ: I am actually, yes.
PIFFS: Are you a physicist?
LAMB: Oh yes, indeed. It's my whole life.
PIFFS: [*languidly*]: Good. Now our procedure is, that before
          we discuss the applicant's qualifications we like to
          subject him to a little test to determine his psycholog-
          ical suitability. You've no objection?
LAMB: Oh, good heavens, no.
PIFFS: Jolly good.

          MISS PIFFS *has taken some objects out of a drawer and
          goes to Lamb. She places a chair for him.*

PIFFS: Please sit down. [*He sits*]. Can I fit these to your
          palms?
LAMB: [*affably*]: What are they?
PIFFS: Electrodes.
LAMB: Oh yes, of course. Funny little things.

          She attaches them to his palms.

PIFFS: Now the earphones.

          She attaches earphones to his head.

LAMB: I say how amusing.
PIFFS: Now I plug in.

          She plugs in to the wall.

LAMB: [*a trifle nervously*]: Plug in, do you? Oh yes, of course.
          Yes, you'd have to, wouldn't you?

          MISS PIFFS *perches on a high stool and looks down on*
          LAMB.

          This help to determine my ...my suitability, does it?
PIFFS: Unquestionably. Now relax. Just relax. Don't think
          about a thing.
LAMB: No.
PIFFS: Relax completely. Rela-a-a-x. Quite relaxed?

          LAMB *nods.* MISS PIFFS *presses a button on the side of
          her stool. A piercing high pitched buzz-hum is heard.*
          LAMB *jolts rigid. His hands go to his earphones. He is*

propelled from the chair. He tries to crawl under the
chair. MISS PIFFS *watches, impassive. The noise stops.*
LAMB *peeps out from under the chair, crawls out,*
stands, twitches, emits a short chuckle and collapses in
the chair.

PIFFS: Would you say you were an excitable person?

LAMB: No — not unduly, no. Of course, I —

PIFFS: Would you say you were a moody person?

LAMB: Moody? No, I wouldn't say I was moody — well, sometimes occasionally I —

PIFFS: Do you ever get fits of depression?

LAMB: Well, I wouldn't call them depression exactly —

PIFFS: Do you often do things you regret in the morning?

LAMB: Regret? Things I regret? Well, it depends what you mean by often, really — I mean when you say often —

PIFFS: Are you often puzzled by women?

LAMB: Women?

PIFFS: Men.

LAMB: Men? Well, I was just going to answer the question about women —

PIFFS: Do you often feel puzzled?

LAMB: Puzzled?

PIFFS: By women.

LAMB: Women?

PIFFS: Men.

LAMB: Oh, now just a minute, I... Look, do you want separate answers or a joint answer?

PIFFS: After your day's work do you ever feel tired? Edgy? Fretty? Irritable? At a loose end? Morose? Frustrated? Morbid? Unable to concentrate? Unable to sleep? Unable to eat? Unable to remain seated? Unable to remain upright? Lustful? Indolent? On heat? Randy? Full of desire? Full of energy? Full of dread? Drained? of energy, of dread? of desire?

Pause.

LAMB: [*thinking*]: Well, it's difficult to say really...

PIFFS: Are you a good mixer?

LAMB: Well, you've touched on quite an interesting point
           there —

PIFFS: Do you suffer from eczema, listlessness, or falling
           coat?

LAMB: Er...

PIFFS: Are you virgo intacta?

LAMB: I beg your pardon?

PIFFS: Are you virgo intacta?

LAMB: Oh, I say, that's rather embarrassing. I mean — in
           front of a lady —

PIFFS: Are you virgo intacta?

LAMB: Yes, I am, actually. I'll make no secret of it.

PIFFS: Have you always been virgo intacta?

LAMB: Oh yes, always. Always.

PIFFS: From the word go?

LAMB: Go? Oh yes, from the word go.

PIFFS: Do women frighten you?

She presses a button on the other side of her stool.
The stage is plunged into redness, which flashes on and off in
time with her questions.

PIFFS: [*building*]: Their clothes? Their shoes? Their voices?
           Their laughter? Their stares? Their way of walking?
           Their way of sitting? Their way of smiling? Their way
           of talking? Their mouths? Their hands? Their feet?
           Their shins? Their thighs? Their knees? Their eyes?
           Their [*Drumbeat*]. Their [*Drumbeat*]. Their [*Cymbal
           bang*]. Their [*Trombone chord*]. Their [*Bass note*].

LAMB: [*in a high voice*]. Well it depends what you mean real-
           ly —

The light still flashes. She presses the other button
and the piercing buzz-hum is heard again. LAMB'S *hands go to*
his earphones. He is propelled from the chair, falls, rolls, crawls,
totters and collapses.

Silence. He lies face upwards. MISS PIFFS *looks at*
him, then walks to LAMB *and bends over him.*

PIFFS: Thank you very much, Mr. Lamb. We'll let you
           know.

MALCOLM BRADBURY

THE REDBRICK PARTY

Emma Fielding put on a wool dress, splashed herself with perfume, and set off for the English Department reception for foreign students. She was a post-graduate student in the department, and was writing a thesis on the fish imagery in Shakespeare's tragedies; there was quite a lot of fish in Shakespeare, and there was more to it, now it was being at last exposed, than you would have thought, or even Sigmund Freud would have thought. The reason for Emma's attendance at the occasion was simple; Treece was, not surprisingly, nervous of the reception and wanted to have some *reliable* people there, and there was no one more reliable in the department than Emma. Treece had, therefore, telephoned Emma and asked "if we might trespass on your time and good nature". If Emma did not have too much of the first, she had an abundance of the second; and so here she was. She was twenty-six, and therefore rather older than most of her fellow-students; older you had to say, and wiser. When you saw her, the word you thought of for her was "handsome"; she looked like the photographs you saw of Virginia Woolf, or those tall, brown-eyed fragile English beauties that fill autobiographies these days, the sort to whom it is not absurd to say, deferentially, "Do you want to go and lie down?" for, it seems, even to be what they are is enough to make them look a little tired; life is so intense.

Treece did not like beautiful women—he had suffered with them too much, in making the discovery that, in our world, to be beautiful is a way of life, which has its own customs and regulations—but he liked Emma; by not being quite beautiful she seemed to have gained everything.

The reception was being held in a large, dirty room with a splintery plank floor, decorated for the occasion with a large circle of wooden chairs and a large metal tea-urn from which Dr. Viola Masefield, likewise co-opted for the occasion, was dispensing tea to a variety of nervous students of all nationalities and colours. Treece was there, trying to get everyone to sit down; no one would. "Vot," demanded an extremely stout German student, greeting Emma with a bow as she entered, "is your vaderland?" "I'm English," said Emma. "Oho," said the German with great cheerfulness. "Then it is your task to entertain me. I am ready."

"I'll bet you are," said Emma. She went over to Dr. Masefield at the tea-urn: "Is there anything I can be doing?" she asked. "Just mingle, I think, if you would," said Dr. Masefield jovially, looking up.

"I think the English nation is much ashamed that it has imprisoned its great national bard, Oscar Vilda," said someone at her side. It was the stout German, who knew when he was on to a good thing.

"Who?" asked Emma.

"Oscar Vilda," said the German. "As told in 'The Ballad of Reading Goal.'"

"Jail," said Emma. "Jail; not goal."

"Write down, please," said the German, taking a piece of paper from his overcoat pocket; Emma did as she was bid.

Professor Treece passed at a trot. "Make them take their overcoats off," he said. He stopped and came back, painfully aware of his task, which was a word for everyone. "Good afternoon, Herr Schumann," he said. "I hope you're going to share Miss Fielding with the rest of us." He caught Emma's eye and blushed. "Oho, no," said the German. "As you say, finders, keepers. She is my *captive*."

"Well, Miss Fielding, the long vacation appears to have invigorated you a great deal. How do you do it?" went on Treece jovially.

"I went to Italy and got drunk every day on Chianti; it's very therapeutic," said Emma.

"Italy," said Treece, who had a far from Lawrentian vision of that country; he regarded it rather as a place where all moral law had long since been overthrown and where a degenerating race was having its last frantic fling. "Were you all right?"

"More or less," said Emma.

"Did you go to Rome?"

"We did," said Emma.

"There are a great many things of architectural interest in Rome," said Treece, "and the railway station is one of them."

"I have been to Rome," said Herr Schumann. The tale he was about to divulge was, however, never told, for at that moment a sudden commotion occurred in a far corner of the room; a Negro student, in an excess of nerves, had spilled a cup of tea over a reader in economics. "My word! Eborebelosa!" Treece said; and he hurried off.

"You are enjoying this party?" inquired the German. "Yes," said Emma. "I think it is a very good party," said the German. "It is permitted to kiss these girls?"

"I don't think so," said Emma. "It's only the middle of the afternoon, isn't it?" "You tell me when is the time," said the German.

"I must go and talk to somebody else," said Emma, and went over to a group of Indian students gathered in a corner. As soon as she announced her name, a sharp silence fell over the group. Their former animation turned to a comatose contemplation of each other's shoes. "You are a tall woman," said someone politely. Silence fell again.

" 'Midwinter spring is its own season'," said one of them, a nun, suddenly. "You know this quotation, of course, and how pertinent are those words, for now, as you see, the sun is shining." She pointed to the window.

"It is of T. S. Eliot," said a voice at Emma's side; it was the German, who had followed her over. " 'Lean, lean on a garden urn...' You know this too?"

Suddenly all the Indians began quoting Eliot. "A hard coming we had of it," cried one. "There were no tigers," intoned another contrapunctally.

"In India," said the nun; all the others fell silent, "the work of Mr. Eliot is very much respected; he is translated; and many people have written his thesis for his doctorate on inclinations of his work."

"In Germany too," said Herr Schumann.

"I am a graduate, of course, though it is true I have not yet received my degree certificate, and I too hope to write a doctor's thesis on the work of your distinguished poet, though he was born in the United States of America, as I expect you know. You understand his work is open to many interpretations. I am a Christian, and his work is open to Christian interpretations."

"Yes, so they tell me," said Emma.

Herr Schumann turned to Emma and, with an ostentatious bow, said: "You permit I bring you a cup of tea." "Yes, please," said Emma, feeling a little tired. "And for you also," said the German to the nun.

"Yes, please, and it will be interesting to reflect that the leaf of the tea we are about to drink comes from my own country, and perhaps indeed has been picked by a member of my numerous family. One of the best poets of the part of India from which I come—it is in the north—is at this moment at your Oxford University writing a thesis on the Oriental imagery of the poems of T. S. Eliot, and on the influence of the *Upanishads*. He has been in correspondence with Mr. Eliot himself."

"Here is your tea," said a voice behind Emma.

"And he tells me," went on the nun, "in a letter that Mr. Eliot has shown him the greatest courtesy."

There was a violent tug at the back of Emma's dress. "Here is your tea," said Herr Schumann. "Thank you," said Emma taking it.

"You have been to Germany, then?" asked the nun of Herr Schumann. "I am from Germany," said Herr Schumann. "What is your reason for coming here?" asked the nun. "It is to learn the English language and to study the literature," said Herr Schumann. "Germany has many poets," said the nun pleasantly. "There is Goethe and Heine and Rilke, to name only a few. It is very good of you to come to England, of course, since you were fighting it only a few years ago. It is very civilized of all of us to forget this so easily. I think we are all very developed persons."

300

"Yes," said the German. "I see you are a nun. I would very much like to be a nun. There are many advantages. Of course, one would have to be a woman."

Emma suddenly saw once again amid the press the face of Professor Treece, mouthing something in her direction. "Ah, Miss Fielding," she heard him say distantly. "There are..." and at once his voice was miraculously magnified; he had somehow reached her side. "...some people I want you to meet. Try and get them sitting down on chairs," he added. "Everyone's standing up, and it's making things very difficult."

Suddenly he was high up in the air, standing on a chair. "Hello, hello," he shouted. "Why doesn't everyone sit down? It's so much more comfortable." No one did; indeed, those who were sitting down became embarrassed about it and stood up. Emma felt Treece's disgrace hardly. Like most people who speculate about the moral problems of human relationships, Treece was really much worse at them than those who are not moved to cogitate; in his care to offend no one, to be honest and true to all, he moved about in a sort of social badlands, where nothing ever really grew. Intention was all. Sympathy for all these people, for being foreigners — lay over the gathering like a woolly blanket; and no one was enjoying it at all.

Foreign students' parties were things that, notoriously, didn't go well; with Treece, to whom disaster was the normal resolution of parties, they went, of course, disastrously. And so at this point on the present occasion there came a striking interruption; and people did not blame life, which could bring such interruptions, but Treece, for not foreseeing them. A group of Negroes, who had been chatting quietly in one corner, dressed in their native robes, had to pray to Allah—or someone like that—in ten minutes' time and wanted to know where there was a consecrated room. "We have no consecrated room," said Treece, embarrassed. *No consecrated rooms!* Here, said the world, is a man who gives a party for foreign students and fails to provide a consecrated room. One of the party offered to consecrate one; all he needed, he said, was a room; he could do the rest. "Boiling water is necessary," he said. Luckily Viola Masefield had a kettle full. It was finally settled that the Senior Common Room should be consecrated; one felt that there was nowhere worthier of it.

"Oh, dear," said Treece to Emma when they had all gone. "One can't foresee everything, can one? What I was saying was, if I remember rightly, that ... yes, I want you to meet one of our friends from Nigeria, a Mr. Eborebelosa. He's rather a difficult case, I'm afraid; he's already spilled a cup of tea over someone in the Economics Department...."

Then, suddenly, they all streamed in again, at the trot, the whole consecrating group. There were dogs' hairs in the Senior Common Room. "But we never have dogs in the Senior Common Room, they must be off people," said Treece, "since people are all we have there."

The Negroes consulted for an anxious moment, and then resolved to do it in the grounds; and they picked up their kettle and sallied forth. The passing traveller, wending his way along Institution Road, would have been refreshed that day with a strange sight — the sight of a group of Negroes, in long robes, ceremonially pouring hot water over one another and making obeisance on the flagstones of the courtyard.

Meanwhile Treece, trying hard to salvage what he could from the wreckage of the occasion, was endeavouring to introduce Emma to Mr. Eborebelosa. "I'd like you to meet..." he said tentatively. "No, no," said Mr. Eborebelosa, looking down. Treece turned to Emma and explained in a low voice that Eborebelosa disliked meeting people and had been closeting himself in lavatories to avoid it. Emma, grasping the problem and sincerely wanting to do something to help Treece, approached Mr. Eborebelosa again, smiling a generous smile, and his agitation grew so intense that the tea began to splash out of the cup in his hand. Emma gently took it from him, just in time, for Eborebelosa became, suddenly, loose-limbed, stepped backward a pace or two, and fell over on to his bottom. Emma took his arm and helped him to his feet. He was shivering all over. "Socially maladept," Treece's phrase for him seemed a ridiculous understatement. "How are you liking England?" asked Emma sweetly. "Not, not," said Mr. Eborebelosa. "But you haven't seen very much of it, have you?" she rebuked him. Eborebelosa tried to work up a scrap of indignation: "Yes, London, Tilbury dicks," said Mr. Eborebelosa. "Docks," said Emma. "Dicks," said Eborebelosa.

"This is a good party, I think?" said a voice by her side; it was of course Herr Schumann. "But when do we have the intoxicating liquors?"

"Leave me alone for a bit, Herr Schumann," said Emma. "Can't you see I'm busy with my friend Mr. Eborebelosa?"

"Oh," said Herr Schumann. "Oho. So that is the way wind is blowing? That is what brews, I see."

"I have friend?" said Mr. Eborebelosa, beaming all at once. He capered about for a moment.

"You have no taste," said Herr Schumann. "I would have given you cakes, chocolates, food of all natures; you have been very unwise. I have many friends in positions of great responsibility to whom I should introduce. Beware. Life will slip you by."

"I am son of a chief," said Mr. Eborebelosa. "I will give you a goat."

"In England, how shall she use a goat? In Europe there is no place for goats. We do not ride on them, we do not drink the milk; goats are defunct. We have gone past the goat. Culture has trod on."

"Now, Herr Schumann..." said Emma.

"Aha, so," said Herr Schumann. "You are his friend, yet you allow him to think he can purchase with goats. 'I want typewriter, how many goats?' You are poor friend, dear woman, I tell you so."

"You would like to wear the clothes of my country," said Eborebelosa to Emma.

"This is white woman..." said Herr Schumann; and then, catching a glint in Emma's eye, he stopped. "So what for do I beat myself to death? Women you must not trust."

Schumann withdrew in a huff, and Emma and Eborebelosa talked pleasantly on, Emma occasionally proffering the teacup to him so that he might take a sip; soon he calmed down and was able to hold it himself. By the time everyone was ready to disperse, after a hard afternoon, Mr. Eborebelosa was becoming enthusiastic about Emma's smile. "I like this smile," he kept saying. "Do it more." Emma, a thoroughly amiable personality, obliged, and Treece kept looking over at the two of them suspiciously as empty grins kept shining forth on Emma's face. Afterwards, Treece came up and congratulated her on her handling of what he called "a difficult case". "I feel really sorry for him," said Emma. "It's simply impossible, of course, to respond fairly to him; there's just no common ground." "Oh," said Treece sharply, "I wouldn't have thought that was true. Indeed, you seem to have disproved it." "Well, it's like talking to children," said Emma. "You get some pleasure out of doing it, but you never really feel you're exhibiting any part of yourself; just exercising in a void, and that just isn't good enough for you yourself." "Oh, you expect too much from life," said Treece, adding with a sweet smile: "You're just like me."

Poor, poor Treece, thought Emma; for she loved to sympathize. Poor man, he has tried to show us all that foreigners aren't funny; but they are. After all, there was one thing that every Englishman knew from his very soul, and that was that, for all experiences and all manners, in England lay the norm; England was the country that God had got to first, *properly*, and here life was taken to the point of purity, to its Platonic source, so that all ways elsewhere were underdeveloped, or impure, or overripe. Everyone in England knew this, and an occasion like the present one was not likely to prove that things had altered. I have lived in England, was the underlying statement, and I know what life is like. What you wanted to say to Treece, under such circumstances, was what Machiavelli told his prince: it is necessary for a man who wishes to maintain himself, to learn how not to be good, and when or when not to use his knowledge; here was a time when one withdrew. It was only Treece who could believe that the destiny of nations was being forged in such small and seedy rooms, with no carpet on the floor, and wooden benches for seats. As for the rest of us, we are unerringly provincial, Emma had to concede; this is just the Midlands, and we don't have to carry the burden of things like that out here.

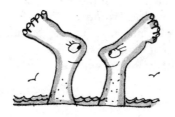

EDWARD LEAR

THE POBBLE WHO HAS NO TOES

I

The Pobble who has no toes
    Had once as many as we;
When they said, "Some day you may lose them all"; —
    He replied,— "Fish fiddle de-dee!"
And his Aunt Jobiska made him drink,
Lavender water tinged with pink,
For she said, "The World in general knows
There's nothing so good for a Pobble's toes!"

II

The Pobble who has no toes,
    Swam across the Bristol Channel;
But before he set out he wrapped his nose,
    In a piece of scarlet flannel.
For his Aunt Jobiska said, "No harm
Can come to his toes if his nose is warm;
And it's perfectly known that a Pobble's toes
Are safe,—provided he minds his nose."

307

III

The Pobble swam fast and well,
    And when boats or ships came near him
He tinkledy-binkledy-winkled a bell,
    So that all the world could hear him.
And all the Sailors and Admirals cried,
When they saw him nearing the further side,—
He has gone to fish, for his Aunt Jobiska's
Runcible Cat with crimson whiskers!"

IV

But before he touched the shore,
    The shore of the Bristol Channel,
A sea-green Porpoise carried away
    His wrapper of scarlet flannel.
And when he came to observe his feet,
Formerly garnished with toes so neat,
His face at once became forlorn
On perceiving that all his toes were gone!

V

And nobody ever knew
    From that dark day to the present,
Whoso had taken the Pobble's toes,
    In a manner so far from pleasant.
Whether the shrimps or crawfish gray,
Or crafty Mermaids stole them away—
Nobody knew; and nobody knows
How the Pobble was robbed of his twice five toes!

VI

The Pobble who has no toes
    Was placed in a friendly Bark,
And they rowed him back, and carried him up,
    To his Aunt Jobiska's Park.
And she made him a feast at his earnest wish

Of eggs and buttercups fried with fish; —
And she said, — "It's a fact the whole world knows,
That Pobbles are happier without their toes."

INCIDENTS IN THE LIFE OF
MY UNCLE ARLY

I

Oh! my aged Uncle Arly,
Sitting on a heap of barley
   Through the silent hours of night,
Close beside a leafy thicket;
On his nose there was a cricket,
In his hat a Railway-Ticket,
      (But his shoes were far too tight.)

II

Long ago, in youth, he squander'd
All his goods away, and wander'd
   To the Timskoop-hills afar.
There on golden sunsets glazing
Every evening found him gazing!
Singing, "Orb! you're quite amazing!
    How I wonder what you are!"

Like the ancient Medes and Persians,
Always by his own exertions
    He subsisted on those hills;
Whiles, by teaching children spelling,
Or at times by merely yelling,
Or at intervals by selling
    "Propter's Nicodemus Pills."

IV

Later, in his morning rambles,
He perceived the moving brambles
    Something square and white disclose:—
'T was a First-class Railway-Ticket;
But on stooping down to pick it
Off the ground, a pea-green cricket
    Settled on my uncle's nose.

V

Never, nevermore, oh! never
Did that cricket leave him ever,—
    Dawn or evening, day or night;
Clinging as a constant treasure,
Chirping with a cheerious measure,
Wholly to my uncle's pleasure,
    (Though his shoes were far too tight.)

VI

So for three and forty winters,
Till his shoes were worn to splinters
    All those hills he wander'd o'er,—
Sometimes silent, sometimes yelling;
Till he came to Borley-Melling,
Near his old ancestral dwelling,
    (But his shoes were far too tight.)

VII

On a little heap of barley
Died my aged Uncle Arly,
    And they buried him one night
Close beside the leafy thicket;
There, his hat and Railway-Ticket;
There, his ever faithful cricket;
        (But his shoes were far too tight.)

THE NUTCRACKERS AND
THE SUGAR TONGS

I

The Nutcrackers sat by a plate on the table;
    The Sugar tongs sat by a plate at his side;
And the Nutcrackers said, "Don't you wish we were able
    Along the blue hills and green meadows to ride?
Must we drag on this stupid existence forever,
    So idle and weary, so full of remorse,
While everyone else takes his pleasure, and never
    Seems happy unless he is riding a horse?

II

"Don't you think we could ride without being instructed,
    Without any saddle or bridle or spur?
Our legs are so long, and so aptly constructed,
    I'm sure that an accident could not occur.
Let us all of a sudden hop down from the table,
    And hustle downstairs, and each jump on a horse!

Shall we try? Shall we go? Do you think we are able?"
    The Sugar tongs answered distinctly, "Of course!"

III

So down the long staircase they hopped in a minute.
    The Sugar tongs snapped, and the Crackers said,
                                    "Crack!"
The stable was open; the horses were in it.
    Each took out a pony and jumped on his back.
The Cat in a fright scrambled out of the doorway;
    The Mice tumbled out of a bundle of hay;
The brown and white Rats, and the black ones from Norway
    Screamed out, "They are taking the horses away!"

IV

The whole of the household was filled with amazement:
    The Cups and the Saucers danced madly about;
The Plates and the Dishes looked out of the casement;
    The Saltcellar stood on his head with a shout;
The Spoons, with a clatter, looked out of the lattice;
    The Mustard pot climbed up the gooseberry pies;
The Soup ladle peeped through a heap of veal patties,
    And squeaked with a ladle-like scream of surprise.

V

The Frying pan said, "It's an awful delusion!"
    The Teakettle hissed, and grew black in the face;
And they all rushed downstairs in the wildest confusion
    To see the great Nutcracker-Sugar-tong race.
And out of the stable, with screamings and laughter
    (Their ponies were cream-colored, speckled with brown),
The Nutcrackers first, and the Sugar tongs after,
    Rode all round the yard, and then all round the town.

They rode through the street, and they rode by the station;
    They galloped away to the beautiful shore;
In silence they rode, and "made no observation,"
    Save this: "We will never go back any more!"
And still you might hear, till they rode out of hearing,
    The Sugar tongs nap, and the Crackers say, "Crack!"
Till, far in the distance their forms disappearing,
    They faded away; and they never came back!

THE DUCK AND THE KANGAROO

I

Said the Duck to the Kangaroo,
    "Good gracious! how you hop
Over the fields, and the water too,
    As if you never would stop!
My life is a bore in this nasty pond,
And I long to go out in the world beyond.
    I wish I could hop like you,"
    Said the Duck to the Kangaroo.

II

"Please give me a ride on your back,"
    Said the Duck to the Kangaroo.

"I would sit quite still, and say nothing but 'Quack,'
      The whole of the long day through.
And we'd go the Dee, and the Jelly Bo Lee,
Over the land and over the sea.
      Please take me a ride! Oh, do!"
      Said the Duck to the Kangaroo.

III

Said the Kangaroo to the Duck,
      "This requires some little reflection.
Perhaps, on the whole, it might bring me luck,
      And there seems but one objection;
Which is, if you'll let me speak so bold,
Your feet are unpleasantly wet and cold,
      And would probably give me the roo —
      Matiz," said the Kangaroo.

IV

Said the Duck, "As I sat on the rocks,
      I have thought over that completely;
And I bought four pairs of worsted socks,
      Which fit my web feet neatly.
And, to keep out the cold, I've bought a cloak,
And every day a cigar I'll smoke,
      All to follow my own dear true
      Love of a Kangaroo."

V

Said the Kangaroo, "I'm ready,
      All in the moonlight pale.
But to balance me well, dear Duck, sit steady,
      And quite at the end of my tail."
So away they went with a hop and a bound.
And they hopped the whole world three times round.
      And who so happy, oh! who,
      As the Duck and the Kangaroo?

AN ALPHABET

The Absolutely Abstemious Ass,
who resided in a Barrel, and only lived on
Soda Water and Pickled Cucumbers.

The Bountiful Beetle,
who always carried a Green Umbrella when it didn't rain,
and left it home when it did.

The Comfortable Confidential Cow,
who sat in her Red Morocco Armchair and
toasted her own Bread at the parlor Fire.

The Dolomphious Duck,
who caught Spotted Frogs for her dinner
with a Runcible Spoon.

The Enthusiastic Elephant,
who ferried himself across the water with the
Kitchen Poker and a New pair of Earrings.

The Fizzgiggious Fish,
who always walked about upon Stilts,
because he had no legs.

The Good-natured Gray Gull,
who carried the Old Owl and his Crimson Carpetbag
across the river, because he could not swim.

The Hasty Higgeldipiggledy Hen,
who went to market in a Blue Bonnet and Shawl,
and bought a Fish for her Supper.

The Inventive Indian,
who caught a Remarkable Rabbit in a
Stupendous Silver Spoon.

The Judicious Jubilant Jay,
who did up her Back Hair every morning with a Wreath of
Roses,
Three feathers, and a Gold Pin.

The Kicking Kangaroo,
who wore a Pale Pink Muslin dress
with Blue spots.

The Lively Learned Lobster,
who mended his own Clothes with
a Needle and Thread.

The Melodious Meritorious Mouse,
who played a merry minuet on the
Pianoforte.

The Nutritious Newt,
who purchased a Round Plum Pudding
for his granddaughter.

The Obsequious Ornamental Ostrich,
who wore Boots to keep his
feet quite dry.

The Perpendicular Purple Polly,
who read the Newspaper and ate Parsnip Pie
with his Spectacles.

The Queer Querulous Quail,
who smoked a Pipe of Tobacco on the top of
a Tin Teakettle.

The Rural Runcible Raven,
who wore a White Wig and flew away
with the Carpet Broom.

The Scroobious Snake,
who always wore a Hat on his Head, for
fear he should bite anybody.

The Tumultuous Tom-tommy Tortoise,
who beat a Drum all day long in the
middle of the wilderness.

The Umbrageous Umbrella-maker,
whose Face nobody ever saw, because it was
always covered by his Umbrella.

The Visibly Vicious Vulture,
who wrote some Verses to a Veal Cutlet in a
Volume bound in Vellum.

The Worrying Whizzing Wasp,
who stood on a Table, and played sweetly on a
Flute with a Morning Cap.

The Excellent Double-extra XX
imbibing King Xerxes, who lived a
long while ago.

The Yonghy-Bonghy-Bo,
whose Head was ever so much bigger than his
Body, and whose Hat was rather small.

The Zigzag Zealous Zebra,
who carried five monkeys on his back all
the way to Jellibolee.

LIMERICKS

There was a Young Person of Smyrna
Whose Grandmother threatened to burn her.
But she seized on the Cat and said, "Granny, burn that!
You incongruous Old Woman of Smyrna!"

* * *

There was an Old Man with a gong
Who bumped at it all the day long.
But they called out, "Oh, law! You're a horrid old bore!"
So they smashed that Old Man with a gong.

* * *

There was an Old Man of Columbia
Who was thirsty and called out for some beer.
But they brought it quite hot, in a small copper pot,
Which disgusted that man of Columbia.

* * *

There was an Old Man in a tree
Who was horribly bored by a Bee.
When they said, "Does it buzz?" he replied, "Yes, it does!
It's a regular brute of a Bee."

There was a Young Lady whose chin
Resembled the point of a pin;
So she had it made sharp and purchased a harp,
And played several tunes with her chin.

* * *

There was an Old Man of Madras
Who rode on a cream-coloured Ass;
But the length of its ears so promoted his fears
That it killed that Old Man of Madras.

* * *

There was a Young Lady whose nose
Was so long that it reached to her toes,
So she hired an Old Lady, whose conduct was steady,
To carry that wonderful nose.

* * *

There was a Young Lady of Norway
Who casually sat in a doorway.
When the door squeezed her flat, she exclaimed, "What of
that?"
This courageous Young Lady of Norway.

* * *

There was an Old Person of Philae
Whose conduct was scroobious and wily.
He rushed up a Palm when the weather was calm
And observed all the ruins of Philae.

* * *

There was an Old Person of Tring
Who embellished his nose with a ring.

He gazed at the moon every evening in June,
That ecstatic Old Person of Tring.

* * *

There was a Young Lady of Lucca
Whose lovers completely forsook her.
She ran up a tree, and said, "Fiddle-de-dee!"
Which embarrassed the people of Lucca.

* * *

There was an Old Lady whose folly
Induced her to sit in a holly;
Whereon, by a thorn her dress being torn,
She quickly became melancholy.

* * *

There was an Old Man on some rocks
Who shut his Wife up in a box.
When she said, "Let me out," he exclaimed, "Without doubt
You will pass all your life in that box."

* * *

There was an Old Man who said, "How
Shall I flee from this horrible Cow?
I will sit on this stile, and continue to smile,
Which may soften the heart of that Cow."

* * *

There was a Young Lady of Russia
Who screamed so that no one could hush her.
Her screams were extreme — no one heard such a scream
As was screamed by that Lady of Russia.

There was an Old Man of Whitehaven
Who danced a quadrille with a Raven.
But they said, "It's absurd to encourage this bird!"
So they smashed that Old Man of Whitehaven.

* * *

There was an Old Lady of Prague
Whose language was horribly vague.
When they said, "Are these caps?" she answered, "Perhaps!"
That oracular Lady of Prague.

* * *

There was a Young Lady of Parma
Whose conduct grew calmer and calmer.
When they said, "Are you dumb?" she merely said, "Hum!"
That provoking Young Lady of Parma.

* * *

There was a Young Person of Crete
Whose toilette was far from complete.
She dressed in a sack spickle-speckled with black,
That ombliferous Person of Crete.

* * *

There was an Old Man with an Owl
Who continued to bother and howl.
He sat on a rail, and imbibed bitter ale,
Which refreshed that Old Man and his Owl.

* * *

There was a Young Lady whose eyes
Were unique as to color and size.
When she opened them wide, people all turned aside,
And started away in surprise.

LEWIS CARROLL

THE MAD GARDENER'S SONG

He thought he saw an Elephant,
    That practised on a fife:
He looked again, and found it was
    A letter from his wife.
"At length I realise," he said,
    "The bitterness of Life!"

He thought he saw a Buffalo
    Upon the chimney-piece:
He looked again, and found it was
    His Sister's Husband's Niece,
"Unless you leave this house," he said,
    "I'll send for the Police!"

He thought he saw a Rattlesnake
    That questioned him in Greek:
He looked again, and found it was
    The Middle of Next Week.
"The one thing I regret," he said,
    "Is that it cannot speak!"

He thought he saw a Banker's Clerk
    Descending from the 'bus:

He looked again, and found it was
    A Hippopotamus.
"If this should stay to dine," he said,
    "There won't be much for us!"

He thought he saw a Kangaroo
    That worked a coffee-mill:
He looked again, and found it was
    A Vegetable-Pill.
"Were I to swallow this," he said,
    "I should be very ill!"

He thought he saw a Coach-and-Four
    That stood beside his bed:
He looked again, and found it was
    A Bear without a Head.

"Poor thing," he said, "poor silly thing!
    It's waiting to be fed!"
He thought he saw an Albatross
    That fluttered round the lamp:

He looked again, and found it was
    A Penny-Postage-Stamp.
"You'd best be getting home," he said,
    "The nights are very damp!"

He thought he saw a Garden-Door
    That opened with a key:
He looked again, and found it was
    A Double Rule of Three:
"And all its mystery," he said,
    "Is clear as day to me!"

He thought he saw an Argument
    That proved he was the Pope:
He looked again, and found it was
    A Bar of Mottled Soap.
"A fact so dread," he faintly said,
    "Extinguishes all hope!"

* * *

How doth the little crocodile
    Improve his shining tail,
And pour the waters of the Nile
    On every golden scale!

How cheerfully he seems to grin,
    How neatly spreads his claws,
And welcomes little fishes in
    With gently smiling jaws!

HUMPTY DUMPTY'S RECITATION

In winter, when the fields are white,
I sing this song for your delight—

In spring, when woods are getting green,
I'll try and tell you what I mean.

In summer, when the days are long,
Perhaps you'll understand the song:

In autumn, when the leaves are brown,
Take pen and ink, and write it down.

I sent a message to the fish:
I told them "This is what I wish."

The little fishes of the sea,
They sent an answer back to me.

The little fishes' answer was
"We cannot do it, Sir, because ——"

I sent to them again to say
"It will be better to obey."

The fishes answered with a grin,
"Why, what a temper you are in!"

I told them once, I told them twice:
They would not listen to advice.

I took a kettle large and new,
Fit for the deed I had to do.

My heart went hop, my heart went thump;
I filled the kettle at the pump.

Then someone came to me and said
"The little fishes are in bed."

I said to him, I said it plain,
"Then you must wake them up again."

I said it very loud and clear;
I went and shouted in his ear.

But he was very stiff and proud;
He said: "You needn't shout so loud!"

And he was very proud and stiff;
He said: "I'd go and wake them, if——"

I took a corkscrew from the shelf:
I went to wake them up myself.

And when I found the door was locked,
I pulled and pushed and kicked and knocked.

And when I found the door was shut,
I tried to turn the handle, but——

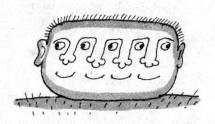

HIAWATHA'S PHOTOGRAPHING

From his shoulder Hiawatha
Took the camera of rosewood,
Made of sliding, folding rosewood;
Neatly put it all together,
In its case it lay compactly,
Folded into nearly nothing;

But he opened out the hinges,
Pushed and pulled the joints and hinges,
Till it looked all squares and oblongs,
Like a complicated figure
In the second book of Euclid.

   This he perched upon a tripod,
And the family in order
Sat before him for their pictures.
Mystic, awful was the process.

   First a piece of glass he coated
With Collodion, and plunged it
In a bath of Lunar Caustic
Carefully dissolved in water:
There he left it certain minutes.

   Secondly, my Hiawatha
Made with cunning hand a mixture
Of the acid Pyro-gallic,
And of Glacial Acetic,
And of Alcohol and water:
This developed all the picture.

   Finally, he fixed each picture
With a saturate solution
Of a certain salt of Soda —
Chemists call it Hyposulphite.
(Very difficult the name is
For a metre like the present,
But periphrasis has done it.)

   All the family in order
Sat before him for their pictures.
Each in turn, as he was taken,
Volunteered his own suggestions,
His invaluable suggestions.

MY FANCY

I painted her a gushing thing,
    With years perhaps a score;
I little thought to find they were
    At least a dozen more;
My fancy gave her eyes of blue,
    A curly auburn head:
I came to find the blue a green,
    The auburn turned to red.

She boxed my ears this morning,
    They tingled very much;
I own that I could wish her
    A somewhat lighter touch;
And if you were to ask me how
    Her charms might be improved,
I would not have them *added to*,
    But just a few *removed!*

She has the bear's ethereal grace,
    The bland hyena's laugh,
The footstep of the elephant,
    The neck of the giraffe;
I love her still, believe me,
    Though my heart its passion hides;

"She's all my fancy painted her,"
But oh! *how much besides!*

WHAT TOTTLES MEANT

"One thousand pounds per annuum
Is not so bad a figure, come!"
Cried Tottles. "And I tell you, flat,
A man may marry well on that!
To say 'the Husband needs the Wife'
Is *not* the way to represent it.
The crowning joy of Woman's life
Is *Man!*" said Tottles (and he meant it).

The blissful Honeymoon is past:
The Pair have settled down at last:
Mamma-in-law their home will share,
And make their happiness her care.
"Your income is an ample one:
Go it, my children!" (And they went it).
"I *rayther* think this kind of fun
Won't last!" said Tottles (and he meant it).

They took a little country-box——
A box at Covent Garden also:
They lived a life of double-knocks,
Acquaintances began to call so:
Their London house was much the same
(It took three hundred, clear, to rent it):
"Life is a very jolly game!"
Cried happy Tottles (and he meant it).

"Contented with a frugal lot"
(He always used that phrase at Gunter's),
He bought a handy little yacht—
A dozen serviceable hunters—
The fishing of a Highland Loch—
A sailing-boat to circumvent it—

329

"The sounding of that Gaelic 'och'
Beats *me!*" said Tottles (and he meant it).

But oh, the worst of human ills
(Poor Tottles found) are "little bills"!
And, with no balance in the Bank,
What wonder that his spirits sank?
Still, as the money flowed away,
He wondered how on earth she spent it.
"You cost me twenty pounds a day,
At least!" cried Tottles (and he meant it).

She sighed. "Those Drawing Rooms, you know!
I really never thought about it:
Mamma declared we ought to go —
We should be Nobodies without it.
That diamond circlet for my brow —
I quite believed that *she* had sent it,
Until the Bill came in just now ——"
"*Viper!*" cried Tottles (and he meant it).

Poor Mrs. T. could bear no more,
But fainted flat upon the floor.
Mamma-in-law, with anguish wild,
Seeks, all in vain, to rouse her child.
"Quick! Take this box of smelling-salts!
Don't scold her, James, or you'll repent it,
She's a *dear* girl, with all her faults ——"
"She *is!*" groaned Tottles (and he meant it).

"I was a donkey," Tottles cried,
"To choose your daughter for my bride!
'Twas *you* that bid us cut a dash!
'Tis *you* have brought us to this smash!
You don't suggest one single thing
That can in any way prevent it —
Then what's the use of arguing?
Shut up!" cried Tottles (and he meant it).

"And, now the mischief's done, perhaps
You'll kindly go and pack your traps?

Since *two* (your daughter and your son)
Are Company, but *three* are none.
A course of saving we'll begin:
When change is needed, *I'll* invent it;
Don't think to put *your* finger in
This pie!" cried Tottles (and he meant it).

See now this couple settled down
In quiet lodgings, out of town:
Submissively the tearful wife
Accepts a plain and humble life:
Yet begs one boon on bended knee:
"My ducky-darling, don't resent it!
Mamma might come for two or three——"
"NEVER!" yelled Tottles. And he meant it.

ALFRED EDWARD HOUSMAN

INFANT INNOCENCE

The Grizzly Bear is huge and wild;
He has devoured the infant child.
The infant child is not aware
He has been eaten by the bear.

FRAGMENT OF A GREEK TRAGEDY

Alcmoen.   *Chorus*

CHO. O suitably-attired-in-leather-boots
Head of a traveller, wherefore seeking whom
Whence by what way how purposed art thou come
To this well-nightingaled vicinity?
My object in enquiring is to know.
But if you happen to be deaf and dumb
And do not understand a word I say,
Then wave your hand, to signify as much.

ALC. I journeyed hither a Bœotian road.

CHO. Sailing on horseback, or with feet for oars?

ALC. Plying with speed my partnership of legs.

CHO. Beneath a shining or a rainy Zeus?

ALC. Mud's sister, not himself, adorns my shoes.

CHO. To learn your name would not displease me much.

ALC. Not all that men desire do they obtain.

CHO. Might I then hear at what your presence shoots?

ALC. A shepherd's questioned mouth informed me that —

CHO. What? for I know not yet what you will say —

ALC. Nor will you ever, if you interrupt.

CHO. Proceed, and I will hold my speechless tongue.

ALC. — This house was Eriphyla's, no one's else.

CHO. Nor did he shame his throat with hateful lies.

ALC. May I then enter, passing through the door?
CHO. Go, chase into the house a lucky foot.
    And, O my son, be, on the one hand, good,
    And do not, on the other hand, be bad;
    For that is very much the safest plan.
ALC. I go into the house with heels and speed.

Chorus

In speculation   *Strophe*
I would not willingly acquire a name
    For ill-digested thought;
    But after pondering much
To this conclusion I at last have come:
      Life is uncertain.
    This truth I have written deep
    In my reflective midriff
    On tablets not of wax,
Nor with a pen did I inscribe it there,
For many reasons: *Life, I say, is not*
      A stranger to uncertainty.
Not from the flight of omen-yelling fowls
    This fact did I discover.
Not did the Delphic tripod bark it out,
    Nor yet Dodona.
Its native ingenuity sufficed
    My self-taught diaphragm.

Why should I mention   *Antistrophe*
The Inachean daughter, loved of Zeus?
    Her whom of old the gods,
    More provident than kind,
Provided with four hoofs, two horns, one tail,
    A gift not asked for
    And sent her forth to learn
    The unfamiliar science
    Of how to chew the cud.
She therefore, all about the Argive fields,
Went cropping pale green grass and nettle-tops,
    Nor did they disagree with her.
But yet, howe'er nutritious, such repasts
    I do not hanker after:

334

Never may Cypris for her seat select
    My dappled liver!
Why should I mention Io? Why indeed?
    I have no notion why.

    But now does my boding heart,   *Epode*
    Unhired, unaccompanied, sing
    A strain not meet for the dance.
    Yea even the palace appears
    To my yoke of circular eyes
    (The right, nor omit I the left)
    Like a slaughterhouse, so to speak,
    Garnished with woolly deaths
    And many shipwrecks of cows.
I therefore in a Cissian strain lament;
    And to the rapid,
Loud, linen-tattering thumps upon my chest
    Resounds in concert
The battering of my unlucky head.

ERIPHYLA (*within*). O, I am smitten with a hatchet's jaw;
    And that in deed and not in word alone.
CHO. I thought I heard a sound within the house
    Unlike the voice of one that jumps for joy.
ERI. He splits my skull, not in a friendly way,
    One more: he purposes to kill me dead.
CHO. I would not be reputed rash, but yet
    I doubt if all be gay within the house.
ERI. O! O! another stroke! that makes the third.
    He stabs me to the heart against my wish.
CHO. If that be so, thy state of health is poor;
    But thine arithmetic is quite correct.

THE SHADES OF NIGHT

    The shades of night were falling fast
    And the rain was falling faster
    When through an Alpine village passed
    An Alpine village pastor.

RUDYARD KIPLING

MY RIVAL

I go to concert, party, ball—
    What profit is in these?
I sit alone against the wall
    And strive to look at ease.
The incense that is mine by right
    They burn before her shrine;
And that's because I'm seventeen
    And She is forty-nine.

I cannot check my girlish blush,
    My colour comes and goes.
I redden to my finger-tips,
    And sometimes to my nose.
But She is white where white should be,
    And red where red should shine.
The blush that flies at seventeen
    Is fixed at forty-nine.

I wish *I* had her constant cheek:
    I wish that I could sing
All sorts of funny little songs,
    Not quite the proper thing.
I'm very *gauche* and very shy,

336

Her jokes aren't in my line;
And worst of all, I'm seventeen
    While She is forty-nine.

The young men come, the young men go,
    Each pink and white and neat,
She's older than their mothers, but
    They grovel at Her feet.
They walk beside Her 'rickshaw-wheels—
    None ever walk by mine;
And that's because I'm seventeen
    And She is forty-nine.

She rides with half a dozen men
    (She calls them "boys" and "mashes"),
I trot along the Mall alone;
    My prettiest frocks and sashes
Don't help to fill my programme-card,
    And vainly I repine
From ten to two A. M. Ah me!
    Would I were forty-nine!

She calls me "darling," "pet," and "dear,"
    And "sweet retiring maid."
I'm always at the back, I know—
    She puts me in the shade.
She introduces me to men—
    "Cast" lovers, I opine;
For sixty takes to seventeen,
    Nineteen to forty-nine.

But even She must older grow
    And end Her dancing days,
She can't go on for ever so
    At concerts, balls, and plays.
One ray of priceless hope I see
    Before my footsteps shine;
Just think, that She'll be eighty-one
    When I am forty-nine!

337

NATURAL THEOLOGY

PRIMITIVE

I ate my fill of a whale that died
    And stranded after a month at sea...
There is a pain in my inside.
    Why have the Gods afflicted me?
Ow! I am purged till I am a wraith!
    Wow! I am sick till I cannot see!
What is the sense of Religion and Faith?
    Look how the Gods have afflicted me!

PAGAN

How can the skin of rat or mouse hold
    Anything more than a harmless flea?...
The burning plague has taken my household.
    Why have my Gods afflicted me?
All my kith and kin are deceased,
    Though they were as good as good could be.
I will out and batter the family priest,
    Because my Gods have afflicted me!

MEDIÆVAL

My privy and well drain into each other
    After the custom of Christendie... .

Fevers and fluxes are wasting my mother.
 Why has the Lord afflicted me?
The Saints are helpless for all I offer —
 So are the clergy I used to fee.
Henceforward I keep my cash in my coffer,
 Because the Lord has afflicted me.

MATERIAL

I run eight hundred hens to the acre,
 They die by dozens mysteriously... .
I am more than doubtful concerning my Maker.
 Why has the Lord afflicted me?
What a return for all my endeavour —
 Not to mention the L. S. D.!
I am an atheist now and for ever,
 Because this God has afflicted me!

PROGRESSIVE

Money spent on an Army or Fleet
 Is homicidal lunacy... .
My son has been killed in the Mons retreat.
 Why has the Lord afflicted me?
Why are murder, pillage and arson
 And rape allowed by the Deity?
I will write to the *Times*, deriding our parson,
 Because my God has afflicted me.

CHORUS

We had a kettle: we let it leak:
 Our not repairing it made it worse.
We haven't had any tea for a week...
 The bottom is out of the Universe!

CONCLUSION

This was none of the good Lord's pleasure,
    For the Spirit He breathed in Man is free;
But what comes after is measure for measure
    And not a God that afflicted thee.
As was the sowing so the reaping.
    Is now and evermore shall be.
Thou art delivered to thine own keeping.
    Only Thyself hath afflicted thee!

HILAIRE BELLOC

ON SLOP: A POET

Where Mr. Slop particularly shines
Is in his six sonorous single lines.
Perhaps where he is less successful is
In all the other verses. These are his.

ON HYGIENE

Of old when folk lay sick and sorely tried
The doctors gave them physic, and they died.
But here's a happier age: for now we know
Both how to make men sick and keep them so.

ON BENICIA: WHO WISHED HIM WELL

Benicia wished me well; I wished her well.
And what I wished her more I may not tell.

ON CHELSEA

I am assured by Dauber's wife
That Dauber's always true to life.
I think his wife would far prefer
That Dauber should be true to her.

ON A PURITAN

He served his God so faithfully and well
That now he sees him face to face, in hell.

ON A GREAT NAME

I heard to-day Godolphin say
He never gave himself away.
Come, come, Godolphin, scion of kings,
Be generous in little things.

*   *   *

Is there any reward?
    I'm beginning to doubt it.
I am broken and bored,
    Is there any reward?
Reassure me, Good Lord,
    And inform me about it.
Is there any reward?
    I'm beginning to doubt it.

HABITATIONS

Kings live in Palaces, and Pigs in sties,
And youth in Expectation. Youth is wise.

TALKING OF BAD VERSE

William, you vary greatly in your verse;
Some's none too good, but all the rest is worse.

LORD LUNDY

WHO WAS TOO FREELY MOVED TO TEARS, AND THEREBY RUINED HIS POLITICAL CAREER

Lord Lundy from his earliest years
Was far too freely moved to Tears.
For instance, if his Mother said,
"Lundy! It's time to go to Bed!"
He bellowed like a Little Turk.
Or if his father, Lord Dunquerque,
Said, "Hi!" in a Commanding Tone,

"Hi, Lundy! Leave the Cat alone!"
Lord Lundy, letting go its tail,
Would raise so terrible a wail
As moved his Grandpapa the Duke
To utter the severe rebuke:
"When I, Sir! was a little Boy,
An Animal was not a Toy!"

His father's Elder Sister, who
Was married to a Parvenoo,
Confided to Her Husband, "Brat!
The Miserable, Peevish Brat!
Why don't they drown the Little Beast?"
Suggestions which, to say the least,
Are not what we expect to hear
From Daughters of an English Peer.
His grandmamma, His Mother's Mother,
Who had some dignity or other,
The Garter, or no matter what,
I can't remember all the Lot!
Said, "Oh! that I were Brisk and Spry
To give him that for which to cry!"
(An empty wish, alas! for she
Was Blind and nearly ninety-three).

The Dear old Butler thought — but there!
I really neither know nor care
For what the Dear Old Butler thought!
In my opinion, Butlers ought
To know their place, and not to play
The Old Retainer night and day.
I'm getting tired and so are you,
Let's cut the Poem into two!

*

LORD LUNDY

(Second Canto)

It happened to Lord Lundy then,
As happens to so many men:
Towards the age of twenty-six,

They shoved him into politics;
In which profession he commanded
The income that his rank demanded
In turn as Secretary for
India, the Colonies, and War.
But very soon his friends began
To doubt if he were quite the man:
Thus, if a member rose to say
(As members do from day to day),
"Arising out of that reply...!"
Lord Lundy would begin to cry.
A Hint at harmless little jobs
Would shake him with convulsive sobs.

While as for Revelations, these
Would simply bring him to his knees,
And leave him whimpering like a child.
It drove his Colleagues raving wild!
They let him sink from Post to Post,
From fifteen hundred at the most
To eight, and barely six — and then
To be Curator of Big Ben!...
And finally there came a Threat
To oust him from the Cabinet!

The Duke — his aged grand-sire — bore
The shame till he could bear no more.
He rallied his declining powers,
Summoned the youth to Brackley Towers,
And bitterly addressed him thus —
"Sir! you have disappointed us!
We had intended you to be
The next Prime Minister but three:
The stocks were sold; the Press was squared;
The Middle Class was quite prepared.
But as it is!... My language fails!
Go out and govern New South Wales!"

*

The Aged Patriot groaned and died:
And gracious! how Lord Lundy cried!

LORD LUCKY

Lord Lucky, by a curious fluke,
Became a most important duke.
From living in a vile Hotel
A long way east of Camberwell
He rose, in less than half an hour,
To riches, dignity and power.
It happened in the following way: —
The Red Duke went out one day
To shoot with several people, one
Of whom had never used a gun.
This gentleman (a Mr. Meyer
Of Rabley Abbey, Rutlandshire),
As he was scrambling through the brake,
Discharged his weapon by mistake,
And plugged about an ounce of lead
Piff-bang into his Grace's Head —
Who naturally fell down dead.
His Heir, Lord Ugly, roared, "You Brute!
Take that to teach you how to shoot!"
Whereat he volleyed, left and right;
But being somewhat short of sight,
His right-hand Barrel only got
The second heir, Lord Poddleplot;
The while the left-hand charge (or choke)
Accounted for another bloke,
Who stood with an astounded air
Bewildered by the whole affair

—And was the third remaining heir.
After the Execution (which
Is something rare among the Rich)
Lord Lucky, while of course he needed
Some help to prove his claim, succeeded.
—But after his succession, though
All this was over years ago,
He only once indulged the whim
Of asking Meyer to lunch with him.

LORD RUMBO AND LORD JUMBO

Lord Rumbo was a Democrat
Who wore a very curious hat
And woollen boots, and didn't think
It right to smoke or take a drink.

He also thought it rather wrong
To hum the chorus of a song.
But what he simply couldn't stand
Was Billiard Tables off the Strand.

Yes! Billiard Tables off the Strand!
Lord Jumbo, on the other hand,
Was quite another sort of cove.
What? Yes by God!—and also Jove.

He was a Tory thick and thin.
His hat was made of Beaver Skin.
He practised every kind of sport
And drank a dreadful deal of Port.

THE YAK

As a friend to the children commend me the Yak.
    You will find it exactly the thing:
It will carry and fetch, you can ride on its back,
    Or lead it about with a string.

The Tartar who dwells on the plains of Thibet
    (A desolate region of snow)
Has for centuries made it a nursery pet,
    And surely the Tartar should know!

Then tell your papa where the Yak can be got,
    And if he is awfully rich
He will buy you the creature — or else he will *not*.
    (I cannot be positive which.)

THE MARMOZET

The species Man and Marmozet
    Are intimately linked;
The Marmozet survives as yet,
    But Men are all extinct.

THE FROG

Be kind and tender to the Frog,
    And do not call him names,
As "Slimy skin," or "Polly-wog,"
    Or likewise "Ugly James,"
Or "Gape-a-grin," or "Toad-gone-wrong,"

Or "Billy Bandy-knees":
The Frog is justly sensitive
    To epithets like these.
No animal will more repay
    A treatment kind and fair;
At least so lonely people say
Who keep a frog (and, by the way,
They are extremely rare).

THE LEARNED FISH

This learned Fish has not sufficient brains
To go into the water when it rains.

FROM "A MORAL ALPHABET"

* * *

O stands for Oxford. Hail! salubrious seat
Of learning! Academical Retreat!
Home of my Middle Age! Malarial Spot
Which People call Medeaval (though it's not).
The marshes in the neighbourhood can vie
With Cambridge, but the town itself is dry,
And serves to make a kind of Fold or Pen
Wherein to herd a lot of Learned Men.

Were I to write but half of what they know,
It would exhaust the space reserved for "O";
And, as my book must not be over big,
I turn at once to "P", which stands for Pig.

MORAL

Be taught by this to speak with moderation
Of places where, with decent application,
One gets a good, sound, middle-class education.

* * *

P stands for Pig, as I remarked before,
A second cousin to the Huge Wild Boar.
But Pigs are civilised, while Huge Wild Boars
Live savagely, at random, out of doors,
And, in their coarse contempt for dainty foods,
Subsist on Truffles, which they find in woods.
Not so the cultivated Pig, who feels
The need of several courses at his meals,
But wrongly thinks it does not matter whether
He takes them one by one or all together.
Hence, Pigs devour, from lack of self-respect,
What Epicures would certainly eject.

MORAL

Learn from the Pig to take whatever Fate
Or Elder Persons heap upon your plate.

* * *

R the Reviewer, reviewing my book,
At which he had barely intended to look;

But the very first lines upon "A" were enough
To convince him the Verses were excellent stuff.
So he wrote, without stopping, for several days
In terms of extreme but well-merited Praise.
To quote but one Passage: "No Person" (says he)
"Will be really content without purchasing three,
While a Parent will send for a dozen or more,
And strew them about on the Nursery Floor.
The Versification might call for some strictures
Were it not for its singular wit; while the Pictures,
Tho' the handling of line is a little defective,
Make up amply in *verve* what they lack in perspective."

MORAL

The habit of constantly telling the Truth
Will lend an additional lustre to Youth.

REBECCA
WHO SLAMMED DOORS FOR FUN AND
PERISHED MISERABLY

A Trick that everyone abhors
In Little Girls is slamming Doors,
A Wealthy Banker's Little Daughter
Who lived in Palace Green, Bayswater
(By name Rebecca Offendort),
Was given to this Furious Sport.

She would deliberately go
And Slam the door like Billy-Ho!
To make her Uncle Jacob start.
She was not really bad at heart,
But only rather rude and wild:
She was an aggravating child...

It happened that a Marble Bust
Of Abraham was standing just
Above the Door this little Lamb
Had carefully prepared to Slam,
And Down it came! It knocked her flat!
It laid her out! She looked like that.

*

Her funeral Sermon (which was long
And followed by a Sacred Song)
Mentioned her Virtues, it is true,
But dwelt upon her Vices too,
And showed the Dreadful End of One
Who goes and slams the door for Fun.

*

The children who were brought to hear
The awful Tale from far and near
Were much impressed, and inly swore
They never more would slam the Door.
— As often they had done before.

GODOLPHIN HORNE WNO
WAS CURSED WITH THE SIN OF PRIDE,
AND BECAME A BOOT-BLACK

Godolphin Horne was Nobly Born;
He held the Human Race in Scorn,
And lived with all his Sisters where
His Father lived, in Berkeley Square.
And oh! the Lad was Deathly Proud!
He never shook your Hand or bowed,
But merely smirked and nodded thus:

How perfectly ridiculous!
Alas! That such Affected Tricks
Should flourish in a Child of Six!
(For such was Young Godolphin's age).
Just then, the Court required a Page,
Whereat the Lord High Chamberlain
(The Kindest and the Best of Men),
He went good-naturedly and took
A Perfectly Enormous Book
Called *People Qualified to Be
Attendant on His Majesty*,
And murmured, as he scanned the list
(To see that no one should be missed),
"There's William Coutts has got the Flu,
And Billy Higgs would never do,
And Guy de Vere is far too young,
And ... wasn't D'Alton's Father hung?
And as for Alexander Byng!—...
I think I know the kind of thing,
A Churchman, cleanly, nobly born,
Come let us say Godolphin Horne?"
But hardly had he said the word
When Murmurs of Dissent were heard.
The King of Iceland's Eldest Son
Said,"Thank you! I am taking none!"
The Aged Duchess of Athlone
Remarked, in her sub-acid tone,
"I doubt if He is what we need!"
With which the Bishops all agreed;
And even Lady Mary Flood
(So Kind, and oh! so *really* good)
Said, "No! He wouldn't do at all,
He'd make us feel a lot too small."
The Chamberlain said, "...Well, well, well!
No doubt you're right... One cannot tell!"
He took his Gold and Diamond Pen
And scratched Godolphin out again.
So now Godolphin is the Boy
Who blacks the Boots at the Savoy.

GILBERT KEITH CHESTERTON

DOLORES REPLIES TO SWINBURNE

Cold passions, and perfectly cruel,
    Long odes that go on for an hour,
With a most economical jewel
    And a quite metaphorical flower.
I implore you to stop it and stow it,
    I adjure you, relent and refrain,
Oh, pagan Priapean poet,
              You give me a pain.

I am sorry, old dear, if I hurt you,
    No doubt it is all very nice
With the lilies and languors of virtue
    And the raptures and roses of vice.
But the notion impels me to anger,
    That vice is all rapture for me,
And if you think virtue is languor
              Just try it and see.

We shall know when the critics discover
    If your poems were shallow or deep;
Who read you from cover to cover,

355

Will know if they sleep not or sleep.
But you say I've endured through the ages
    (Which is rude) as Our Lady of Pain,
You have said it for several pages,
                        So say it again.

VARIATIONS OF AN AIR:

Composed on Having to Appear in a Pageant
as Old King Cole.

Old King Cole was a merry old soul,
And a merry old soul was he;
He called for his pipe,
He called for his bowl,
And he called for his fiddlers three.

AFTER LORD TENNYSON

Cole, that unwearied prince of Colchester,
Growing more gay with age and with long days
Deeper in laughter and desire of life,
As that Virginian climber on our walls
Flames scarlet with the fading of the year;
Called for his wassail and that other weed
Virginian also, from the Western woods
Where English Raleigh checked the boats of Spain,
And lighting joy with joy, and piling up
Pleasure as crown for pleasure, bade men bring
Those three, the minstrels whose emblazoned coats
Shone with the oyster-shells of Colchester;
And these three played, and playing grew more fain
Of mirth and music; till the heathen came,
And the King slept beside the northern sea.

AFTER W. B. YEATS

Of an old King in a story
    From the grey sea-folk I have heard,
Whose heart was no more broken
    Than the wings of a bird.

As soon as the moon was silver
    And the thin stars began,
He took his pipe and his tankard,
    Like an old peasant man.

And three tall shadows were with him
    And came at his command;
And played before him for ever
    The fiddles of fairyland.

And he died in the young summer
    Of the world's desire;
Before our hearts were broken
    Like sticks in a fire.

AFTER WALT WHITMAN

Me clairvoyant,
Me conscious of you, old camarado,
Needing no telescope, lorgnette, field-glass, opera-glass,
                            myopic pince-nez,
Me piercing two thousand years with eye naked and
                                not ashamed;
The crown cannot hide you from me;
Musty old feudal-heraldic trappings cannot hide you from me,
I perceive that you drink.
(I am drinking with you. I am as drunk as you are.)
I see you are inhaling tobacco, puffing, smoking, spitting
(I do not object to your spitting),
You prophetic of American largeness,
You anticipating the broad masculine manners of these States;

I see in you also there are movements, tremors, tears, desire for
the melodious,
I salute your three violinists, endlessly making vibrations,
Rigid, relentless, capable of going on for ever;
They play my accompaniment; but I shall take no notice of
any accompaniment;
I myself am a complete orchestra.
So long.

A BALLAD OF ABBREVIATIONS

The American's hustler, for he says so,
 And surely the American must know.
He will prove to you with figures why it pays so
 Beginning with his boyhood long ago.
When the slow-maturing anecdote is ripest,
 He'll dictate it like a Board of Trade Report,
And because he has no time to call a typist,
 He calls her a Stenographer for short.

He is never known to loiter or malinger,
 He rushes, for he knows he has "a date";
He is always on the spot and full of ginger,
 Which is why he is invariably late.
When he guesses that it's getting even later,
 His vocabulary's vehement and swift,
And he yells for what he calls the Elevator,
 A slang abbreviation for a lift.

Then nothing can be nattier or nicer
 For those who like a light and rapid style.
Than to trifle with a work of Mr. Dreiser
 As if comes along in waggons by the mile

He has taught us what a swift selective art meant
  By description of his dinners and all that,
And his dwelling, which he says is an Apartment,
  Because he cannot stop to say a flat.

We may whisper of his wild precipitation,
  That its speed is rather longer than a span,
But there really is a definite occasion
  When he does not use the longest word he can.
When he substitutes, I freely make admission,
  One shorter and much easier to spell;
If you ask him what he thinks of Prohibition,
  He may tell you quite succinctly it is Hell.

THE SHAKESPEARE MEMORIAL

Lord Lilac thought it rather rotten
That Shakespeare should be quite forgotten,
And therefore got on a Committee
With several chaps out of the City,
And Shorter and Sir Herbert Tree,
Lord Rothschild and Lord Rosebery,
And F. C. G. and Comyns Carr,
Two dukes and a dramatic star,
Also a clergyman now dead;
And while the vain world careless sped
Unheeding the heroic name —

The souls most fed with Shakespeare's flame
Still sat unconquered in a ring,
Remembering him like anything.

Lord Lilac did not long remain,
Lord Lilac did not come again.
He softly lit a cigarette
And sought some other social set
Where, in some other knots or rings,
People were doing cultured things,
— Miss Zwilt's Humane Vivarium
— The little men that paint on gum
— The exquisite Gorilla Girl....
He sometimes, in this giddy whirl
(Not being really bad at heart),
Remembered Shakespeare with a start—
But not with that grand constancy
Of Clement Shorter, Herbert Tree,
Lord Rosebery and Comyns Carr
And all the other names there are;
Who stuck like limpets to the spot,
Lest they forgot, lest they forgot.

Lord Lilac was of slighter stuff;
Lord Lilac had had quite enough.

HARRY GRAHAM

FROM "RUTHLESS RHYMES"

OPPORTUNITY

When Mrs. Gorm (Aunt Eloïse)
Was stung to death by savage bees,
Her husband (Prebendary Gorm)
Put on his veil, and took the swarm.
He's publishing a book next May
On "How to Make Bee-keeping Pay".

MR. JONES

"There's been an accident," they said,
"Your servant's cut in half; he's dead!"
"Indeed!" said Mr. Jones, "and please,
Send me the half that's got my keys."

L'ENFANT GLACÉ

When Baby's cries grew hard to bear,
I popped him in the Frigidaire.
I never would have done so if
I'd known that he'd be frozen stiff.

My wife said: "George, I'm so unhappé
Our darling's now completely *frappé!*"

WASTE

I had written to Aunt Maud,
Who was on a trip abroad,
When I heard she'd died of cramp
Just too late to save the stamp.

INDIFFERENCE

When Grandmamma fell off the boat,
And couldn't swim (and wouldn't float),
Matilda just stood by and smiled.
I almost could have slapped the child.

COMPENSATION

Weep not for little Léonie
Abducted by a French *Marquis*!
Though loss of honour was a wrench,
Just think how it's improved her French!

WINTER SPORTS

The ice upon our pond's so thin
That poor Mamma has fallen in!
We cannot reach her from the shore
Until the surface freezes more.
Ah me, my heart grows weary waiting—
Besides, I want to have some skating.

POETICAL ECONOMY

What hours I spent of precious time,
    What pints of ink I used to waste,
Attempting to secure a rhyme
    To suit the public taste,
Until I found a simple plan
Which makes the lamest lyric scan!

When I've a syllable *de trop*,
    I cut it off, without apol.:
This verbal sacrifice, I know,
    May irritate the schol.;
But all must praise my dev'lish cunn.
Who realise that Time is Mon.

My sense remains as clear as cryst.,
    My style as pure as any Duch.
Who does not boast a bar sinist.
    Upon her fam. escutch.;
And I can treat with scornful pit.
The sneers of ev'ry captious crit.

I gladly publish to the pop.
    A scheme of which I make no myst.,

363

And beg my fellow scribes to cop.
    This-labour-saving syst.
I offer it to the consid.
Of ev'ry thoughtful individ.

The author, working like a beav.,
    His readers' pleasure could redoub.
Did he but now and then abbrev.
    The work he gives his pub.
(This view I most partic. suggest
To A. C. Bens, and G. K. Chest.)

If Mr. Caine rewrote *The Scape.*,
    And Miss Correll condensed *Barabb.*,
What could they save in foolscap pape.
    Did they but cult. the hab.
Which teaches people to suppress
All syllables that are unnec.!

If playwrights would but thus dimin.:
    The length of time each drama takes,
(*The Second Mrs. Tanq.* by Pin.
    Or even *Ham.*, by Shakes.)
We could maintain a watchful att.
When at a Mat. on Wed. or Sat.

Have done, ye bards, with dull monot.!
    Foll. my examp., O, Stephen Phill.,
O, Owen Seam., O, William Wat.,
    O, Ella Wheeler Wil.,
And share with me the grave respons.
Of writing this amazing nons.!

THE COCKNEY OF THE NORTH

(W. B. Yeats)

I will arise and go now, and go to Inverness,
    And a small villa rent there, of lath and plaster built;
Nine bedrooms will I have there, and I'll don my native dress,
    And walk about in a d—— loud kilt.

And I will have some sport there, when grouse
                                  come driven slow,
    Driven from purple hill-tops to where the loaders quail;
While midges bite their ankles, and shorts are flying low,
    And the air is full of the grey-hen's tail.

I will arise and go now, for ever, day and night,
    I hear the taxis bleating and the motor-buses roar,
And over tarred macadam and pavements parched and white
    I've walked till my feet are sore!
For it's oh, to be in Scotland! now that August's nearly there,
    Where the capercailzie warble on the mountain's
                                    rugged brow;
There's pleasure and contentment, there's sport
                                and bracing air,
    In Scotland — now!

EDMUND CLERIHEW BENTLEY

FROM "BIOGRAPHY FOR BEGINNERS"

SIR CHRISTOPHER WREN

Sir Christopher Wren
Said, "I am going to dine with some men.
If anybody calls
Say I am designing St. Paul's."

ADAM SMITH

Adam Smith
Was disowned by all his kith,
But he was backed through thick and thin
By all his kin.

SIR HUMPHRY DAVY

Sir Humphry Davy
Abominated gravy.
He lived in the odium
Of having discovered Sodium.

J. S. MILL

John Stuart Mill,
By a mighty effort of will,
Overcame his natural bonhomie
And wrote "Principles of Political Economy".

LORD CLIVE

What I like about Clive
Is that he is no longer alive.
There is a great deal to be said
For being dead.

GEORGE III

George the Third
Ought never to have occurred.
One can only wonder
At so grotesque a blunder.

SAVONAROLA

Savonarola
Declined to wear a bowler,
Expressing the view that it was gammon
To talk of serving God and Mammon.

T. S. ELIOT

THE HIPPOPOTAMUS

And when this epistle is read among you, cause
that it be read also in the Church of the Laodiceans.

The broad-backed hippopotamus
Rests on his belly in the mud;
Although he seems so firm to us
He is merely flesh and blood.

Flesh and blood is weak and frail,
Susceptible to nervous shock;
While the True Church can never fail
For it is based upon a rock.

The hippo's feeble steps may err
In compassing material ends,
While the True Church need never stir
To gather in its dividends.

The 'potamus can never reach
The mango on the mango-tree;

But fruits of pomegranate and peach
Refresh the Church from over sea.

At mating time the hippo's voice
Betrays inflexions hoarse and odd,
But every week we hear rejoice
The Church, at being one with God.

The hippopotamus's day
Is passed in sleep; at night he hunts;
God works in a mysterious way—
The Church can sleep and feed at once.

I saw the 'potamus take wing
Ascending from the damp savannas,
And quiring angels round him sing
The praise of God, in loud hosannas.

Blood of the Lamb shall wash him clean
And him shall heavenly arms enfold,
Among the saints he shall be seen
Performing on a harp of gold.

He shall be washed as white as snow,
By all the martyr'd virgins kist,
While the True Church remains below
Wrapt in the old miasmal mist.

GROWLTIGER'S LAST STAND

Growltiger was a Bravo Cat, who travelled on a barge:
In fact he was the roughest cat that ever roamed at large.

From Gravesend up to Oxford he pursued his evil aims,
Rejoicing in his title of "The Terror of the Thames".

His manners and appearance did not calculate to please;
His coat was torn and seedy, he was baggy at the knees;
One ear was somewhat missing, no need to tell you why,
And he scowled upon a hostile world from one forbidding eye.

The cottagers of Rotherhithe knew something of his fame;
At Hammersmith and Putney people shuddered at his name.
They would fortify the hen-house, lock up the silly goose,
When the rumour ran along the shore:
                              GROWLTIGER'S ON THE LOOSE!

Woe to the weak canary, that fluttered from its cage;
Woe to the pampered Pekinese, that faced Growltiger's rage;
Woe to the bristly Bandicoot, that lurks on foreign ships,
And woe to any Cat with whom Growltiger came to grips!

But most to Cats of foreign race his hatred had been vowed;
To Cats of foreign name and race no quarter was allowed.
The Persian and the Siamese regarded him with fear —
Because it was a Siamese had mauled his missing ear.

Now on a peaceful summer night, all nature seemed at play,
The tender moon was shining bright, the barge at Molesey lay.
All in the balmy moonlight it lay rocking on the tide —
And Growltiger was disposed to show his sentimental side.

His bucko mate, GRUMBUSKIN, long since
                              had disappeared,
For to the Bell at Hampton he had gone to wet his beard;
And his bosum, TUMBLEBRUTUS, he too had stol'n
                              away —
In the yard behind the Lion he was prowling for his prey.

In the forepeak of the vessel Growltiger sate alone,
Concentrating his attention on the Lady GRIDDLEBONE.
And his raffish crew were sleeping in their barrels and their
                              bunks —

As the Siamese came creeping in their sampans and their
                                                    junks.

Growltiger had no eye or ear for aught but Griddlebone,
And the Lady seemed enraptured by his manly baritone,
Disposed to relaxation, and awaiting no surprise —
But the moonlight shone reflected from a hundred bright blue
                                                    eyes.

And closer still and closer the sampans circled round,
And yet from all the enemy there was not heard a sound.
The lovers sang their last duet, in danger of their lives —
For the foe was armed with toasting forks and cruel carving
                                                    knives.

Then GILBERT gave the signal to his fierce Mongolian
                                                    horde;
With a frightful burst of fireworks the Chinks they swarmed
                                                    aboard.
Abandoning their sampans, and their pullaways and junks,
They battened down the hatches on the crew within their
                                                    bunks.

Then Griddlebone she gave a screech, for she was badly
                                                    skeered;
I am sorry to admit it, but she quickly disappeared.
She probably escaped with ease, I'm sure she was not
                                                    drowned —
But a serried ring of flashing steel Growltiger did surround.

The ruthless foe pressed forward, in stubborn rank on rank;
Growltiger to his vast surprise was forced to walk the plank.
He who a hundred victims had driven to that drop,
At the end of all his crimes was forced to go ker-flip, ker-flop.

Oh there was joy in Wapping when the news flew through
                                                    the land;
At Maidenhead and Henley there was dancing on the strand.
Rats were roasted whole at Brentford, and at Victoria Dock,
And a day of celebration was commanded in Bangkok.

MACAVITY: THE MYSTERY CAT

Macavity's a Mystery Cat: he's called the Hidden Paw—
For he's the master criminal who can defy the Law.
He's the bafflement of Scotland Yard, the Flying Squad's
                                                    despair:
For when they reach the scene of crime—*Macavity's not
                                                    there!*

Macavity, Macavity, there's no like Macavity,
He's broken every human law, he breaks the law of gravity.
His powers of levitation would make a fakir stare,
And when you reach the scene of crime—*Macavity's not
                                                    there!*
You may seek him in the basement, you may look up in
                                                the air—
But I tell you once and once again, *Macavity's not there!*

Macavity's a ginger cat, he's very tall and thin;
You would know him if you saw him, for his eyes are
                                                sunken in.
His brow is deeply lined with thought, his head is highly
                                                domed;
His coat is dusty from neglect, his whiskers are uncombed.

He sways his head from side to side, with movements like
a snake;
And when you think he's half asleep, he's always wide awake.
Macavity, Macavity, there's no one like Macavity,
For he's a fiend in feline shape, a monster of depravity.
You may meet him in a by-street, you may see him
in the square—
But when a crime's discovered, then *Macavity's not there!*

He's outwardly respectable. (They say he cheats at cards.)
And his footprints are not found in any file of
Scotland Yard's.
And when the larder's looted, or the jewel-case is rifled,
Or when the milk is missing, or another Peke's been stifled,
Or the greenhouse glass is broken, and the trellis past repair
Ay, there's the wonder of the thing! *Macavity's not there!*

There may be a scrap of paper in the hall or on the stair—
But it's useless to investigate— *Macavity's not there!*
And when the loss has been disclosed, the Secret Service say:
"It must have been Macavity!"—but he's a mile away.
You'll be sure to find him resting, or a-licking of his thumbs,
Or engaged in doing complicated long division sums.

Macavity, Macavity, there's no one like Macavity,
There never was a Cat of such deceitfulness and suavity.
He always has an alibi, and one or two to spare:
At whatever time the deed took place—
MACAVITY WASN'T THERE!
And they say that all the Cats whose wicked deeds are widely
known
(I might mention Mungojerrie, I might mention Griddlebone)
Are nothing more than agents for the Cat who all the time
Just controls their operations: the Napoleon of Crime!

GUS: THE THEATRE CAT

Gus is the Cat at the Theatre Door.
His name, as I ought to have told you before,
Is really Asparagus. That's such a fuss
To pronounce, that we usually call him just Gus.
His coat's very shabby, he's thin as a rake,
And he suffers from palsy that makes his paw shake.
Yet he was, in his youth, quite the smartest of Cats—
Put no longer a terror to mice and to rats.
For he isn't the Cat that he was in his prime;
Though his name was quite famous, he says, in its time.
And whenever he joins his friends at their club
(Which takes place at the back of the neighbouring pub)
He loves to regale them, if someone else pays,
With anecdotes drawn from his palmiest days.
For he once was a Star of the highest degree—
He has acted with Irving, he's acted with Tree.
And he likes to relate his success on the Halls,
Where the Gallery once gave him seven cat-calls.
But his grandest creation, as he loves to tell,
Was Firefrorefiddle, the Fiend of the Fell.

"I have played," so he says, "every possible part,
And I used to know seventy speeches by heart.

375

I'd extemporize back-chat, I knew how to gag,
And I knew how to let the cat out of the bag,
I knew how to act with my back and my tail;
With an hour of rehearsal, I never could fail.
I'd a voice that would soften the hardest of hearts,
Whether I took the lead, or in character parts.
I have sat by the bedside of poor Little Nell;
When the Curfew was rung, then I swung on the bell.
In the Pantomime season I never fell flat,
And I once understudied Dick Whittington's Cat.
But my grandest creation, as history will tell,
Was Firefrorefiddle, the Fiend of the Fell."

Then, if someone will give him a toothful of gin,
He will tell how he once played a part in *East Lynne*.
At a Shakespeare performance he once walked on pat,
When some actor suggested the need for a cat.
He once played a Tiger — could do it again —
Which an Indian Colonel pursued down a drain.
And he thinks that he still can, much better than most,
Produce blood-curdling noises to bring on the Ghost.
And he once crossed the stage on a telegraph wire,
To rescue a child when a house was on fire.
And he says: "Now, these kittens, they do not get trained
As we did in the days when Victoria reigned.
They never get drilled in a regular troupe,
And they think they are smart, just to jump through a hoop."
And he'll say, as he scratches himself with his claws,
"Well, the Theatre's certainly not what it was.
These modern productions are all very well,
But there's nothing to equal, from what I hear tell,
    That moment of mystery
      When I made history
As Firefrorefiddle, the Fiend of the Fell."

WYNSTAN HUGH AUDEN

FROM "LETTER TO LORD BYRON"

Excuse, my lord, the liberty I take
    In thus addressing you. I know that you
Will pay the price of authorship and make
    The allowances an author has to do.
    A poet's fan-mail will be nothing new.
And then a lord — Good Lord, you must be peppered,
Like Gary Cooper, Coughlin, or Dick Sheppard,

With notes from perfect strangers starting, "Sir,
    I liked your lyrics, but *Childe Harold's* trash,"
"My daughter writes, should I encourage her?"
    Sometimes containing frank demands for cash,
    Sometimes sly hints at a platonic pash,
And sometimes, though I think this rather crude,
The correspondent's photo in the rude.

And as for manuscripts — by every post...
    I can't improve on Pope's shrill indignation,
But hope that it will please his spiteful ghost
    To learn the use in culture's propagation
    Of modern methods of communication;
New roads, new rails, new contacts, as we know
From documentaries by the G. P. O.

For since the British Isles went Protestant
    A church confession is too high for most.
But still confession is a human want,
      So Englishmen must make theirs now by post
      And authors hear them over breakfast toast.
For, failing them, there's nothing but the wall
Of public lavatories on which to scrawl.

So if ostensibly I write to you
    To chat about your poetry or mine,
There's many other reasons: though it's true
      That I have, at the age of twenty-nine
      Just read *Don Juan* and I found it fine.
I read it on the boat to Reykjavik
Except when eating or asleep or sick.

Now home is miles away, and miles away
    No matter who, and I am quite alone
And cannot understand what people say,
      But like a dog must guess it by the tone;
      At any language other than my own
I'm no great shakes, and here I've found no tutor
Nor sleeping lexicon to make me cuter.

The thought of writing came to me today
    (I like to give these facts of time and space);
The bus was in the desert on its way
      From Möthrudalur to some other place:
      The tears were streaming down my burning face;
I'd caught a heavy cold in Akureyri,
And lunch was late and life looked very dreary.

Professor Housman was I think the first
    To say in print how very stimulating
The little ills by which mankind is cursed,
      The colds, the aches, the pains are to creating;
      Indeed one hardly goes too far in stating
That many a flawless lyric may be due
Not to a lover's broken heart, but 'flu.

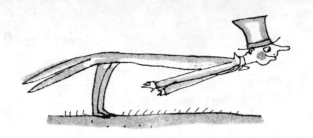

SHORTS

* * *

Pick a quarrel, go to war,
Leave the hero in the bar;
Hunt the lion, climb the peak:
No one guesses you are weak.

* * *

The friends of the born nurse
Are always getting worse.

* * *

When he is well
She gives him hell,
But she's a brick
When he is sick.

* * *

You're a long way off becoming a saint
So long as you suffer from any complaint;
But, if you don't, there's no denying
The chances are that you're not trying.

* * *

I'm afraid there's many a spectacled sod
Prefers the British Museum to God.

*　*　*

I'm beginning to lose patience
With my personal relations:
They are not deep,
And they are not cheap.

*　*　*

Those who will not reason
Perish in the act:
Those who will not act
Perish for that reason.

*　*　*

Let us honour if we can
The vertical man.
Though we value none
But the horizontal one.

*　*　*

These had stopped seeking
But went on speaking,
Have not contributed
But have diluted.

These ordered light
But had no right,
These handed on
War and a son.

Wishing no harm
But to be warm,
These fell asleep
On the burning heap.

Private faces in public places
Are wiser and nicer
Than public faces in private places.

* * *

With what conviction the young man spoke
When he thought his nonsense rather a joke;
Now, when he doesn't doubt any more,
No one believes the booming old bore.

* * *

To the man-in-the-street who, I'm sorry to say,
    Is a keen observer of life,
The word *intellectual* suggests right away
    A man who's untrue to his wife.

* * *

When Statesmen gravely say "We must be realistic",
The chances are they're weak and, therefore, pacifistic,
But when they speak of Principles, look out: perhaps
Their generals are already poring over maps.

* * *

Why are the public buildings so high? How come you don't
                                              know?
Why, that's because the spirits of the public are so low.

* * *

As the poets have mournfully sung,
Death takes the innocent young,
    The rolling in money,
    The screamingly funny,
And those who are very well hung.

ACADEMIC GRAFFITI

* * *

Henry Adams
Was mortally afraid of Madams:
In a disorderly house
He sat quiet as a mouse.

* * *

St. Thomas Aquinas
Always regarded wine as
A medicinal juice
That helped him to deduce.

* * *

Johann Sebastian Bach
Was a master of his *Fach*:
Nothing could be more *kluge*
Than his *Kunst der Fuge*.

382

* * *

Thomas Lovell Beddoes
Could never walk through meadows
Without getting the glooms
And thinking of tombs.

* * *

Ludwig van Beethoven
Believed it proven
That, for mortal dust,
What must be, must.

* * *

William Blake
Found Newton hard to take,
And was not enormously taken
With Francis Bacon.

* * *

Lord Byron
Once succumbed to a Siren:
His flesh was weak,
Hers Greek.

* * *

Among the prosodists, Bysshe
Was the syllable-counting old sissy,
Guest
The accentual pest.

* * *

Dante
Was utterly *enchanté*
When Beatrice cried in tones that were peachy:
Noi siamo amici.

* * *

Charles Dickens
Could find nothing to say to chickens,
But gossipping with rabbits
Became one of his habits.

* * *

Sir Rider Haggard,
Was completely staggered
When his bride-to-be
Announced "I AM SHE!"

* * *

Joseph Haydn
Never read Dryden
Nor did John Dryden
Ever hear Haydn.

* * *

No one could ever inveigle
Georg Wilhelm Friedrich Hegel
Into offering the slightest apology
For his *Phenomenology*.

* * *

Henry James
Abhorred the word *Dames*,
And always wrote "*Mommas*"
With inverted commas.

* * *

When the young Kant
Was told to kiss his aunt,
He obeyed the Categorical Must,
But only just.

* * *

Mallarmé
Had too much to say:
He could never quite
Leave the paper white.

* * *

John Milton
Never stayed in a Hilton
Hotel,
Which was just as well.

* * *

Thomas More
Caused a furore
Every time he bellowed his
Irish Melodies.

* * *

When Sir Walter Scott
Made a blot,
He stamped with rage
And started a new page.

* * *

Paul Valéry
Earned a meager salary,
Walking through the *Bois*,
Observing his *Moi*.

FROM "MARGINALIA"

* * *

Afraid after long
separation of meeting
a hostile stranger,
the two old friends re-affirmed
their pact with peals of laughter.

* * *

Fear and Vanity
incline us to imagine
we have caused a face
to turn away which merely
happened to look somewhere else.

* * *

Justice: permission to peck
a wee bit harder
than we have been pecked.

* * *

The introvert is deaf
to his neighbour's cry
at the extrovert's pinch.

КОММЕНТАРИИ

В предлагаемых комментариях, помимо справок об авторах, расшифровываются, насколько это возможно, исторические, литературные, библейские аллюзии, приводятся источники цитат, адреса пародий (в отдельных случаях даже отрывки из пародируемых произведений), поясняются культурные, страноведческие и исторические реалии, а также слова, словосочетания и выражения, отсутствующие в «Большом англо-русском словаре» под ред. профессора И. Р. Гальперина (изд. 2-е, стереотипное). Даются в них и переводы отдельных предложений или их фрагментов, если они представляют определенные трудности для понимания.

В комментарии не включены те топонимические сведения, которые не имеют существенного значения для понимания описываемых в рассказах и стихах событий, а также те иноязычные слова и выражения, которые «англизировались» и включены в словарь И. Р. Гальперина. В комментариях не даются справки об исторических фигурах, литературных произведениях, сведения о которых содержатся в общедоступных справочниках,— в противном случае излишне дотошные комментарии к юмористической антологии приобрели бы пародийный характер.

Специально следует остановиться на языковых трудностях, возникающих в тех случаях, когда некоторые авторы (в первую очередь это касается Бирбома, пародирующего Киплинга, и Бейтса) в комических целях передают на письме особенности произношения и грамматики, характерные для английского просторечья. Чтобы облегчить понимание просторечно-диалектных форм и не пояснять их всякий раз в постраничных комментариях, ниже приводится глоссарий, где разъясняются слова и словосочетания, представляющие собой отклонения от стандартной орфографии. Глоссарию предшествуют предварительные замечания о типах наиболее распространенных отклонений от орфографической и грамматической нормы.

I. Отступления от норм произношения:

1. употребление в конце слова альвеолярного носового **n** вместо велярного носового ŋ: goin'; speakin';

2. опущение (в особенности в лондонском просторечии— кокни) звука **h** в начале слова (h-dropping): 'im = him; 'is = his;

3. диереза (выпадение звука или слога в результате ассимиляции или диссимиляции): em = them; dunno = don't know;

4. различные типы стяжений с ассимилятивной заменой звуков: dessay = daresay.

II. Отступления от грамматической нормы:

1. изменение глагольных парадигм: they was just old nails = they were just old nails; we makes our mistakes = we make our mistakes;

2. опущение вспомогательного глагола "do" в вопросительных предложениях: You promise?

3. опущение вспомогательного глагола "have" в Present Perfect: I never done anything = I have never done anything;

4. использование двойного отрицания: You ain't going tell nobody? = You aren't going to tell anybody?

5. просторечное употребление "them" вместо артикля: it got into my teeth eating them nails = it got into my teeth eating the nails.

Глоссарий

ad = had; aint = isn't; alf = half; an' = and; andle = handle; arsh = harsh; arskin = asking; as = has; ave = have; avent = haven't.

battew = better; brasted = bastard.

conduc = conduct; cos = because; course = of course.

d = had; dessay = daresay; dooty = duty; dorg = dog; dunno = don't know.

e = he; ell = hell; em = them; er = her; ere = here.

gal = girl; gawd = god; git = get; gorn = gone.

hanarchy = anarchy; hevidence = evidence; hexperts = experts; hup = up.

im = him; inscrootable = inscrutable; is = his.

jool = rule.

Lawd = Lord; librery = library; lorst = lost.

mossel = morsel.

noo = new.

o = of, on; oly = holy; ome = home; orf = off; ort = are; ot = what, that; oughta = ought to; ow = how.

po' = poor; pore = poor; premptory = peremptory.

rayther = rather.

's = is, has; sarjint = sargeant; skeered = scared; soopr = super.

ter = to; thass = that's; tis = it is; twas = it was.

ullo = hallo; ustle = hustle.

westcit = westcoat; wi' = with; wos = was; wot = what; wotever = whatever.

y = you; yer = you, your; yuss = yes.

I. Prose

F. ANSTEY

Ф. Энсти — псевдоним прозаика и очеркиста Томаса Энсти Гатри (1856—1934), автора многочисленных романов и рассказов с увлекательной интригой и живым юмором, рассчитанных главным образом на юного читателя. С 1887 по 1930 г. Энсти проработал в редакции «Панча» — цитадели британского юмора. Рассказы и очерки Энсти, публиковавшиеся в «Панче», впоследствии вошли в сборники: *Voces populi* (1890), *The Talking Horse* (1892), *Mr. Punch's Pocket Ibsen* (1893) и др. Славу писателю принес роман *The Brass Bottle* (1890) — современная переработка одной из сказок Шахерезады, — переведенный на многие языки мира. «Старик Хоттабыч» Л. Лагина — одна из многочисленных версий этого романа Ф. Энсти.

A Canine Ishmael

Рассказ вошел в сборник *The Talking Horse*.

15. Telemachus — Телемах, сын Одиссея и Пенелопы из «Одиссеи» Гомера.

15—16. Thirty Years' War — Тридцатилетняя война 1618—1648 гг. между Габсбургами — сторонниками католицизма, и антигабсбургской коалицией — сторонниками протестантизма.

JEROME K. JEROME

Джером Клапка Джером (1859—1927) — прозаик, журналист, драматург, очеркист. Прежде чем стать профессиональным литератором, Джером работал клерком в железнодорожной компании, учителем в школе, актером в репертуарной труппе — театральный опыт лег в основу первой его книги *On the Stage and Off* (1888). Джером явился одним из инициаторов и создателей иллюстрированного журнала «Бездельник» (*Idler*), в котором кроме него печатались такие заокеанские знаменитости, как Брет Гарт и Марк Твен. Из-под пера Джерома вышло огромное число романов, пьес, путевых очерков, мемуаров, рассказов главным образом юмористического характера, однако мировую известность писателю принесли две книги: *Three Men in a Boat* (1889) и — в меньшей степени — ее продолжение: *Three Men on the Bummell* (1900). *Overhauling a Bicycle* и *The Statues of Prague* — главы из книги *Three Men on the Bummell*.

The Statues of Prague

28. Pilsener (*нем.*) — пльзенский.

Ems — название минеральной воды; Эмс — водный курорт в Германии недалеко от Висбадена.

Apollinaris water — минеральная вода; Аполлинарис — название источника в долине реки Ар в Германии.

35. Karlsbrücke, Franz-Josefsbrücke ... Ringplatz — топонимика Праги; Brücke (*нем.*) — мост; Platz (*нем.*) — площадь; Ring (*нем.*) — кольцо.

36. the statue of the Duke of Wellington — памятник английскому полководцу герцогу Веллингтону (1769—1852), находится на Пиккадилли-Серкус, в центре Лондона.

Westminster Bridge — Вестминстерский мост через Темзу, построен в 1854—1862 гг., находится в Вестминстере, центральном районе Лондона.

JAMES MATTHEW BARRIE

Джеймс Барри (1860—1937) — прозаик, драматург. Учился в академии Дамфрис и в Эдинбургском университете. Начинал как журналист; журналистской деятельности посвятил роман *When a Man's Single* (1888), писал также книги автобиографического характера (*Margaret Ogilvy*, 1896), очерки (*A Window in Thrums*, 1889), пьесы, самой известной из которых стала *Peter Pan* (1904), переработанная из повести *The Little White Bird* (1902). Некоторые книги Барри (в первую очередь пьеса *The Admirable Chrichton*, 1902; сборник рассказов *My Lady Nicotine*, 1890) написаны в юмористическом ключе.

The Perils of Not Smoking

The Perils of Not Smoking — глава из книги *My Lady Nicotine*.

34. Arcadians — *зд.* курильщики трубочного табака «Аркадия» (Arcadia).

36. Mr. Irving at the Lyceum — имеется в виду известный английский актер и режиссер Генри Ирвинг (настоящее имя Джон Генри Бродрибб, 1838—1905), с 1878 по 1898 г. Ирвинг руководил лондонским театром «Лицеум».

HECTOR HUGH MUNRO (SAKI)

Гектор Хью Манро (1870—1916)—прозаик, юморист, очеркист; шотландец по происхождению, более известный в англоязычной юмористике как Саки (Saki)—псевдоним, заимствованный им у Омара Хайяма; родился в Бирме, где его отец работал полицейским инспектором. После смерти матери двухлетнего Манро отправили в Англию к родственникам, воспитавшим мальчика в строгости и умеренности. Литературную деятельность Манро начал в 1895 г. фельетонистом консервативной *Westminster Gazette* и корреспондентом *Morning Post* на Балканах, в России и в Париже (1902—1908). За первым сборником юмористических рассказов Манро (*Reginald*, 1904), многие из которых первоначально публиковались в газете *Daily Express* и журнале *Bystander*, последовали *Reginald in Russia* (1910), *The Chronicles of Clovis* (1911) и *Beasts and Superbeasts* (1914). Еще при жизни (писатель погиб на войне в расцвете сил и таланта) многие критики называли Саки «английским О. Генри»—с американским новеллистом Манро роднят неуемное воображение, острая, непредсказуемая интрига, меткие, отточенные характеристики персонажей. В то же время юмор Манро отличается язвительностью и желчностью.

Reginald's Christmas

Рассказ из сборника *Reginald*.

39. to-be-left-till-called-for cousin—ср. по-русски: «седьмая вода на киселе».

sins of the fathers should be visited by the children = I ... visit the sins of the fathers upon the children (*The Book of Common Prayer: 2nd Commandment*).

Durbar—Дарбар, официальное торжество или фестиваль, устраивался в Индии английской колониальной администрацией.

40. okapi—окапи, редкое парнокопытное животное семейства жирафов.

put on a first-aid-to-the-injured expression—надулась (*букв.*: на лице появились первые признаки обиды).

Wee MacGregor—малютка Макгрегор, т. е. Роб Рой Макгрегор (Rob Roy McGregor), герой одноименного романа Вальтера Скотта.

"At the end of the passage" ... Kipling ... "Earthworms out of Tuscany" — героиня на ходу придумывает роман «под» Киплинга, играя на омонимии слова passage: 1) проход, коридор; 2) морское путешествие. «Земляные черви из Тосканы» — пародия на научно-популярную беллетристику в духе дарвинистских теорий.

41. Austin's odes — речь идет о второстепенном и весьма плодовитом английском поэте Альфреде Остине (1835—1913), авторе многочисленных од.

progressive halma — настольная игра, напоминающая нарды.

The Reticence of Lady Anne

Рассказ из сборника *Reginald in Russia*.

43. Iphigénie en Tauride (*фр.*) — опера итальянского композитора Алессандро Скарлатти (1660—1725) «Ифигения в Тавриде».

44. Satyr lines ... goat continuations... — сатиры, лесные божества, демоны плодородия в свите Диониса; изображались с хвостом и копытами.

Tea

Рассказ из сборника *The Toys of Peace* (1912).

46. Minorca hens — порода кур.

47. Muscovy duck = Musc-duck — порода тропических уток.

Mayfair — Мейфэр, фешенебельный район Лондона.

48. with Goodwood on us — из-за приближающихся скачек; Goodwood — ипподром в графстве Суссекс, где в июле проводятся ежегодные призовые скачки.

series of rushes—like the infant Moses — омонимическая игра: rush — 1) запарка, спешка; 2) тростник; согласно библейской легенде, младенец Моисей лежал в корзине, которая стояла в тростнике у реки.

Filbold Studge,
the Story of a Mouth That Helped

Рассказ из сборника *The Chronicles of Clovis*.

52. National Liberal Club — радикальный клуб в Лондоне в Уайт-Холле, основан в 1882 г.

53. 'tis not in mortals to countermand success — измененная цитата из трагедии «Катон» (*Cato*, 1713) английского писателя Джозефа Аддисона (Addison, 1672-1719):

> 'Tis not in mortals to command success,
> But we'll do more, Sempronius,—
> We'll deserve it. (Act I, Sc. 2)

MAX BEERBOHM

Макс Бирбом (1872—1956) — прозаик, критик, эссеист, пародист, после окончания Оксфордского Мертон-колледжа (Merton College) в 1898 г. сменил самого Б. Шоу на «почетном посту» театрального критика солидного лондонского еженедельника *Saturday Review*. Впрочем, дар критика в полной мере проявился у Бирбома не в серьезных статьях, рецензиях и монографиях, а в литературной пародии, ставшей под его пером мощным критическим оружием: в 1912 г. Бирбом выпустил пародийный сборник *A Christmas Garland*, где очень досталось чуть ли не всем англоязычным писателям первой величины: Уэллсу, Беннету, Голсуорси, Конраду, Честертону, Генри Джеймсу. Проявил себя Бирбом и в поэтической пародии (*The Poet's Corner*, 1904), а также в качестве новеллиста (*Seven Men*) и эссеиста (*More; Yet Again; And Even Now*).

A Good Prince

Рассказ вошел в сборник *Seven Men*.

54. The Green Park — Грин-парк в Лондоне, тянется вдоль Пиккадилли.

Almanach de Gotha — генеалогический, дипломатический и статистический справочник, выпускавшийся с 1763 г. на французском языке Юстусом Пертом Готским (Justus Perthes of Gotha).

55. Henri Quatre (*фр.*) — Генрих IV (1553—1610), французский король с 1589 г.

Sandringham — Сандринхем, одна из загородных резиденций английских королей (в графстве Норфолк).

56. St. James's Palace — Сент-Джеймсский дворец, бывшая королевская резиденция в Лондоне; построен в XVI в.

Prince Edward — в дальнейшем английский король Эдвард VI (1841—1910).

the House of Hanover — имеется в виду Ганноверская династия английских королей (1714—1901).

Attendons! *(фр.)* — Подождем!

An Incident

Очерк написан в 1954 г. и вошел в посмертный сборник эссе и радиопередач Бирбома "Mainly on the Air. Broadcast Talks and Essays" (1958).

56. Henry James — Генри Джеймс (1843—1916), американский писатель, большую часть жизни прожил в Европе; Джеймс очень высоко ценил пародийный талант Бирбома.

57. Carlton Hotel — отель «Карлтон» в Лондоне, где находится ведущий клуб консерваторов, основанный в 1832 г. герцогом Веллингтоном.

the Savile — «Савил», лондонский клуб писателей, издателей, режиссеров, основан в 1868 г.

Rye — Рай, город в Англии, в графстве Суссекс.

Grafton Galleries — картинная галерея на Графтон-террас, улице в северной части Лондона.

Kensington — Кенсингтон, фешенебельный район на юго-западе Лондона.

58. Augustus John — Огастес Джон (1878—1961), английский живописец.

Rudyard Kipling

Пародия на прозу Киплинга, где высмеивается пристрастие писателя к просторечным и диалектным формам, вошла в сборник *A Christmas Garland*.

58. Police Station Ditties — аллюзия на стихи Киплинга *Departmental Ditties* (1886).

Slushby — говорящая фамилия; от slush — вздор, болтовня.

59. pitmanised — записал; от pit *(сленг)* — нагрудный карман; отсюда pitman — записная книжка; to pitmanise — записывать.

Drawn a blank to-night? — Сегодня не ладится? От to draw blank *(сленг)* — терпеть неудачу.

60. Sec. = secretary; **Yard** = Scotland Yard; **Div.** = Division.
billicock (*сленг*) — шляпа, котелок.

62. a thing of beauty and a joy for ever — слегка видоизмененная
цитата из поэмы Джона Китса (Keats, 1795-1821) *Endymion*:

> A thing of beauty is a joy forever,
> Its loveliness increases; it will never
> Pass into nothingness; but still will keep
> A bower quiet for us, and a sleep
> Full of sweet dreams, and health, and quiet breathing.

Frog's-march him! — Тащи его! To give smb. the frog's march
(*сленг*) — тащить волоком.

MAURICE BARING

Морис Бэринг (1874—1945) сменил множество самых различных профессий: был поэтом и лингвистом, пародистом и дипло-
матом, критиком и переводчиком, корреспондентом на фронтах
первой мировой войны и военным летчиком. Стихи, которыми он
начинал свою литературную карьеру (*Pastels and Other Rhymes*,
1891; *The Black Prince*, 1902), больше десятка романов, рассказы, эссе прочно забылись — в историю английской литературы Бэринг вошел как юморист, в первую очередь благодаря вы-
шедшей в 1934 г. в издательстве „Heinemann" книге *Unreliable
History*, состоящей из трех частей (*Diminutive Dramas, Dead
Letters, Lost Diaries*) и написанной в жанре так называемого «па-
родийного дописывания» классических произведений.

King Lear's Daughter

В этом отрывке, взятом из раздела «Забытые письма» книги
«Невероятная история», Бэринг «модернизирует» «Короля Лира».

66. ...to throw up Cordelia at one every moment — постоянно
ставит Корделию в пример; to throw up smb. at smb. — ставить
кого-то кому-то в пример, выделять.

The Rehearsal

«Репетиция» вошла в первый раздел *Unreliable History —
Diminutive Dramas*.

67. The Globe Theatre — «Глобус», театр в Лондоне (построен в 1599 г.), где ставились все пьесы Шекспира, написанные после 1594 г.

They are all men — во времена Шекспира женские роли исполнялись мужчинами.

67—68. Colman ... Foote — используя в бурлеске «Репетиция» имена таких крупных деятелей английского театра XVIII в., как Джордж Колмен-старший (1732—1794) и Сэмюел Фут (1720—1770), Бэринг обращается к приему исторической экстраполяции, широко распространенному в комической литературе.

68. Gray's Inn — Грейз инн, район в Лондоне, где когда-то находился один из «Судебных иннов» — гильдии лондонских юристов.

Psyche — Психея, в греческой мифологии олицетворение человеческой души, изображавшейся в виде бабочки или девушки.

Kenilworth — Кенилуорт, город в Англии, в графстве Уорвикшир.

71. Mr. Burbage — Ричард Бербедж (1567?—1619), английский трагедийный актер; с 1595 по 1618 г. играл главные роли в шекспировских пьесах.

72. O dearest chuck ... need — Бэринг пародирует рифмованные подражания Шекспиру, популярные в начале XIX в.

85. the Queen — у английской королевы Елизаветы I Тюдор (1533—1603) были рыжие волосы.

EDMUND V. KNOX

Эдмунд Нокс (1881—1951) — издатель, юморист, журналист; родился в многодетной семье англиканского священника. Окончив Оксфорд и послужив отечеству во время первой мировой войны, Нокс в 1920 г. устроился работать в «Панч», а с 1932 г. стал главным редактором журнала, сменив на этом посту известного юмориста и пародиста Оуэна Симена (см. ниже). Шуточные стихи, эпиграммы, рассказы, бурлески Нокса, печатавшиеся под псевдонимом "Evoe" в «Панче», «Обзервере», «Спэктейторе», «Санди Таймс», в дальнейшем вошли в сборники: *The Brazen Lyre* (1911), *Parodies Regained* (1921), *Folly Calling* (1938).

Нокс не только сочинял и издавал юмористические произведения, но и широко их пропагандировал, на протяжении многих лет издавая «Библиотеку юмора» ("Library of Humour") в издательстве "Methuen".

The Perfect Guest

76. Lord Macaulay — Томас Бабингтон Маколей (1800—1859), английский историк, публицист и политический деятель.

Wilfred — святой Уилфрид (634—709), английский священнослужитель, архиепископ Йоркский.

PELHAM GRENVILLE WODEHOUSE

Пэлем Гренвилл Вудхаус (1881—1975) по праву считается наиболее заметной фигурой в английской юмористике XX в. как по объему литературной продукции (в общей сложности свыше 90 книг), так и по ее качеству — сквозные персонажи его романов и рассказов: слуга-интеллектуал Дживз, повеса Берти Вустер, незадачливый детектив Маллинер, газетчик Псмит — давно уже стали фигурами нарицательными. Впрочем, путь к славе Вудхаусу предстоял довольно долгий. Родившись в провинциальном английском городке Гилфорде и закончив Далуич-колледж (Dulwich College), Вудхаус, сын колониального чиновника, несколько лет проработал клерком в банке, затем, уйдя на вольные хлеба, вел юмористическую рубрику «Между прочим» (*By the Way*) в лондонской *Globe*, сочинял рассказы и повести из школьной жизни для юношеского журнала «Капитан» (*The Captain*) и, только переехав в США в 1910 г., стал писать всерьез: романы, рассказы, пьесы, киносценарии, эссе, либретто и т. д. В 1955 г. Вудхаус принял американское гражданство, а в 1975 г. был удостоен звания «Рыцарь Британской империи». Самый большой успех выпал на долю книг Вудхауса с участием Дживза: *The Inimitable Jeeves* (1923), *Carry On, Jeeves* (1925), *Very Good, Jeeves* (1958), *My Man Jeeves* (1963) и др. Из романов писателя особенного внимания заслуживают *Uneasy Money* (1917), *Piccadilly Jim* (1918), *The Indiscretions of Archie* (1921), *The Code of the Woosters* (1938).

Do Thrillers Need Heroines?

Эссе вошло в сборник Вудхауса *Louder and Funnier* (1932).

79. Ascot — «Аскот», ипподром близ города Виндзора, где в июне проходят традиционные призовые скачки — событие в жизни английской аристократии.

Lord's — «Лордз», крикетный стадион в Лондоне.

Eton and Harrow match — крикетный матч между учащимися двух старейших, привилегированных английских школ — Итона и Харроу.

Limehouse — Лаймхаус, район лондонских доков.

82. Football Coupon — карточка, заполняемая участниками футбольного почтового тотализатора.

Jeeves Exerts the Old Cerebellum
No Wedding Bells for Bingo

Эти взаимосвязанные новеллы вошли в сборник *The Inimitable Jeeves*. Комический эффект в романах и рассказах из серии «Дживз» создается тем, что лакей Дживз отличается подчеркнуто интеллигентным стилем поведения и речи; хозяин же, наоборот, развязной манерой; Дживз изъясняется «высоким» стилем, Берти Вустер говорит преимущественно на сленге.

83. ...exerts the old cerebellum — *букв.* напрягает старые мозги.

The stable is not sanguine — Конюхам (*букв.* на конюшне) эта лошадь оптимизма не внушает.

84. biffs (*сленг*) — *зд.* носится, мечется.

85. a livelier iris ... dove — Берти неточно цитирует строки из поэмы английского поэта Альфреда Теннисона (Tennyson, 1809-1892) *Locksley Hall*:

In the spring a livelier iris changes on the barnish'd dove;
In the spring a young man's fancy lightly turns to thoughts of love.

Serpentine — Серпантин, искусственное озеро в Гайд-парке с лодочной станцией и пляжем.

86. Ritz — «Ритц», лондонская фешенебельная гостиница на Пиккадилли.

on the right side of the ledger — ср. по-русски: «в плюсе»; в гроссбухе доходы обычно пишутся справа, расходы — слева.
map (*сленг*) — лицо.

87. mazzard (*сленг*) — голова, лицо.

tum (*сленг*) — живот, брюхо (от stomach).

Claridge's — «Клариджез», фешенебельный отель в Лондоне в районе Мейфэр.

sole frite au gourment aux champignons (*фр.*) — жареный язык с шампиньонами.

Borgia family — существует легенда, согласно которой члены итальянской аристократической семьи Борджиа (Родриго, 1431—1503) и его дети (сын Цезарь, 1476—1507, и дочь Лукреция, 1480—1519) владели секретом изготовления смертельного яда, с помощью которого они расправлялись со своими врагами.

88. Camberwell — Камберуэлл, район в южной части Лондона.

...swinging a dashed efficient shoe (*сленг*) — ср. по-русски: «чувствует себя как рыба в воде».

the old lemon (*сленг*) — старикан (*букв.*: старый дурень); см. ниже: old egg, old crumpet.

89. the whole binge (*сленг*) — *зд.* (расскажешь) всю историю; binge — *букв.*: пьянка, попойка. Ср. по-русски: «вот такая пьянка».

90. ...to shoot young Bingo in on him — ср. по-русски: «напустить на него Бинго».

91. kins = keen.

Sporting Times — вероятно, имеется в виду *Sporting Life* — ежедневная лондонская спортивная газета.

91—92. "A Red, Red Summer Rose", "Madcap Myrtle"... — *зд.* Вудхаус пародирует расхожие названия душещипательных романов.

92. the goods and beyond ... troops — ср. по-русски: «ровно то, что прописал доктор», «как нельзя более кстати».

clergyman's throat — воспаление голосовых связок; *букв.*: горло священника.

an undoubted hit in the right quarter — ср. по-русски: «попал в точку».

95. pitch it strong — ср. по-русски: «будь на высоте», «не тушуйся».

96. the bally things — весь этот вздор; bally = bloody; см. ниже: bally troubles.

persp. = perspiration.

97. Good egg! (*сленг*) = Здорово!

98. brace up and bite the bullet — готовься к самому худшему, возьми себя в руки.

The Level Business Head

Этот рассказ из сборника *Lord Emsworth and Others* (1937) входит в цикл рассказов с участием светского проходимца и вымогателя Стэнли Акриджа и его богатой и жадной тетушки Джулии.

100. Wimbledon Common — улица в Уимблдоне, аристократическом предместье Лондона.

102. tawny = tawny port.

Waterloo Cup — «Кубок Ватерлоо», популярные ежегодные соревнования борзых.

Gawblimey! — Черт возьми! (Gaw = God).

103. Bond Street — Бонд-стрит, одна из главных торговых улиц Лондона, известна, в частности, своими ювелирными магазинами.

Euston — Юстон, лондонский вокзал.

104. the dog had handed in his dinner-pail — собака сыграла в ящик.

105. Oh, the tweetums! — Какие лапочки!

106. Hell hath no fury like a woman scorned... — Стэнли цитирует трагедию английского драматурга Уильяма Конгрива (Congreve, 1670-1729) *The Mourning Bride*:
Heaven has no rage like love to hatred turned,
Nor hell a fury like a woman scorned.
(Act III, Sc. 2)

These things take it out of a fellow — Такое перенести нелегко; to take smth. out of smb. — ослаблять, огорчать; ср. по-русски: «от этого сляжешь».

Lewes Races — собачьи бега в г. Льюэсе (графство Суссекс).

107. Sandown = Sandown Park — «Сандаун-парк», ипподром близ Лондона.

108. He's wide (*сленг*) — Он разбогател.

110. Gerroutofit = Get out of it.

117. roopiness — от roup — аукцион.

ALLAN PATRICK HERBERT

Алан Патрик Херберт (1890—1971) — романист и эссеист; закончил Оксфорд, участвовал в первой мировой войне, в 1918 г. стал адвокатом; на протяжении многих лет (1935—1949) представлял в парламенте Оксфордский университет. Наряду с серьезными произведениями (романы *Holy Deadlock*, 1934; *Plain Jane*; сборник рассказов *Riverside Nights*) Херберт написал достаточно много юмористических книг, куда вошли юморески, пародии, эпиграммы, шаржи и очерки, впервые увидевшие свет на страницах «Панча» за подписью «А. Р. Н.». «Когда мы громко, от души смеемся,— заметил Херберт в своей лекции *The English Laugh* (1950),— то забываем про все, что нас окру-

жает, и смотрим на собственную жизнь со смехом и любовью—
словно ангелы с небес».

Literature
Engaged

Literature и *Engaged* — выдержки из книги Херберта *The Trials of Topsy* (1928), пародии на эпистолярный жанр, заставляющей вспомнить гоголевских Меджи и Фидель, и одновременно— на светскую хронику; объект насмешки, а также схожесть пародийных приемов (в частности, использование говорящих фамилий: Topsy Trout, Haddock, Fatface и др.) сближают «Испытания Топси» с юморесками и пародиями Дж. Б. Мортона, П. Флеминга, Дж. Кольера.

120. a wee bit difficile — характерное для автора письма совмещение шотландского просторечия wee и французских слов; dificile (*фр.*) — трудный.

121. "Who's who" — «Кто есть кто», ежегодный биографический справочник.

Wadham — Уодем-колледж, в Оксфорде, основан в 1612 г. Николасом Уодемом.

Marlborough Club — аристократический клуб в Лондоне (основан в 1863 г.).

Hurlingham — «Харлингем», лондонский аристократический спортивный клуб; основан в 1869 г.

122. Whitechapel — Уайтчепел, один из беднейших районов лондонского Ист-Энда.

misogamist — противник брака (от греческого misein = to hate; gamos = marriage).

123. to flabbify — втянуть; неологизм от flabby — вялый. Неологизмы вообще характерны для «словотворчества» леди Топси Траут.

124. p'raps = perhaps.

NAT GUBBINS

Натаниел Габбинс (1893—1971) — журналист, очеркист. Проработав больше 20 лет штатным репортером столичных *Daily Mirror* и *Daily Express*, Габбинс стал вести юмористическую рубрику в *Sunday Express* под названием «Сидя на заборе» (*Sitting on the Fence*). Среди прочих материалов этой рубрики была и «лингвистическая тема»: пародии на учебники иностранных языков, самоучители, разговорники — довольно распространенное явление в английской газетной юмористике.

A Visit to Wales

Рассказ вошел в антологию английского юмора *Laughter in a Damp Climate. An Anthology of British Humour.* L., 1963.

JOHN B. MORTON

Прозаик, журналист Джон Бингем Майкл Мортон (1893—1979) с блеском совмещал профессии юмориста и ученого-историка. Закончив престижную Харроу-скул, а следом оксфордский Вустер-колледж (Worcester College), Мортон всю жизнь проработал газетчиком, с 1924 по 1965 г. ведя страницу юмора в лондонской *Daily Express* за подписью «Лицо без определенных занятий» (Beachcomber). Подобно многим газетчикам-юмористам XX в. (американцам Р. Бенчли и Ф. Салливану, ирландцу Флэнну О'Брайену, своим соотечественникам А. П. Херберту, Э. Ноксу, П. Флемингу и другим), Мортон создает целую галерею сквозных персонажей, с которыми читатель «Дейли экспресс» встречался из номера в номер: это и ушлый капитан с красноречивой фамилией Foulenough — карикатура на бесстрашных героев комиксов, и прославленный эскулап, и прозорливые детективы, и неподкупные служители Фемиды. Юмористические рассказы, фельетоны, пародии Мортона, публиковавшиеся на страницах «Дейли экспресс», впоследствии вошли в сборник *The Best of Beachcomber* (1963).

The Case of Juliette Milton

Рассказ относится к циклу *The Chronicles of Mr. Justice Cocklecarrot*, где действует один из сквозных персонажей Мортона судья «Морковка». «История Джулиет Мильтон» — многоадресная пародия: здесь высмеиваются и светская хроника, и традиционные для английских периодических изданий «Письма к редактору», и процедура судебного заседания.

137. the fairies ... Knockfierna in County Limerick — Мортон намекает на гномов из ирландского фольклора; Лимерик — графство в Ирландии.

138. Evil be to him who thinks evil — девиз рыцарей ордена Подвязки, учрежденного в 1349 г. английским королем Эдуардом III (1312—1377) Плантагенетом.

Lothario — герой трагедии английского драматурга Николаса

Роу (Rowe, 1674-1718) *The Fair Penitent* (1703); в переносном смысле — распутник, развратник.

after bringing down … Oldham — to bring the house down — иметь успех (в театре), «сорвать аплодисменты»; Old Victoria — Олд-Вик, театральная труппа, прославившаяся постановкой шекспировских пьес; Oldham — Олдэм, город недалеко от Манчестера, в графстве Ланкашир.

139. Chelsea — Челси, район художников, творческой богемы в западной части Лондона.

140. m'lud = my lord; **m'ludship** = my lordship.
Fire ahead! (*сленг*) — Начинай! Приступай!

The Thunderbolt

Эта пародия на спортивную хронику также вошла в сборник избранных произведений Мортона *The Best of Beachcomber*.

145. Miss Mae West — Мей Уэст (1892—1980), американская актриса.
The pooblic… — менеджер Футтла Ботьюлос — иностранец, он допускает ошибки в произношении и грамматике: pooblic = public; chimprion = champion; until he will be have won = until he has won.

146. The fight's as good as over — можно считать, что поединок закончился.

147. Mrs. Dietrich — Марлен Дитрих (род. 1901), американская киноактриса (немка по национальности).
Faust in Gounod's opera — опера «Фауст» (1859) французского композитора Шарля Гуно (1818—1893).

148. Burlington House — Берлингтон-Хаус, здание на Пиккадилли в Лондоне, в котором находится Королевская академия искусств.
Sock him, feller! (*амер. сленг*) — Врежь ему, приятель!
Gabriele d'Annunzio — Габриеле Д'Аннунцио (1863—1938), итальянский писатель, политический деятель.
Atta (*амер. сленг*) = Attaboy.

149. old-stager — ср. по-русски: «ветеран сцены».

DOMENIC B. WYNDHAM LEWIS

Доминик Бивен Уиндхем Льюис (1894—1969) больше известен как биограф, однако в свое время под псевдонимом «Тимоти

Робкий» (Timothy Shy) опубликовал немало фельетонов, юморесок и пародий в английской периодике, в том числе в «Панче».

The Case of the Village Blacksmith

Этот рассказ, в котором обыгрывается стихотворение *Village Blacksmith* американского поэта Г. У. Лонгфелло (1807—1882), вошел в антологию *A Treasury of British Humor,* N. Y., 1942.

152. Mr. Drinkwater — Джон Дринкуотер (1882—1937), английский поэт и драматург, автор ряда исторических пьес.

Eliza Cook — Элайза Кук (1818—1889), английская поэтесса.

153. ...one stanza of your... — в стихотворении Лонгфелло *Wreck of the Hesperus* о дочери шкипера говорится:

> Blue were her eyes as the fairy flax,
> Her cheeks like the dawn of day
> And her bosom white as the hawthorn buds,
> That ope in the month of May.

thinking of your "Excelsior"... — в пятой строфе стихотворения Лонгфелло *Excelsior* (1842) сказано:

> "O stay," the maiden said, "and rest
> Thy weary head upon this breast!"

154. Baby ... you said it. — «Ловлю тебя на слове, крошка» (американское просторечье).

Poet Laureate — поэт-лауреат; пожизненное почетное звание, присваиваемое в Англии известным поэтам.

in church on Sunday mornings ... hard rough hand ... singing high and shrill... — вот соответствующие выдержки из «Деревенского кузнеца»:

> He goes on Sunday to the church...
> He hears his daughter's voice,
> Singing in the village choir...
> And with his hard, rough hands he wipes
> A tear out of his eyes.

VICTOR SAWDON PRITCHETT

Прежде чем стать профессиональным писателем, Виктор Соден Притчетт (род. 1900), будущий романист, новеллист, литературовед, работал продавцом, коммивояжером, репортером в Испании и Марокко. Своим становлением Притчетт обязан солидному периодическому изданию *New Statesman and Nation*, где состоялся его дебют критика и фельетониста и где он несколько лет вел еженедельную рубрику *Books in General*. В романах (*Clare Drummer*, 1929; *Dead Man Leading*, 1937) и в особенности в новеллах (*The Spanish Virgin*, 1930; *The Key to My Heart*, 1963; *Blind Love*, 1969) Притчетта превалирует сатирический настрой, а некоторые типажи (например, из романа *Mr. Beluncle*, 1951) заставляют вспомнить его кумира — Диккенса; в 50-е годы в США большим успехом пользовались не только лекции Притчетта о комическом духе английского романа, но и публичные выступления писателя с чтением романов Диккенса.

Oedipus Complex

Новелла вошла в сборник Притчетта *Collected Stories*, 1956.
157. Barmouth — Бармут, курортный город в Северном Уэльсе.
158. Freud ... Oedipus complex — Зигмунд Фрейд (1856—1939), австрийский врач-психиатр и психолог; основатель психоанализа; Эдипов комплекс, по Фрейду,— результат вытеснения в раннем детстве враждебных импульсов по отношению к отцу.
159. Buckingham Palace — Букингемский дворец, главная королевская резиденция в Лондоне (построен в 1703 г.).

JOHN COLLIER

Джон Генри Нойес Кольер (1901—1980) — романист, новеллист, сценарист, одинаково хорошо известен по обе стороны Атлантики — отчасти потому, что с начала 40-х годов он безвыездно жил в Америке, работая сценаристом в Голливуде, а отчасти, поскольку его сатирические гротески и фантасмагории во многом навеяны фантазиями По, «черным юмором» Бирса, изобретательностью О. Генри. В 30—40-е годы рассказы Кольера, удававшиеся ему больше, чем романы, широко печатались в английских и американских периодических изданиях, а затем выходили отдельными сборниками: *Devil and All* (1934), *Presenting Moonshine* (1941), *The Touch of Nutmeg* (1943).

Рассказы *The Frog Prince* и *Variation on a Theme* вошли в сборник избранных произведений Кольера *Fancies and Goodnights* (1951).

The Frog Prince

162. blasé roué (*фр.*) — пресыщенный распутник.
near-man (*сленг*) — недочеловек, «недоделанный».

163. faint heart never won fair lady — ср. по-русски: «смелость города берет».

164. Palm Beach — Палм-Бич, курортный город во Флориде (США).

165. Ritz-Carlton — «Риц-Карлтон», фешенебельный отель в Нью-Йорке.

Variation on a Theme

169. He was rather like one of those prisoners... — возможно, намек на Сервантеса, сочинявшего свои книги в тюрьме.

170. I had to dump it — пришлось ее бросить; to dump (*амер. сленг*) — бросать, избавляться от чего-либо; Горилла Симпсон вообще сыплет американскими ходовыми словечками и выражениями: you said it; see here; cut it out, sister; poor fish; this'll go big и т. д.

Your characters ... more in the round — *зд.* ваши персонажи будут более неоднозначными.

the Hawthornden — премия Хоторндена, ежегодная литературная премия за лучшее художественное произведение в прозе или в стихах, написанное английским автором не старше сорока лет; учреждена в 1919 г.

171. Queen Anne — английская королева Анна Стюарт (1665—1714).

175. to set the Thames on fire — ср.: покажет, где раки зимуют.
176. the critic who makes or breaks — критик, с которым шутки плохи.

woman of Junoesque proportions — женщина с фигурой (формами) Юноны; Юнона — в римской мифологии одна из главных богинь, жена Юпитера.

zabaglione (*ит.*) — сабайон (сладкий крем).

177. Brighton — Брайтон, курорт в графстве Суссекс.

his host's "striking gold" — как его хозяин «заколачивает монету».

178. Bloomsbury — район в центральной части Лондона, где по традиции живут представители творческой интеллигенции.

GRAHAM GREENE

В творчестве Грэма Грина (род. 1904), «живого классика» английской литературы XX в., социально-психологический гротеск в полной мере проявился в таких произведениях, как романы

Our Man in Havana (1958), *The Comedians* (1966), *Travels with My Aunt* (1969). «Чистый» юмор, юмор ради юмора у Грина достаточно редок, хотя в ряде очерков и новелл встречается, в частности в рассказах, собранных в 1967 г. под интригующим заглавием *May We Borrow Your Husband?*

Рассказы *Awful When You Think of It* и *The Root of All Evil* вошли в сборник *May We Borrow Your Husband?*

Awful When You Think of It

181. Reading and Slough — Рединг, столица графства Беркшир; Слоу — город в графстве Бакингемшир.

182. What's yours? — Что будете пить?

The other half? — Как поживает супруга (*букв.* ваша половина)?

My round — Теперь моя очередь (теперь я угощаю).

183. Imps — Импс, акции компании «Импириал груп» (Imperial Group).

a damn good one — отличный анекдот.

184. Doubles all round — Всем по двойной порции (виски).

The Root of All Evil

187. Gasthof (*нем.*) — постоялый двор, трактир.

188. Schloss (*нем.*) — замок.

191. Strasse (*нем.*) — улица.

194. It's not beyond Puckler — *зд.* с Пуклера станется.

196. sin of Sodom — Содомский грех, содомия.

HERBERT ERNEST BATES

С 1926 г., времени выхода его первой книги, Герберт Эрнест Бейтс (1905—1974) выпустил больше 30 новеллистических сборников, впоследствии объединенных в *Thirty Tales* (1934), *Country Tales* (1940), *Selected Stories* (1957), *Seven by Five* (1963). Писал Бейтс и романы (*Fair Stood the Wind for France*, 1944; *The Purple Plain*, 1947), повести, воспоминания, литературные эссе, очерки. Большую часть жизни Бейтс прожил на ферме, в графстве Кент, и, соответственно, черпал темы из сельской жизни; характерна сельская тематика и для комических рассказов писателя, где действует остроумный выдумщик дядюшка Сайлес — в каком-то смысле английский аналог Сандро из Чегема Искандера.

Finger Wet, Finger Dry

Рассказ вошел в *Selected Stories* (1957) Бейтса, а также в антологию английского юмора *Laughter in a Damp Climate*.

197. Finger Wet, Finger Dry — провалиться мне на этом месте. **He's just stuffin' you** — «Заливает».

198. ...went a belly-flopper — забил крыльями.

199. You cork it in — держи язык за зубами.

Sometimes Sam was on nights ... days — Иногда Сэм работал по ночам, а иногда — днем.

So I made no more to do — Делать было нечего.

don't wear a chair out — не просиживай стул.

hide the thimble — игра «спрячь наперсток» — то же, что русская игра «кольцо-кольцо, ко мне на крыльцо».

PETER FLEMING

Питер Флеминг (род. 1907) — журналист, фельетонист, прозаик; родился в Лондоне; после окончания Итона и Оксфорда, где будущий писатель издавал еженедельник *Isis*, работал в редакциях *Evening Standard, Spectator*, печатал эссе и фельетоны за подписью «Мотылек» (Moth) и «Сова» (Strix), был специальным корреспондентом *Times*, участвовал во второй мировой войне. Известность Флемингу принесли фантастический роман о визите Гитлера в Англию *Flying Visit* (1940) и сборник рассказов *A Story to Tell and Other Tales* (1942). Многие произведения Флеминга навеяны путевыми впечатлениями: *Brazilian Adventure* (1933), *News from Tartary* (1936). Газетные и журнальные публикации Флеминга собраны в сборнике *My Aunt's Rhinoceros and Other Reflections* (1958).

Эссе и фельетоны Флеминга *Advice to the Reader, Immortal Longings, On Going to the Moon, Pistols Weaken* первоначально были напечатаны в журнале «Спектейтор», впоследствии вошли в сборник *My Aunt's Rhinoceros and Other Reflections*.

Advice to the Reader

203. C'est une étrange entreprise que celle de faire rire les honnêtes gens. — **Molière** (*фр.*) — Странная затея смешить честных людей. — Мольер.

Captain of the XI — капитан сборной школы по футболу.

206. Elia — псевдоним английского писателя Чарльза Лэма

(Lamb, 1775-1834), под которым он выпустил сборник эссе автобиографического характера *Essays of Elia* (1820-1823).

Milne — Алан Александр Милн (1882—1956), английский писатель, поэт, драматург, автор популярных детских книг.

On Going to the Moon

208. un-Elizabethan attitude — во времена английской королевы Елизаветы I Тюдор английские мореплаватели совершили немало географических открытий.

Ottoman Empire — Оттоманская (Османская) империя, название султанской Турции; сложилась империя в XV—XVI вв., распалась после первой мировой войны.

210. British Council — Британский совет, правительственная организация по развитию культурных связей с зарубежными странами в целях пропаганды английского образа жизни.

Pistols Weaken

210. Anthony Hope — псевдоним английского писателя сэра Энтони Хокинса (Hawkins, 1863-1933), автора занимательных романов и пьес: *The Prisoner of Zenda* (1894), *Rupert of Hentzau* (1898).

210—201. Bulldog Drummond ... the Callaghans... the Cautions — герои романов Энтони Хоупа.

JAMES B. BOOTHROYD

Джеймс Б. Бутройд (род. 1910) — банковский служащий по профессии; с 1938 г. регулярно пишет для «Панча», а с 1950 г., уйдя из банка, становится членом редколлегии этого журнала. Сотрудничает Бутройд и с другими крупными периодическими изданиями, рецензирует книги, пьесы, сочиняет сценарии; одно время писатель вел сатирическую радиопрограмму *Monday Night at Home*. Юмористические рассказы Бутройда составили несколько сборников: *The House about a Man* (1961), *Home and Away* (1963), *You Can't Be Serious* (1967).

Рассказы *X = 0, Disposing of the Weapon* вошли в сборник *You Can't Be Serious*; рассказ *Knowing a Thing or Two* — в сборник *The House about a Man*.

X = 0

212. Harrowgate — Хэрроугейт, город в графстве Йоркшир, лечебный курорт.

214. the tube was going in the TV — ср. по-русски: кинескоп «садится».

Disposing of the Weapon

214. touched his forelock ... forensic — разберется сам (to touch the forelock — принимать решение), и меня не посадят на скамью подсудимых (forensic — *зд.* суд).

Tonbridge ... Tunbridge — Тонбридж (Танбридж), городок в графстве Кент.

Home Guard — войска местной обороны, ополчение во время второй мировой войны, созданное на случай вторжения гитлеровцев в Англию.

215. Wehrmacht (*нем.*) — «вермахт», вооруженные силы фашистской Германии.

Lee-Enfields — «Ли-Энфилд», винтовка калибра 7,69 мм.

216. Hawkhurst — Хокхерст, округ, расположенный частично в графстве Кент, а частично в графстве Суссекс.

217. Dunkirk — имеется в виду Дюнкеркская операция в мае 1940 г. по эвакуации в Англию англо-французских войск.

Woolton Pie — «Вултонский пирог», укрепления в Вултоне, городе в графстве Ланкашир, в связи с возможным вторжением немецко-фашистских войск.

Anderson shelters — семейные бомбоубежища, сооружавшиеся в Англии во время второй мировой войны и названные по имени Дж. Андерсона, тогдашнего министра внутренних дел Великобритании.

Knowing a Thing or Two

228. Palace of Westminster — Вестминстерский дворец, здание английского парламента в Лондоне.

Not a sausage (*сленг*) — Ничего не вышло.

Do-It-Yourself programme — «Сделай сам», популярная программа английского телевидения.

GEORGE MIKES

Джордж Микеш (род. 1912) — писатель-юморист, журналист, историк; родился в Венгрии в семье адвоката, учился в Будапештском университете; еще до второй мировой войны переехал в Англию, где снискал славу блестящего юмориста, досконально овладевшего не только английским языком, но и умением шутить по-английски. Со времени огромного успеха *How to Be an Alien* (1946) писатель выпустил более 20 книг, многие из которых затрагивают одну и ту же тему — юмористическое «освоение» различных национальных культур: *How to Scrape Skies* (1948) — американской, *Über alles* (1953) — немецкой, *Italy for Beginners* (1956) — итальянской. Известен Микеш и как фельетонист, рецензент, широко печатающийся в британской периодике, а антология *Eight Humorists*, составленная Микешем в 1954 г., свидетельствует о том, что Микеш — не только практик, но и серьезный теоретик юмористического жанра.

How to Be an Alien

224. Alice Duer Miller (1874—1942) — американская писательница.

228. Comment allez-vous? (*фр.*) — Как поживаете? (по аналогии с повторяющимся How do you do?).

235. Curzon Street society — метонимия высшего общества; Кэрзон-стрит — улица в Лондоне с роскошными магазинами, гостиницами и особняками.

237. the War of Spanish Succession — война за испанское наследство (1701—1714) между франко-испанской коалицией и Англией, Голландией, Австрией и Пруссией закончилась подписанием Утрехтского и Раштаттского (1714) мира.

Les rivières sont les chemins qui marchent (*фр.*) — Реки — это двигающиеся дороги.

240. the Beveridge Plan — сэр Уильям Генри Беверидж (1879—1963), английский экономист; речь идет о докладе Бевериджа в 1942 г., послужившем основой для принятия ряда законов о государственной системе медицинского обслуживания и социального обеспечения.

241. a famous English statesman... — Микеш намекает на премьер-министра Великобритании в 1937—1940 гг. Невилла Чемберлена (1869—1940), сторонника умиротворения гитлеровского режима, подписавшего Мюнхенское соглашение 1938 г.

High Court — Высокий суд правосудия, высший суд первой инстанции в Великобритании.

a great politician ... "a jolly good fellow" — имеется в виду Уинстон Черчилль.

242. Richmond — имеется в виду Ричмонд-парк, самый большой городской парк Англии; расположен на юго-западной окраине Лондона.

the Brains Trust — «Мозговой трест», ответы видных политических деятелей и специалистов на вопросы радиослушателей и телезрителей.

243. contemptible bourgeois habit — блумзберийцев традиционно отличает критическое отношение к буржуазной морали, религии, эстетике.

Sir Thomas Wyatt and John Ford — сэр Томас Уайетт (1503? — 1542), один из крупнейших поэтов раннего английского Возрождения; Джон Форд (1586—1640), английский поэт и драматург.

244. Blimps — филистер, олицетворение косности и шовинизма — по имени комического персонажа карикатур Д. Лоу (David Low) полковника Блимпа.

245. Brahmanism — индуистская религия и философия.

their aitches — пропуск фарингальского фрикативного [h] характерен для лондонского кокни.

246. "Henry V" or "Pygmalion" — речь идет об известных английских фильмах: «Пигмалион» (1938) по пьесе Б. Шоу (режиссеры Дж. Асквит, Л. Хоуард) и «Генрих V» (1944) по пьесе Шекспира (режиссер и исполнитель главной роли Лоуренс Оливье).

Galli Curci — Амелита Галли Курчи (1882—1963), итальянская певица.

Deanna Durbin — Дина Дурбин (род. 1921), американская актриса.

247. Toscanini — Артуро Тосканини (1867—1957), итальянский дирижер.

Noel Coward — Ноэл Коуард (1899—1973), английский актер, драматург, композитор.

248. Peter Pan — мальчик, который никогда не взрослеет, герой одноименной детской книги Джеймса Барри (см. коммент. на с. 390).

249. Wolseley — «вулзи», марка легкового автомобиля компании «Бритиш Лейланд».

"and thou shalt fear ... thy life" — «...будешь трепетать ночью и днем и не будешь уверен в жизни твоей» (Второзаконие: 28, 66).

250. West End — Уэст-Энд, западная, фешенебельная часть Лондона.

Hampstead Heath — Хампстед-Хит, лесопарк на северной окраине Лондона, где проводятся ярмарки с аттракционами.

253. Haymarket — раньше на лондонской улице Хеймаркет на месте театра «Хеймаркет» и театра «Ее Величества» находился сенной рынок.

255. the oracles of Delphi — по преданию, город Дельфы в Древней Греции был знаменит своими оракулами.

256. Journalism, or the Freedom of the Press — в этом разделе Микеш пародирует стиль крупнейших лондонских газет и выступлений в парламенте.

257. R. A. F. = Royal Air Force.
Fleet Air Arm — авиация ВМС.

258. an Oxford Blue — «темно-синий», студент, защищающий спортивную честь Оксфордского университета.

260. Pascal's "Pensées" — «Мысли» Паскаля; pensées (*фр* — мысли.

ROALD DAHL

Новеллист, поэт, детский писатель, норвежец по происхождению, Роалд Дал (род. 1916) пришел в литературу не сразу. Прежде чем опубликовать в американских журналах (*The New Yorker, Playboy* и др.) свои первые рассказы, 26-летний автор «успел» после окончания школы принять участие в экспедиции на Ньюфаундленд, поработать в компании «Шелл», побывать в Африке, проявить героизм летчика в начале второй мировой войны, получить тяжелое ранение. Навеянные военным опытом первые рассказы Дала впоследствии вошли в сборник *Over to You* (1946), однако известность писателю принесли рассказы из более поздних сборников *Someone Like You* (1948), *Kiss-Kiss, Twenty-Nine Kisses from Roald Dahl, Switch Bitch*, которые отличаются лаконизмом, отточенным стилем, непредсказуемыми — в духе Саки и О. Генри — концовками, а главное, «черным юмором», дающим себя знать даже в детских книгах писателя: *James and the Giant Peach, Charlie and the Chocolate Factory, The Magic Finger, The Enormous Crocodile*, также ставших бестселлерами. Неизменным успехом пользуются и телеэкранизации по книгам Дала.

The Great Automatic Grammatisator

Рассказ вошел в сборник *Someone Like You*.

261. Adolph Knipe — имя и фамилия героя ассоциируются по звучанию с именем и фамилией крупного американского издателя Альфреда Нопфа (Alfred Knopf).

264. "Roget's Thesaurus" — «Тэзаурус», толковый словарь

английского языка, составлен английским лексикографом Питером Марком Роже (1779—1869).

270. he said, epexegetically — уточнил он; epexegetically — от epexegesis (*греч.*) — *букв.* объяснительное расширение.

271. breviped — с короткими ногами; brevis (*лат.*) — короткий; pes, pedis (*лат.*) — нога.

"Saturday Evening Post", "Collier's", "Ladies' Home Journal" — популярные английские периодические издания.

272. "Reader's Digest" — «Ридерз дайджест», ежемесячный американский иллюстрированный журнал, в основном перепечатывающий, причем в сокращенном виде, материалы из других изданий.

NORMAN FREDERICK SIMPSON

Драматурга, школьного учителя по профессии Нормана Фредерика Симпсона (род. 1919) принято причислять к абсурдистам, цитировать в одном ряду с С. Беккетом, Э. Ионеско, Г. Пинтером. Алогизм привычных явлений, несоответствие формы выражения существу выражаемого — и в самом деле отличительные признаки таких пьес Симпсона, как *A Resounding Tinkle* (1956), где действует чета Парадоксов и где под Гипотетическим императивом высмеивается английское богослужение; *One Way Pendulum* (1959), жанр которой определен самим драматургом как «фарс в новом измерении» и которая пародирует судопроизводство; *The Cresta Run* (1965), где высмеивается шпиономания. Драматургия Симпсона, в частности скетчи *Gladly Otherwise, One to Another* (1959), одноактная пьеса *The Hole* (1958), заставляют, однако, вспомнить и «нонсенсы» его знаменитых соотечественников Лира, Кэрролла, а также мрачный юмор Дж. Мортона, Дж. Кольера, Р. Дала.

Телевизионная пьеса *One Blast and Have Done* впервые поставлена в театре "The Queen" 28 сентября 1960 г. Телевизионная пьеса *Oh* — в том же театре, 8 июня 1960 г.

One Blast and Have Done

281. One Blast and Have Done — *зд.* Один раз подую и уйду.
I'm on the cadge really — *зд.* Я, собственно, с просьбой.

283. timpani — литавры.
Just as well it was a Monday — Понедельник — одно слово; у англичан понедельник тоже считается тяжелым днем, отсюда Monday feelings, Black Monday и т. д.

284. It isn't as if she's exactly a Peach Melba — Прямо как красотка Мелба; Нелли Мелба (1861—1931) — австралийская певица-сопрано.

"Rock of Ages" — протестантский церковный гимн.

285. "Shenandoah" — имеется в виду спиричуэл «Шенандо»; Шенандо — река в США (Виргиния).

HAROLD PINTER

Драматург Гарольд Пинтер (род. 1930), в отличие от Симпсона, уже с юных лет связал свою жизнь с театром: под псевдонимом "David Baron" работал актером, учился в Королевской академии драматического искусства и в Театральной школе сценического искусства. В таких трагикомедиях и трагифарсах раннего Пинтера, весьма точно названных «пьесы угрозы» ("plays of menace"), как *The Room* (1957), *The Dumb Waiter* (1957), *The Birthday Party* (1958), *A Slight Ache* (1959), *The Caretaker* (1959), *The Collection* (1960), *Homecoming* (1965), отчетливо ощущается влияние французских абсурдистов, в первую очередь С. Беккета и Э. Ионеско. Настроение безысходности, бессмысленности существования проявляется и в более поздних пьесах Пинтера *Old Times* (1971), *No Man's Land* (1975) и даже — подспудно — в таких, казалось бы, легкомысленных, развлекательных сценках и этюдах, какими являются одноактные *Request Stop* и *Applicant*, включенные в спектакль *Pieces of Eight*, поставленный лондонским театром «Аполлон» в 1959 г.

Request Stop

291. Shepherds Bush — Шепердз-Буш, район на западной окраине Лондона.

293. Marble Arch — Марбл-Арч, триумфальная арка; сооружена в 1828 г. перед въездом в Букингемский дворец; в 1851 г. перенесена в Гайд-Парк, в настоящее время находится за его пределами.

Applicant

295. On heat — ср. по-русски: «На взводе».

296. falling coat — эпилепсия, то же, что и falling sickness.
virgo intacta (*лат.*) — девственник.
From the word go? — *зд.* Абсолютно? Полностью? (*букв.*: от начала до конца).

MALCOLM BRADBURY

Имя Малькольма Бредбери (род. 1932) хорошо известно и в академических и в литературных кругах Англии. Его творческие интересы весьма обширны: Бредбери—профессор Нориджского университета, выступает в университетах Англии и США с лекциями по теории и истории литературы, он же—романист, новеллист, искусствовед, литературный критик. Бредбери разрабатывает жанр «университетского романа», в котором написаны такие книги, как *Eating People is Wrong* (1959), *History Man* (1975). Известен Бредбери и как пародист: в свою книгу *Who Do You Think You Are* (1976) писатель включил печатавшиеся в периодике, в том числе и в «Панче», меткие пародии на таких известных современных английских и американских писателей, как Э. Уилсон, К. Эмис, А. Мердок, М. Спарк, Ч. П. Сноу и Дж. Д. Сэлинджер.

Действие романа *Eating People is Wrong*, глава из которого включена в настоящую антологию, происходит в провинциальном английском университете на кафедре английского языка.

The Redbrick Party

297. The Redbrick Party — в заглавии романа обыгрывается термин redbrick: от redbrick universities — «краснокирпичные университеты», разговорное название провинциальных университетов, появившихся в Англии на рубеже веков и построенных из красного кирпича.

298. "Vot"... — немец произносит английские слова на немецкий манер: vot = what; vaderland = fatherland.

Oscar Vilda = Oscar Wilde — Оскар Уайльд (1854—1900), английский писатель, поэт, драматург, критик; немец намекает на то, что в 1895 г. Уайльд был приговорен к двум годам тюремного заключения за гомосексуализм.

Jail... — немец путает слова gaol [dʒeil] — тюрьма, и goal [goul] — цель.

finders, keepers — имеется в виду детский стишок:

> Finders, keepers,
> Losers, weepers.

299. Chianti — кьянти, сухое красное итальянское вино.

Lawrentian vision — английский писатель Д. Г. Лоуренс (Lawrence, 1885-1930) многие годы прожил в Италии.

Midwinter spring is its own season... Lean, lean on a garden urn ...

a hard coming we had of it... There were no tigers — студенты из Индии цитируют произведения англо-американского поэта Томаса Стирнза Элиота (см. ниже), в частности отрывок из первой части поэмы *Little Gidding* (1942), строки из стихотворения *Journey of the Magi* (1927).

300. the "Upanishads" — Упанишады (*букв.* сокровенное знание), основа всех ортодоксальных религиозно-философских систем Индии.

II. Verse

EDWARD LEAR

Создатель страны «нонсенса», отменявшей упорядоченность викторианского века, поэт и художник Эдвард Лир (1812—1888) родился в бедной многодетной семье и работать пошел с 15 лет, а с 18 стал профессиональным художником. Всю жизнь Лир много странствовал, давал уроки рисования (в том числе и королеве Виктории), выпускал видовые альбомы типа *Views in Rome* (1841) или *Excursions in Italy* (1846), писал картины и сочинил несколько книг: *A Book of Nonsense* (1846), *More Nonsense* (1872), посвященные детям графа Дарби, в имении которого Лир несколько лет жил, а также *Nonsense Songs, Stories, Botany and Alphabets* (1871) и *Laughable Lyrics* (1877). Одна из заслуг Лира состоит в том, что он литературно «узаконил» встречавшиеся прежде лишь в устной традиции шуточные «лимерики», пятистрочные стихи, написанные анапестом и рифмующиеся по схеме «аавва». Как и во всех произведениях Лира, в лимериках решительно отвергаются правила и установления «здравомыслящего общества». В своих «нонсенсах» Лир обыгрывает написание и звучание слов, каламбурит, придумывает новые слова и словосочетания: географические названия типа the great Gromboolian plain, имена героев, скажем Mr. and Mrs. Discobolos, эпитеты scroobious, mumbian и т. д., над расшифровкой некоторых лексикографы бьются и по сей день.

Стихи Лира, вошедшие в настоящую антологию, печатаются по книге: *Edward Lear's Nonsense Books*. N. Y., 1967.

307. Bristol Channel — вероятно, по аналогии с British Channel.

308. Runcible Cat — runcible — одно из любимых, бессмысленных словечек Лира, теперь вошедших в английский язык: runcible spoon — вилка с широкими зубцами; см. также аналогичные аллитеративные сочетания: Dolomphious Duck, Fizzgiggious Fish, Higgeldipiggledy Hen, Scroobious Snake.

roo-Matiz — характерный для Лира каламбур; roomatiz = rheumatism; matiz (*исп.*) — оттенок.

317. Xerxes — Ксеркс I (519—465 до н. э.), царь персов, с 486 г. возглавил поход персов в Грецию.

318. Smyrna, Philae, Tring, Lucca, Whitehaven — Смирна, древнегреческое название турецкого города Измир; Филэ, остров на Ниле; Тринг, город в Англии, в графстве Херстфордшир; Лукка, город в Италии; Уайтхэвен, город в Англии, в графстве Кумбрия.

LEWIS CARROLL

Продолжатель традиции «литературы нонсенса», сын приходского священника, выпускник, затем профессор Оксфорда, Льюис Кэрролл (наст. имя — Чарлз Латуидж Доджсон, 1832—1898) в отличие от Лира практически не покидал Англии (путешествие в Россию в 1867 г. было скорее исключением) и серьезно занимался наукой — математикой, логикой. Ставшие классикой мировой литературы философские сказки Кэрролла *Alice in Wonderland* (1865) и *Through the Looking-Glass* (1871) представляют собой своеобразный синтез науки и искусства и дают неограниченную возможность для самых различных интерпретаций. Хотя «Алиса в Стране чудес», «В Зазеркалье», а также «Охота на Снарка» (*The Hunting of the Snark*, 1876), «Сильви и Бруно» (*Sylvie and Bruno*, 1889-1893) трактуются литературными критиками порой излишне серьезно, получают даже психоаналитические толкования, налицо сказочно-юмористическая, смеховая, фольклорная основа творчества Кэрролла, его незаурядные изобретательность и фантазия, проявившиеся, в частности, и в поэтических «нонсенсах», пародиях и стилизациях, какими изобилуют обе «Алисы», да и другие книги Кэрролла.

The Mad Gardener's Song

Стихотворение из романа Кэрролла «Сильви и Бруно»; приводим первые две строфы «Песни безумного садовника» в переводе Д. Орловской:

> Ему казалось — на трубе
> Увидел он Слона.
> Он посмотрел — то был Чепец,
> Что вышила жена.

И он сказал: «Я в первый раз
Узнал, как жизнь сложна».
Ему казалось — на шкафу
Красуется Павлин.
Он присмотрелся — это был
Сестры Невестки Сын.
И он сказал: «Как хорошо,
Что я здесь не один». (...)

How Doth the Little Crocodile...

Стихотворение о крокодиле, вошедшее в «Алису в Стране чудес», представляет собой пародию на стихи английского богослова и поэта Исаака Уоттса (Watts, 1674-1748) «Противу праздностей и шалостей» из сборника «Божественные песни для детей» (*Divine Songs for Children*, 1715). Приведем стихотворение Кэрролла и текст пародируемого стихотворения по-русски в переводе Д. Орловской:

К э р р о л л:

Как дорожит своим хвостом
Малютка крокодил! —
Урчит и вьется над песком,
Прилежно пенит Нил!
Как он умело шевелит
Опрятным коготком! —
Как рыбок он благодарит,
Глотая целиком.

У о т т с
(«Противу праздностей и шалостей»):

Как дорожит любым деньком
Малюточка пчела! —
Гудит и вьется над цветком,
Прилежна и мила.
Как ловко крошка мастерит
Себе опрятный дом!
Как щедро деток угостит
Припрятанным медком!

И я хочу умелым быть,
Прилежным, как она, —
Не то для праздных рук найдет
Занятье Сатана!
Пускай в ученье и в труде

419

Я буду с ранних лет—
Тогда и дам я на суде
За каждый день ответ.

Humpty Dumpty's Recitation

Стихотворение Шалтая-Болтая «Зимой, когда белы поля...» из «Алисы в Зазеркалье» перебивается прозаическим комментарием Алисы и самого Шалтая-Болтая, что создает дополнительный юмористический эффект.

Hiawatha's Photographing

Пародия Кэрролла на поэму Лонгфелло «Песнь о Гайавате» (*Hiawatha*, 1855) вошла в сборник *The Collected Verse of Lewis Carroll*, N. Y., 1933.

My Fancy

Стихотворение написано в 1862 г. и вошло в сборник *The Collected Verse.*

329. She's all my fancy painted her... — скрытая, измененная цитата из стихотворения английского поэта и журналиста Уильяма Ми (Mee, 1788-1862):

> She's all my fancy painted her,
> She's lovely, she's divine.

What Tottles Meant

Стихотворение написано в 1867 г.

329. flat (*амер. сленг*) = flat-footed — категорично, решительно.

country-box.../A box at Covent Garden — «Ковент-Гарден», название королевского оперного театра в Лондоне; Кэрролл обыгрывает два значения слова box: (1) домик; (2) ложа.

They lived a life of double-knocks — ср. по-русски: «денег не считали»; to take the knocks — жить на широкую ногу.

330. traps (*сленг*) — вещи, «пожитки».

ALFRED EDWARD HOUSMAN

Альфред Эдвард Хаусмен (1859—1936) — поэт, филолог-античник, профессор Лондонского и Кембриджского университетов, известен стихами (сборники *A Shropshire Lad*, 1896; *Last*

Poems, 1922; *More Poems,* 1936), большая часть которых не только не располагает к юмору, но создает у читателя настроение безысходности, неустроенности, обманутых надежд. Вместе с тем перу Хаусмена принадлежит и несколько очень смешных стихотворений и стилизаций и, в частности, пародия на древнегреческие трагедии, а если говорить точнее, на их английские переводы, которых Хаусмен по долгу службы перечитал за свою жизнь немало.

Infant Innocence

Шуточное стихотворение Хаусмена навеяно, по всей видимости, мотивами ряда стихов английского поэта Уильяма Блейка (Blake, 1757-1827) из сборника *Songs of Innocence: The Little Boy Lost; The Little Boy Found; Infant Joy* и т. д.

Fragment of a Greek Tragedy

Пародия Хаусмена включена в известный сборник англо-американской стихотворной пародии, изданный и составленный английским поэтом и критиком Дж. К. Сквайром (1884—1958), *Apes and Parrots* (1928). В пародии воссоздается древнегреческий миф, согласно которому Алкмеон, сын Амфиария и Эрифилы, убивает свою мать, отомстив ей за предательство, после чего впадает в безумие.

334. Delphic ... Dodona — речь идет о святилище Додоны в греческом городе Эпире, где, по преданию, находился старейший оракул Зевса.

Antistrophe — антистрофа, в античной трагедии четная строфа хоровой песни, повторявшая по ритму нечетную строфу.

The Inachean daughter — имеется в виду Ио́, в греческой мифологии дочь аргосского царя Инаха, возлюбленная Зевса.

335. Cypris — Киприда, одно из имен Афродиты, в греческой мифологии богини любви и красоты.

Epode — в античном стихосложении лирическое стихотворение, в котором длинный стих чередуется с коротким.

RUDYARD KIPLING

«Бард империализма», лауреат Нобелевской премии Джозеф Редьярд Киплинг (1865—1936) снискал себе громкую славу и как поэт, автор патриотических по содержанию и балладных по форме стихотворений (*Barrack-room Ballads,* 1892; *Departmental Ditties,* 1886), и как новеллист, автор экзотических историй и сказок из индийской жизни (*Plain Tales from the Hills*, 1888), и как романист (*The Light That Failed*, 1890; *Kim*, 1901), и как детский писатель: повесть *Captains Courageous* (1897), *Just So Stories* (1902), *The Jungle Book* (1894, 1895). Большинство книг Киплинга, независимо от того, в каком жанре они написаны, представляют собой проповедь «права сильного», панегирик официальной идеологии и отличаются грубоватым юмором и образным просторечием, ставшими мишенью ряда пародий, в том числе и Бирбома (см. коммент. на с. 393). Между тем и сам Киплинг не гнушался пародией, искусно и остроумно подражая стилю Вордсворта, Гейне, Браунинга, Морриса, Суинберна.

Стихотворения *My Rival* и *Natural Theology*, вошедшие в изданную в США антологию английского юмора *A Treasury of British Humor* (1942), высмеивают популярную строфику и тематику английской дидактической и философской поэзии XIX в.

Natural Theology

339. L. S. D. = librae, solidi, denarii (*лат.*) — фунты, шиллинги, пенсы.

Mons retreat — сражение при бельгийском городе Монсе состоялось 23 августа 1914 г. и закончилось поражением английского экспедиционного корпуса.

340. As was the sowing so the reaping — обыгрывается пословица: «Что посеешь, то и пожнешь».

Thou = you; **thine** = your; **Thyself** = yourself (*арх.*).

HILAIRE BELLOC

Хилэр Беллок (1870—1953) — английский прозаик, поэт, эссеист, историк; родился в Париже (мать Беллока — француженка), окончил Оксфорд, в 1902 г. принял английское подданство, с 1906 по 1910 г. был членом парламента от либералов, писал эссе (*On Nothing*, 1908; *On Everything*, 1909; *On Anything*, 1910); биографии — Дантона (1899), Робеспьера (1901), Наполеона (1932); исторические труды, романы (*A Change in the Cabinet*, 1909; *The Green Overcoat*, 1912; *The Postmaster-General*, 1932), но в истории литературы, по всей вероятности, Беллок останется в основном как поэт-юморист, прямой наследник Лира и Кэрролла, автор таких сборников в духе поэзии «нонсенса», как *The Bad Child's Book of Beasts* (1896), *More Beasts for Worse Children* (1897), *Cautionary Tales* (1907), *New Cautionary Tales* (1930) и др.

Стихотворения Беллока, включенные в настоящую антологию, вошли в сборник: Hilaire Belloc. *Complete Verse.* L.: 1970.

345. Parvenoo — английское написание французского слова parvenu — вульгарный; «парвеню».

346. Big Ben — «Биг Бен» («Большой Бен»), колокол часов-курантов на здании парламента в Лондоне.

347. Camberwell — Камбуруэлл, жилой район в южной части Лондона.

Rutlandshire = Rutland — Ратлэнд, графство в Англии.

348. Strand — Стрэнд, одна из главных улиц в центре Лондона, где расположены театры, фешенебельные магазины и гостиницы.

350-351. "O" stands for Oxford... "R" the Reviewer — отрывки из сборника Беллока *A Moral Alphabet.*

352. Bayswater — район в Лондоне.

353. Berkeley Square — Баркли-сквер, площадь в центре Лондона.

354. "Savoy" — «Савой», одна из самых фешенебельных лондонских гостиниц.

GILBERT KEITH CHESTERTON

В многогранном творчестве эссеиста, прозаика, журналиста Гилберта Кита Честертона (1874—1936) поэзия, в том числе и комическая, занимает далеко не последнее место, а такие стихотворения, как *Elegy in a Country Churchyard* (1922), *The Song against Grocers* (1915), *The Secret People* (1915), стали классикой английской литературы. Стойкий демократизм, антибуржуазность, парадоксальный ум, тончайшее литературное чутье, остроумие проявились не только в лучших романах писателя (*The Napoleon of Notting Hill*, 1904; *The Man Who Was Thursday — a Nightmare*, 1908), детективных рассказах, литературно-художественных биографиях, эссе (*All Things Considered*, 1908; *Small Trifles*, 1909; *Generally Speaking*, 1928), но и в стихах, объединенных в сборники: *Greybeards at Play* (1902), *The Wild Knight and Other Poems* (1905), *The Ballad of the White Horse* (1911), *Poems* (1915), *Collected Poems* (1926).

Особенно удавалась Честертону поэтическая пародия: писатель создал непревзойденные образцы жанра, точно улавливая особенности стиля столь непохожих представителей поэтического цеха, как Браунинг и Лонгфелло, Йетс и Уитмен, Суинберн и Теннисон.

Стихотворения и пародии Честертона, вошедшие в настоящую антологию, печатаются по сборнику: G. K. Chesterton. *Collected poems*. L.: 1926.

Dolores Replies to Swinburne

Пародия на стихотворение «Долорес» одного из самых пародируемых английских поэтов Алджернона Чарлза Суинберна (Swinburne, 1837-1909) воспроизводит строфику и ритмику оригинала, строится в виде ответа лирического героя поэту и содержит намеки и аллюзии эпиграмматического характера.

355. Priapean poet — Честертон намекает на то, что образцом для любовной лирики Суинберна была откровенная и чувственная античная эротическая поэзия; Приап — в древнегреческой мифологии бог садов, стад, покровитель виноделия.

356. Our Lady of Pain — т. е. Долорес; *букв*. Дева Страданий.

Variations of an Air

Тематическим стержнем пародий Честертона на английского поэта Теннисона, ирландского поэта У. Б. Йетса (Yeats, 1865-1939) и американского поэта У. Уитмена (Whitman, 1819-1892) служит шуточный стишок про легендарного британского короля Кола (Cole, Coel). В пародийное «попурри» Честертона вошли также пародии на Р. Браунинга (Browning, 1812-1889) и А. Суинберна.

356. prince of Colchester — по преданию, в английском городе Колчестере, графство Эссекс, была резиденция короля Кола.

English Raleigh ... Spain — имеется в виду английский мореплаватель, поэт, драматург, историк Уолтер Рэли (1552—1618), который в 1588 г. явился одним из руководителей разгрома испанской «Непобедимой Армады».

357. after W. B. Yeats — в пародии на Йетса воспроизводится строфика и ритмика ряда ранних стихотворений поэта из сборника *The Wind among the Reeds* (1899), в частности *The Cap and the Bells*.

after Walt Whitman — Честертон пародирует стихотворение Уитмена «Песня о себе» (*Song of Myself*) из сборника «Листья травы» (*Leaves of Grass*, 1855).

camarado (*исп.*) — друг, товарищ.

A Ballad of Abbreviations

В стихотворении, где Честертон по обыкновению критикует американские порядки и нравы, обыгрываются различия между британским и американским вариантом английского языка: lift = elevator; typist = stenographer, flat = apartment и т. д.

358. Board of Trade — Министерство торговли (внутренней и внешней); существовало в Англии с 1786 по 1970 г.

Mr. Dreiser — Честертон намекает на обстоятельность, многословие американского писателя Теодора Драйзера (1871—1945).

359. Prohibition — речь идет о Сухом законе, который действовал в США в 20—30-х годах и над которым часто издевался Честертон.

The Shakespeare Memorial

359. Shorter — Клемент Шортер (1858—1921), английский журналист, издатель; с 1891 по 1900 г. издавал *Illustrated London News*, где печатался Честертон.

Sir Herbert Tree — Герберт Бирбом Три (1853—1917), английский актер, режиссер, поставил около двадцати пьес Шекспира.

Lord Rothschild — лорд Ротшильд (1840—1915), барон, член английского парламента, финансист, глава английского банковского дома.

Lord Rosebery — лорд Розбери (1847—1919), английский политик, государственный деятель; был женат на дочери барона Ротшильда.

F. C. G. — имеется в виду сэр Фрэнсис Кэрразерс Гоулд (Francis Carruthers Gould, 1844-1925), английский журналист, памфлетист, один из издателей *Westminster Gazette*.

Comyns Carr — Коминз Карр (настоящее имя Артур Стреттелл, 1882—1941), английский экономист, государственный деятель.

HARRY GRAHAM

Попечитель Британского музея, участник Бурской и первой мировой войн, поэт и драматург Гарри Грэхем (1874—1936) едва ли останется в литературе как автор популярных в свое время пьес *By Candle Light, White Horse Inn, Sybil, Land of Smiles*. Гораздо плодотворнее Грэхем трудился на ниве юмора, сочинив несколько очень веселых книг: *Departmental Ditties, The Bolster Book, The Perfect Gentleman, The World We Laugh In* и др. Что же касается «Безжалостных рифм» (*Ruthless Rhymes for Heartless Homes*), этого первого, пожалуй, в англоязычных литературах образчика «черного юмора», то они пользуются успехом и по сей день. А в первые годы XX в. в Англии не было, кажется, ни одной студенческой газеты, где бы не печатались такие, например, стихи:

> In the drinking well,
> Which the plumber built her,
> Aunt Eliza fell;
> We must buy a filter.

From "Ruthless Rhymes"

361. L'enfant glacé (*фр.*) — замороженный ребенок; по аналогии с café glacé — кофе с мороженым.

Frigidaire (*фр.*) — холодильник, ледник; здесь Грэхем обыгрывает вдобавок французскую идиому mettre qch. au frigidaire — отложить что-либо в долгий ящик.

362. unhappé — записанное на французский манер английское слово unhappy.

frappé (*фр.*) — двойной смысл: 1) охлажденный, 2) «чокнутый».

Poetical Economy

Комический эффект стихотворения строится на рифмующихся усеченных формах.

363—364. apol. = apology; **schol.** = scholar; **cun.** = cunning; **Mon.** = Money; **cryst.** = crystal; **Duch.** = Duchess; **sinist.** = sinister; **fam.** = family; **escutch.** = escutcheon; **pit.** = pity; **crit.** = critic; **pop.** = populace; **myst.** = mystery; **cop.** = copy; **syst.** = system; **consid.** = consideration; **individ.** = individual; **beav.** = beaver; **redoub.** = redouble; **abbrev.** = abbreviate; **pub.** = publisher; **partic.** = particularly; **A. C. Bens.** = A. C. Benson (1862—1925), английский эссеист, издатель; президент колледжа Магдалины в Кембридже; **G. K. Chest.** = G. K. Chesterton; **The Scape.** = *The Scapegoat* (1891), роман английского писателя Томаса Генри Кейна (Caine, 1853-1931); **Miss Correll.** = Mary Correlli, псевдоним английской писательницы Мэри Макей (Mackey, 1855-1924); **Barabb.** = Barabbas (1893), роман Мэри Коррелли; **pape** = paper; **hab.** = habit; **unnec.** = unnecessary; **dimin.** = diminish; **The Second**

Mrs. Tanq. = *The Second Mrs. Tanqueray* (1893), пьеса английского драматурга Артура Уинга Пинеро (Pinero, 1855-1934); **Pin.** = Pinero; **Ham.** = Hamlet; **Shakes.** = Shakespeare; **att.** = attitude; **Wed.** = Wednesday; **Sat.** = Saturday; **monot.** = monotony; **foll.** = follow; **examp.** = example; **Stephen Phill.** = Stephen Phillips (1849-1915), английский драматург и поэт; **Owen Seam.** = Owen Seaman (1860-1941), английский пародист, главный редактор «Панча»; **William Wat.** = Sir William Watson (1858-1935), английский поэт; **Ella Wheeler Wil.** = Ella Wheeler Wilcox (1850-1919), американская поэтесса и журналистка; **respons.** = response; **nons.** = nonsense.

The Cockney of the North

Грэхем пародирует стихотворение Йетса *The Lake Isle of Innisfree* из сборника *The Rose* (1893). Приводим первую строфу стихотворения Йетса:

> I will arise and go now, and go to Innisfree
> And a small cabin build there, of clay and wattles made;
> Nine bean-rows will I have there, a hive for the honey bee,
> And live alone in the bee-loud glade.

365. Inverness — приморский курорт в Шотландии, центр туризма.

EDMUND CLERIHEW BENTLEY

Поэт, журналист, прозаик Эдмунд Клерихью Бентли (1875—1956) был членом редколлегии «Дейли ньюс», писал передовицы для «Дейли телеграф», известен также как автор детективных романов и шуточных стишков, в которых обыгрываются биографии великих людей,— в истории литературы за этими стишками закрепилось название «клерихью» — по имени автора. Благодаря «клерихью», вошедшим в сборники *Biography for Beginners, More Biography, Baseless Biography*, в английской комической литературе у Бентли довольно высокая репутация: вместе с Гарри Грэхемом он считается продолжателем «поэзии несуразиц» в духе Лира, Кэрролла и Беллока.

From "Biography for Beginners"

366. Sir Christopher Wren — Кристофер Рен (1632—1723), английский архитектор, математик и астроном; Рен строил собор св. Павла в Лондоне.

Adam Smith — Адам Смит (1723—1790), шотландский экономист и философ.

kith ... kin — в стихотворении обыгрывается выражение kith and kin — родня.

Sir Humphry Davy — Гемфри Дэви (1778—1829), английский химик и физик; получил электролизом калий и натрий.

367. John Stuart Mill — Джон Стюарт Милль (1806—1873), английский философ, экономист, общественный деятель; работа Милля «Принципы политической экономии» написана в 1848 г.

Lord Clive — Роберт Клайв (1725—1774), английский политик; потеряв рассудок, покончил с собой.

George III — Георг III (1738—1820), английский король Ганноверской династии с 1760 г.; с 1811 г. психически болен.

368. Savonarola — Джироламо Савонарола (1452—1498), настоятель монастыря домениканцев во Флоренции; выступал против тирании, обличал папство, призывал церковь к аскетизму.

THOMAS STEARNS ELIOT

Вклад в комическую литературу классика англоязычной поэзии XX в., лауреата Нобелевской премии Томаса Стирнза Элиота (1885—1965), автора таких масштабных философских произведений, как, скажем, поэма *The Waste Land* (1922), поэтическая драма *Murder in the Cathedral* (1935), статья *Tradition and the Individual Talent* (1919), крайне невелик. Ограничивается этот вклад, пожалуй, лишь хрестоматийным стихотворением «Гиппопотам» (1920), в котором проявились антицерковные настроения Элиота 10-х годов, а также широко известным, в том числе и русскому читателю по маршаковским переводам, сборником *Old Possum's Book of Practical Cats* (1939), откуда и взяты вошедшие в настоящую антологию стихотворения.

The Hippopotamus

369. The hippopotamus — бегемот, одно из средневековых иносказательных обозначений дьявола; комический эффект уподобления церкви гиппопотаму достигается также снижающе-бытовыми аналогиями, смешением просторечия и библейского языка.

And when ... Laodiceans — «Когда это послание прочитано будет у вас, то распорядитесь, чтобы оно было прочитано и в Лаодикийской церкви» (Послание апостола Павла к колосянам: IV, 16).

Flesh and blood is weak and frail — в своем послании Павел призывает верующих к «небрежению о насыщении плоти».

True Church ... rock — «И на сем камне я создам Церковь Мою» (Матфей: XVI, 18).

370. Blood of the Lamb — Кровью Агнца окропленный; пародийный намек на Откровение святого Иоанна: «...они омыли одежды свои и убелили одежды свои кровью Агнца» (VII, 14).

Growltiger's Last Stand

371—372. Gravesend, Rotherhithe, Hammersmith, Putney, Molesey, Hampton, Wapping, Maidenhead, Henley, Brentford — населенные пункты на Темзе, в Южной Англии «по пути следования» грозного Граултайгера.

371. sate (*устар. поэтич.*) = sat.

Macavity: the Mystery Cat

373. Scotland Yard, the Flying Squad — Скотланд-Ярд, традиционное название лондонской полиции; Flying Squad — «Летучий отряд», лондонское отделение уголовного розыска (Criminal Investigation Department).

374. Peke = Pekinese.

Gus: the Theatre Cat

В стихотворении обыгрываются фразеологизмы со словом cat: cat-calls, to let the cat out of the bag и т. д. Кроме того, Гас сыплет театральными словечками: back-chat; I knew how to gag; character parts и т. д.

376. Little Nell — Малютка Нелл, героиня романа Диккенса «Лавка древностей» (*The Old Curiosity Shop*, 1841).

Dick Whittington's Cat — одна из многочисленных сценических версий о коте Дика Виттингтона, английского аналога «Кота в сапогах» Перро; согласно легенде, кот предсказал Ричарду Виттингтону, сыну мелкого лондонского торговца, что тот станет лорд-мэром Лондона — что в 1397 г. и произошло.

"East Lynne" — «Ист Линн» (1861), роман английской писательницы Эллен Вуд (Wood, 1814-1887).

Victoria — Виктория (1819—1901), королева Великобритании с 1837 г., последняя из Ганноверской династии.

Выпускник Оксфорда, участник Гражданской войны в Испании, Уистан Хью Оден (1907—1973) одинаково свободно владел пером лирика и пародиста, сатирика и социального критика; отличает Одена и исключительное жанровое многообразие: помимо стихов и поэм — «левых», антибуржуазных, антифашистских в молодости (*Poems*, 1928; *Poems*, 1930; *The Orators*, 1932; *Look, Stranger*, 1936; *Another Time*, 1940) и более остраненных, философских, эстетских после войны (*The Shield of Achilles*, 1955; *Homage to Clio*, 1960; *City without Walls*, 1969), он широко известен как публицист (*Letters from Iceland*, 1937), драматург (*The Dog beneath the Skin*, 1935; *On the Frontier*, 1938), критик, переводчик поэзии. Комическая стихия характерна в равной степени для ранних и поздних книг Одена. Его шуточные куплеты, эпиграммы, пародии, короткие, емкие максимы в стихах ("shorts") заставляют вспомнить Беллока и Грэхема, а *Academic Graffiti* — «клерихью» Эдмунда Бентли.

Стихотворения, включенные в настоящую антологию, вошли в сборник Одена *Collected Poems*, L., 1976.

From "Letter to Lord Byron"

Поэма, написанная в 1936 г. и стилизованная под байроновского «Дон Жуана», вошла в книгу *Letters from Iceland*, написанную Оденом в соавторстве с поэтом Луисом Макнисом (MacNeice, 1907-1963) после их совместной поездки по Исландии; приводим лишь первые станзы поэмы.

377. Gary Cooper, Coughlin ... Dick Sheppard — популярные киноактеры.

"Childe Harold" — имеется в виду поэма Байрона «Паломничество Чайльд-Гарольда» (*Childe Harold's Pilgrimage*, 1818).

Pope — английский поэт Александр Поп (1688—1744), крупнейший представитель английского классицизма, любимый поэт Байрона.

G. P. O. = General Post Office — Главное почтовое управление.

378. Reykjavik ... Möthrudalur ... Akureyri — топонимика Исландии.

Professor Housman — т. е. Alfred Edward Housman.

Shorts

В настоящий сборник вошли *Shorts* 1929—1931 гг., 1940 г.

380. the British Museum — Британский музей в Лондоне, один из крупнейших музеев мира, основан в 1753 г.

Academic Graffiti

В сборник *Academic Graffiti* (1971) вошли шуточные стихи Одена 1952—1970 гг.

382. Henry Adams — Генри Брукс Адамс (1838—1918), американский писатель, автор девятитомной истории США (1889—1891).

St. Thomas Aquinas — Фома Аквинский (1225—1274), философ и теолог.

Fach (*нем.*) — ремесло, профессия; **kluge** (*нем.*) — умный; **Kunst der Fuge** (*нем.*) — искусство фуги.

383. Thomas Lovell Beddoes — Томас Лавелл Беддоуз (1803—1849), английский поэт и драматург; его стихи и пьесы отличаются мрачным, «кладбищенским» колоритом.

Bysshe — т. е. Перси Биши Шелли.

384. enchanté (*фр.*) — очарован; Беатриче — возлюбленная Данте; **noi siamo amici** (*итал.*) — мы друзья.

Sir Rider Haggard — Генри Райдер Хаггард (1856—1925), английский писатель, автор многих приключенческих романов; **"She"** (1887) — роман Хаггарда.

Dryden — Джон Драйден (1631—1700), английский писатель, один из основоположников английского классицизма.

Phenomenology — имеется в виду работа Гегеля «Феноменология духа» (1807).

385. Categorical Must — Категорический императив — центральный принцип этики Канта.

Hilton — «Хилтон», фешенебельная лондонская гостиница на Парк-Лейн; в настоящее время отели «Хилтон» разбросаны по всему миру (отсюда: a Hilton).

Thomas Moore ... Irish Melodies — Томас Мур (1779—1852), английский поэт-романтик, по происхождению ирландец; в сборнике «Ирландские мелодии» (1807—1834) Мур воспевал освободительную войну Ирландии против Англии.

386. Bois (*фр.*) — лес; имеется в виду Bois de Boulogne — Булонский лес в Париже; **Moi** (*фр.*) — я.

А. Ливергант

АНТОЛОГИЯ АНГЛИЙСКОГО ЮМОРА

(*На английском языке*)

СБОРНИК

Составитель Александр Яковлевич Ливергант

Издательский редактор В. Я. Бонар
Художник А. Б. Маркевич
Художественный редактор В. Б. Тихомиров
Технический редактор А. П. Агафошина

ИБ № 4736

Сдано в набор 4.09.89. Подписано в печать 21.08.90.
Формат 84 × 108¹/₃₂. Бумага офсетная. Гарнитура таймс.
Печать офсет. Условн. печ. л. 22,68. Усл. кр.-отт. 23.32.
Уч.-изд. л. 21,56. Тираж 25000экз. Заказ № 1151.
Цена 3 р. 00 к. Изд. № 5081.

Издательство «Радуга» В/О «Совэкспорткнига» Государственного комитета СССР
по печати
119859, Москва, ГСП-3, Зубовский бульвар, 17

Можайский полиграфкомбинат В/О «Совэкспорткнига» Государственного комитета СССР по печати
143200, Можайск, ул. Мира, 93